SOIL BIOLOGY AND CONSERVATION OF THE BIOSPHERE

SOIL BIOLOGY AND CONSERVATION OF THE BIOSPHERE

Edited by

J. SZEGI

AKADÉMIAI KIADÓ, BUDAPEST 1977

Proceedings of the VIIth Meeting of the Soil Biology
Section of the Society for Soil Science of the
Hungarian Association of Agricultural Sciences
held at the Keszthely University of Agriculture,
Hungary 2–4 September 1975.

Supervised by
T. PÁTKAI

ISBN 963 05 1273 4

Printed in Hungary

CONTENTS

FOREWORD

Accelerated intensification of agricultural production has necessitated the increased application of chemicals, having a determining influence on soil forming processes, as well as on the biosphere in general.

More recently the processes of soil formation are at least as much under the influence of human factors as under the influence of natural soil forming factors in the usual interpretation. The intensive application of mineral fertilizers and particularly chemicals for plant protection influence both abiotic and biotic processes in soils and alter soil fertility. Not only the amount of chemicals applied in agriculture is increasing year by year but many new components have been introduced which have diverse effects on biological and biochemical processes in soils. In order to protect and increase soil fertility, thorough studies and knowledge of their effects are necessary. It is possible to reinforce the beneficial effects of the application of chemicals and diminish or exclude reverse effects of chemicals only by this way.

The topics of the VIIth Meeting of the Soil Biology Section of the Hungarian Soil Science Society on Soil Biology and Conservation of the Biosphere, which were devoted to the above mentioned problems are timely both theoretically and practically, bearing a direct significance to the up-to-date practice of agriculture. As soil forming always entails biological and non-biological processes, the dynamics of soil formation and soil fertility can only be interpreted by studying the abiotic and biotic processes in soils conjointly.

The Hungarian Soil Science Society, sponsoring the VIIth Meeting of the Soil Biology Section on Soil Biology and Conservation of the Biosphere, has always paid due attention to the biology of soils, and its Commission 3 (Soil Biology) has successfully organized numerous meetings on different problems of biological processes related to the fertility and agricultural utilization of soils.

Those meetings, including the participation of eminent scientists from abroad were crowned with success and gained a reputation for the Society both at home and abroad.

Based on these good experiences, the organizers of this meeting selected current topics for discussions and this meeting has certainly aroused interest in many actual problems and aims of soil biology and promoted an exchange of ideas and has led to adopting the results and experiences.

One of the largest departments of the Research Institute for Soil Science and Agricultural Chemistry of the Hungarian Academy of Sciences — co-sponsoring the organization of the VIIth Meeting of the Biology Section — is the Soil Microbiology Department, which took the lion's share in organizing this meeting, fulfilling a main task of one of the Institute's programmes; multilateral study of soil forming processes and soil fertility.

This volume represents a cross-section of the research programme and the achievements of not only Hungarian scientists but experts of numerous countries too, and will help the readers apart from getting acquainted with numerous questions related to soil biology and soil formation, also to adopt the results for both research and practice.

I. Szabolcs
President of the Hungarian
Soil Science Society

OPENING ADDRESS

Preservation of the harmony between man and the environment in recent years, has become one of the most urgent tasks of science. Numerous institutions in Hungary as in other countries are dealing with different aspects of biospheric protection.

One of the research projects of high priority of the Hungarian Academy of Sciences is the problem of conservation of the biosphere and its rational utilization.

The Coordinating Committee was formed in 1971 by the Academy to harmonize these research projects carried out by the research institutes of the Academy and other departments concerned.

Revealing the properties of soil physics, chemistry and biology serving the basic requirements of living nature is one of important aspects of biosphere research. Of course the task of soil biology in biosphere research is exceptionally manifold and is connected interdisciplinarily with numerous other scientific branches. Therefore on behalf of the Academy we welcome the VIIth Scientific Session of the Soil Biology Section of the Soil Science Society which has placed the research tasks of environmental protection related to soil biology, on the agenda for discussion.

The lectures to be heard here will reflect what results have been achieved in neighbouring countries in this field and moreover we may gain an insight into the soil microbiology research of the Academy at the termination of the four-year research cycle.

Ecological research in soil biology has an exceptionally great tradition in the figures of **Winogradsky**, **Omeliansky**, Bejerinck, Löhnis, Stoklasa, Waksman, **Fehér**, **Mishustin** and others. In the last two decades as a consequence of the sudden development of agricultural production, several problems so far unknown have emerged which have instigated soil biology research. Among these two should be mentioned. One is plant protection chemicals and extensive application of chemicals regulating the population, the other the expansion of the production systems in agriculture.

In countries with developed chemical industries carrying on intensive agricultural production the different plant protection chemicals reach the soil in ever greater amounts and through it in many cases the waters and they are having an ever

11

greater effect on the soil biological processes i.e. the biological cycle of materials. Since the organisms living in the soil are integrated elements of the ecological systems, upsetting the biological balance may have unforeseeable consequences, not merely because the evolutionary trends are delayed but on account of what may follow from this viz. the fertility of the soil and the quality of the crop may be affected. As a consequence the investigation of the secondary effect of pesticides is assuming an ever more extensive role in soil biology. This was one of the themes of the soil biology symposium organized in Budapest in 1970. At this scientific meeting there are 15 lectures devoted to this topic.

The other problem which is closely connected with the rapid development of agriculture is the setting up of production systems and generally the expansion of industrial production in plant cultivation and animal breeding. There are numerous soil biological problems to be solved in this field. These are for example studying the transformation of large masses of organic materials of plant origin remaining after mechanical harvesting. No doubt, however, in the culture ecosystems influenced by human activity the plant remains reaching the soil have a very important role in maintaining the soil biological balance and their role with the intensification of chemization will become more vital.

Ploughing in of the organic materials of plant origin into the soil followed by a rather intensive soil biological activity in part accelerates detoxication of pesticides and partly promotes the storage of plant nutrients reaching the soil with large dose fertilization. Nevertheless we have to count with the fact that in the course of mineralization of the free organic materials in the soil, the extent of binding of nutrients reaching the soil with fertilizers may increase too. The importance of this is reflected in the programme of this meeting. The production plants becoming widespread in animal breeding present a formidable problem to soil biology with respect to the elimination of wastes from meat producing factories.

The rapid growth of agricultural production primarily has demanded that our main attention be focussed on processes above the soil. Plant breeding mechanization and chemization has certainly caused revolutionary changes in plant cultivation. The processes below the soil surface should be the centre of our focus for a considerable part of the biological and energy cycle of the biosphere is carried on at this level.

I. Láng
Deputy Secretary General
Hungarian Academy of Sciences

LIST OF CONTRIBUTORS

ÁBRAHÁM, L. National Institute for Agricultural Quality Testing, 1024 Budapest, Keleti Károly St. 24, Hungary

BAKALIVANOV, D. "Poushkarov" Institute for Soil Science, Sofia 24, Shosse Bankya 5, Bulgaria

BAKONDI-ZÁMORY, É. (Mrs) National Institute for Agricultural Quality Testing, 1024 Budapest, Keleti Károly St. 24, Hungary

BALICKA, N. (Mrs) University of Agronomy, Institute of Soil Chemistry, Soil Science and Microbiology, 50–930 Wroclaw, Grunwaldzka 53, Poland

BAYOUMY, M. B. Eötvös Loránd University, Institute of Systematic Zoology and Ecology, 1088 Budapest, Puskin St. 3. Hungary

BARABÁS, I. (Mrs) Biological Centre of the Hungarian Academy of Sciences, Institute of Genetics, Szeged, Hungary

BERESTETSKY, O. All-Union Research Institute of Agricultural Microbiology, Leningrad, Pushkin-6, Podbelshky St. 3, USSR

BUDAY, F. University of Agricultural Sciences, Department of Microbiology, 2100 Gödöllő, Hungary

BUKOWSKI, Z. Agricultural Academy, Department of Agricultural Chemistry and Microbiology, Krakow, Poland

BUTI, I. (Miss) Research Institute for Soil Science and Agricultural Chemistry of the Hungarian Academy of Sciences, 1022 Budapest, Herman Ottó St. 15, Hungary

CHANOVA, D. K. (Mrs) "Poushkarov" Institute for Soil Science, Sofia 24, Shosse Bankya 5, Bulgaria

CORTÉS, N. (Mrs) University of Oriente, School of Biological Sciences, Laboratory of Microbiology, Santiago de Cuba, Cuba

CSUTÁK, J. Eötvös Loránd University, Institute of Systematic Zoology and Ecology, 1088 Budapest, Puskin St. 3, Hungary

CZUKOR, I. (Mrs) Research Institute for Canning and Paprika Industry, 1453 Budapest P.O.B. 11, Hungary

DÓRA, GY. "Maurice Thorez" Open-cut Mines, 3272 Visonta, Hungary

DERIMOVA-PÁNTOS, T. (Mrs) University of Forestry and Timber Industry, Department of Soil Science, 9400 Sopron, Hungary

DI GLÉRIA, E. (Miss) "Rozmaring" Agricultural Cooperative, 1028 Budapest, Patakhegyi St. 83–85, Hungary

DOBROVOLNÁ–VASULKOVÁ, E. (Mrs) Botanical Institute of the Czechoslovak Academy of Sciences, Brno, Stará 18, Czechoslovakia

DRĂGAN–BULARDA, M. Babeş–Bolyai University, Department of Plant Physiology, Cluj–
Napoca, Romania

EL BAHRAWI, S. A. Tanta University, Faculty of Agriculture, Tanta, Egypt

EMTSEV, V. T. Timiryazev Agricultural Academy, Department of Microbiology, 125008
Moscow, Timiryazev St. 49, Building N^O 9, USSR.

FARGUES, J. I.N.R.A. Station de Recherches de Lutte Biologique, Versailles, France

FARKAS, E. (Mrs) University of Horticulture and Viticulture, Department of Chemistry, 1118
Budapest, Ménesi St. 44, Hungary

FERNÁNDEZ, M. (Mrs) University of Oriente, School of Biological Sciences, Laboratory of
Microbiology, Santiago de Cuba, Cuba

FÜLEKY, GY. Research Institute for Soil Science and Agricultural Chemistry of the Hungarian
Academy of Sciences, 1022 Budapest, Herman Ottó St. 15, Hungary

GALGÓCZY, B. University of Agricultural Sciences, Department of Chemistry, 8361 Keszthely,
Deák F. St. 16, Hungary

GAMAL EL-DIN, H. Research Institute for Soil Science and Agricultural Chemistry of the
Hungarian Academy of Sciences, 1022 Budapest, Herman Ottó St. 15, Hungary

GARCIA PEÑA, R. High School of Agronomy, National Centre of Agronomy, Ciego de Avila,
Camaguey, Cuba

GERGELY, Z. University of Agricultural Sciences, Department of Microbiology, 2100 Gödöllő,
Hungary

GÄRTNER–BÁNFALVI, Á. National Institute for Agricultural Quality Testing, Budapest,
Hungary

GULYÁS, F. Research Institute for Soil Science and Agricultural Chemistry of the Hungarian
Academy of Sciences, 1022 Budapest, Herman Ottó St. 15, Hungary

GYURKÓ, P. University of Forestry and Timber Industry, Department of Soil Science, 9400
Sopron, Hungary

HADYIVALCHEVA, E. N. (Mrs) "Poushkarov" Institute for Soil Science, Sofia 24, Shosse
Bankya 5, Bulgaria

HAIDER, K. Institute of Soil Biochemistry, Braunschweig, G.F.R.

HAMED, A. S. National Research Centre, Department of Soil Science and Microbiology, Dokki,
Cairo, Egypt

HARGITAI, L. University of Horticulture and Viticulture, Department of Soil Science, 1118
Budapest, Ménesi St. 44, Hungary

HELMECZI, B. University of Agricultural Sciences, Department of Soil Science and Microbiology, 4001 Debrecen, Böszörményi St. 138, Hungary

HLEBAROVA, S. I. (Mrs) "Poushkarov" Institute for Soil Science, Sofia 24, Shosse Bankya 5,
Bulgaria

IBRAHIM, A. N. Al Azhar University, Faculty of Agronomy, Department of Botany, Cairo, Egypt

IMRE, J. Regional Laboratory of the National Institute for Agricultural Quality Testing, 6722
Szeged, Alsókikötősor St. 5, Hungary

IVANOVA, E. P. (Mrs) "Poushkarov" Institute for Soil Science, Sofia 24, Shosse Bankya 5,
Bulgaria

KABATA–PENDIAS, A. (Mrs) Institute of Soil Science and Plant Cultivation, Pulawy 24–100,
Poland

KÁDÁR, I. Research Institute for Soil Science and Agricultural Chemistry of the Hungarian
Academy of Sciences, 1022 Budapest, Herman Ottó St. 15, Hungary

KECSKÉS, M. Research Institute for Soil Science and Agricultural Chemistry of the Hungarian
Academy of Sciences, 1022 Budapest, Herman Ottó St. 15, Hungary

KILBERTUS, G. University of Nancy-1, Laboratory of Botany and Microbiology, Centre de
2me Cycle, Case Officialle N^O 140, 54037 Nancy–Cedex. France

KISS, S. Babeş–Bolyai University, Department of Plant Physiology, Cluj–Napoca, Romania

14

KISS, GY. Plant Protection Centre of the Ministry of Agriculture and Food, 1118 Budapest, Buda-
örsi St. 141/145, Hungary

KISS, M. (Mrs) University of Agricultural Sciences, Department of Microbiology, Gödöllő,
Hungary

KLIMES—SZMIK, A. Research Institute for Soil Science and Agricultural Chemistry of the
Hungarian Academy of Sciences, 1022 Budapest, Herman Ottó St. 15, Hungary

KOBUS, J. Institute of Soil Science and Plant Cultivation, Pulawy 24-100, Poland

KONKOLY, I. Supply Trust for the Agriculture, 1065 Budapest, Bajcsy-Zsilinszky St. 57,
Hungary

KÓNYA, K. University of Agricultural Sciences, Department of Plant Production, 2100 Gödöllő,
Hungary

KOSINKIEWICZ, B. (Mrs) University of Agronomy, Institute of Soil Chemistry, Soil Science
and Microbiology, 50—930 Wroclaw, Grunwaldzka St. 53, Poland

KOSTOV, O. S. "Poushkarov" Institute for Soil Science, Sofia 24, Shosse Bankya 5, Bulgaria

KOVÁCS—LIGETFALUSI, I. (Mrs) University of Forestry and Timber Industry, Department of
Soil Science, 9400 Sopron, Hungary

KÖVES—PÉCHY, K. (Mrs) Research Institute for Soil Science and Agricultural Chemistry of the
Hungarian Academy of Sciences, 1022 Budapest, Herman Ottó St. 15, Hungary

KOZÁK, M. Research Institute for Soil Science and Agricultural Chemistry of the Hungarian
Academy of Sciences, 1022 Budapest, Herman Ottó St. 15, Hungary

KREŻEL, Z. (Mrs) University of Agronomy, Institute of Soil Chemistry, Soil Science and
Microbiology, 50—930 Wroclaw, Grunwaldzka St. 53, Poland

KUBÁT, J. Research Institute of Plant Production, 161—06 Prague 6, Ruzyné, Czechoslovakia

KUBISTA, K. University of Agriculture, Department of Microbiology, Prague—Suchdol,
Czechoslovakia

LÁNG, I. Hungarian Academy of Sciences, 1051 Budapest, Roosevelt Square 9, Hungary

LATKOVICS, I. (Mrs) Research Institute for Soil Science and Agricultural Chemistry of the
Hungarian Academy of Sciences, 1022 Budapest, Herman Ottó St. 15, Hungary

LUBCZYNSKA, J. (Mrs) University of Agronomy, Institute of Soil Chemistry, Soil Science and
Microbiology, 50—930 Wroclaw, Grunwaldzka St. 53, Poland

MANNINGER, E. Research Institute for Soil Science and Agricultural Chemistry of the
Hungarian Academy of Sciences, 1022 Budapest, Herman Ottó St. 15, Hungary

MAREČKOVÁ, H. (Mrs) Research Institute of Crop Production, 161—06 Prague 6, Ruzyné,
Czeshoslovakia

MÁTÉ, F. Research Institute for Soil Science and Agricultural Chemistry of the Hungarian
Academy of Sciences, 1022 Budapest, Herman Ottó St. 15, Hungary

MÁTÉ, E. (Mrs) Council of Budapest County, Agricultural Department of the Executive
Committee, 1052 Budapest, Városház St. 7, Hungary

MENDLIK, A. (Mrs) Geochemical Research Laboratory of the Hungarian Academy of Sciences,
1112 Budapest, Budaörsi st. 45, Hungary

MILUSHEVA, J. (Mrs) "Poushkarov" Institute for Soil Science, Sofia 24, Shosse Bankya 5,
Bulgaria

MISHUSTIN, E. N. Institute of Microbiology of the Academy of Sciences of USSR, Moscow
V-132, Profsoyuznaya St. 7, USSR

MOLNÁR, J. Experimental Station of the Research Institute for Viticulture and Enology, 3300
Eger, Lenin St. 141, Hungary

MUROMTSEV, G. S. All-Union Research Institute for Agricultural Microbiology, Leningrad,
Pushkin 6, Podbelshky St. 3, USSR

MÜLLER, G. Martin Luther University, Department of Soil Science and Microbiology, 402
Halle, Weidenplan 14, GDR

NAGY, R. (Mrs) Research Institute for Viticulture and Enology, 1022 Budapest, Herman Ottó St. 15, Hungary

NOVÁK, B. Research Institute of Crop Production, 161–06 Prague 6, Ruzyné, Czechoslovakia

NOVAKOVÁ, J. (Mrs) University of Agriculture, Department of Microbiology, Prague–Suchdol, Czechoslovakia

NYÍRI, L. Research Institute for Soil Cultivation, 5300 Karcag, Hungary

OLÁH, G. M. Université Laval, Laboratoire de Mycologie, Quebec, Canada

OLÁH, J. "Maurice Thorez" Open-cut Mines, 3272 Visonta, Hungary

PANTERA, H. (Mrs) Institute of Fertilization and Soil Science, 55–230 Laskowice–Olawskie, Poland

PÁNTOS-DERIMOVA T. (Mrs) University of Forestry and Timber Industry, Department of Soil Science, 9400 Sopron, Hungary

PÁNTOS, GY. University of Forestry and Timber Industry, Department of Soil Science, 9400 Sopron, Hungary

PAPP, J. Plant Protection Centre of the Ministry of Agriculture and Food, 1118 Budapest, Buda-örsi St. 141/145, Hungary

PAPP, L. "Kossuth Lajos" University, Department of Botany, 4010 Debrecen, Hungary

PÁTKAI, T. Research Institute for Soil Science and Agricultural Chemistry of the Hungarian Academy of Sciences, 1022 Budapest, Herman Ottó St. 15, Hungary

POBOZSNY, M. (Miss) Research Group of Soil Zoology of the Hungarian Academy of Sciences, 1088 Budapest, Puskin St. 3, Hungary

POZSGAI, J. University of Agricultural Sciences, Department of Plant Protection, 8360 Keszthely, Hungary

PUSZTAI, T. (Mrs) "Eötvös Loránd" University, Department of Genetics, 1088 Budapest, Muzeum Boul. 4/a, Hungary

RANKOV, V. "Maritsa" Vegetable Crops Research Institute, Plovdiv, Bulgaria

REISINGER, O. University of Nancy-1, Laboratory of Botany and Microbiology, Centre de 2me Cycle, Case Officielle N° 140, 54037 Nancy–Cedex, France

RODRIGUEZ–PEREZ, M. (Mrs) University of Oriente, School of Biological Sciences, Laboratory of Microbiology, Santiago de Cuba, Cuba

SÁIZ–JIMÉNEZ, C. Centre of Edafology and Applied Biology, Sevilla, Spain

SALEM, K. G. Agricultural Research Centre, Weed Control Department Cairo, Egypt

SALEM, S. H. Zagazig University, Faculty of Agronomy, Department of Microbiology Dokki, Egypt

SAUT, A. M. University of Veterinary Science, Department of Parasitology, 1183 Budapest, Landler Jenő St. 2, Hungary

SARKADI, J. Research Institute for Soil Science and Agricultural Chemistry of the Hungarian Academy of Sciences, 1022 Budapest, Herman Ottó St. 15, Hungary

SOÓS, T. "Phylaxia" Veterinary Biologicals and Feedstuffs, 1107 Budapest, Szállás St. 5, Hungary

SCHAEFER, R. Orsay University, Faculty of Sciences, Department of Ecology, 91405 Orsay, France

SZABOLCS, I. Research Institute for Soil Science and Agricultural Chemistry of the Hungarian Academy of Sciences, 1022 Budapest, Herman Ottó St. 15, Hungary

SZEGI, J. Research Institute for Soil Science and Agricultural Chemistry of the Hungarian Academy of Sciences, 1022 Budapest, Herman Ottó St. 15, Hungary

SZEMES, I. Research Institute for Soil Science and Agricultural Chemistry of the Hungarian Academy of Sciences, 1022 Budapest, Herman Ottó St. 15, Hungary

SZENDE, K. Research Institute for Soil Sciences and Agricultural Chemistry of the Hungarian Academy of Sciences, 1022 Budapest, Herman Ottó St. 15, Hungary

SZEPES, GY. (Mrs) National Institute of Agricultural Quality Testing, 1024 Budapest, Keleti Károly St. 24, Hungary

SIDORENKO, O. Institute of Microbiology of the Academy of Sciences of USSR, Moscow V-132, Profsoyuznaya St. 7, USSR

SZOLNOKI, J. Geochemical Research Laboratory of the Hungarian Academy of Sciences, 1088 Budapest, Museum Boul. 4/a, Hungary

TAKÁTS, T. University of Forestry and Timber Industry, Department of Soil Science, 9400 Sopron, Hungary

TALEVA, A. T. "Poushkarov" Institute for Soil Science, Sofia 24, Shosse Bankya 5, Bulgaria

TÁTRAI, N. Company of Geodesy and Cartography, 2800 Tatabánya, Táncsics M. St. 102, Hungary

TESAŘOVA, M. (Miss) Botanical Institute of Czechoslovak Academy of Sciences, 662 61 Brno, Stará 18, Czechoslovakia

TEWFIK, M. S. Agricultural Research Centre, Weed Control Department, Cairo, Egypt

TIMÁR, É. M. (Mrs) Research Institute for Soil Science and Agricultural Chemistry of the Hungarian Academy of Sciences, 1022 Budapest, Herman Ottó St. 15, Hungary

TORMA, V. "Egyetértés" Agricultural Cooperative, 7847 Kovácshida, Hungary

TÓTH, Á. University of Horticulture and Viticulture, Department of Chemistry 1114 Budapest, Villányi St. 29—31, Hungary

TÓTH, B. University of Agricultural Sciences, Department of Chemistry, 8361 Keszthely, Deák F. St. 16, Hungary

TÓTH, J. A. Kossuth Lajos University, Department of Botany, 4010 Debrecen, Hungary

TROJANOWSKI, J. M. Curie—Sklodowska University, Department of Biochemistry, 20—033 Lublin, Academicka St. 19, Poland

UHERKOVICH, R. "Zrinyi" Agricultural Cooperative, 7968 Felsőszentmárton, Hungary

ULEHLOVÁ, B. (Mrs) Botanical Institute of the Czechoslovak Academy of Sciences, Brno, Stará 18, Czechoslovakia

URBINA, A. Research Institute for Agronomy, Santiago de Chile, Chile

VARJÚ, P. University of Forestry and Timber Industry, Department of Soil Science, 9400 Sopron, Hungary

VÉGH, K. (Miss) Research Institute for Soil Science and Agricultural Chemistry of the Hungarian Academy of Sciences, 1022 Budapest, Herman Ottó St. 15, Hungary

VELEV, B. "Maritsa" Vegetable Crops Research Institute, Plovdiv, Bulgaria

VINTIKOVA, H. (Mrs) Research Institute of Crop Production Prague 6, Ruzyné Czechoslovakia

VOINOVA—RAIKOVA, ZH. "Poushkarov" Institute for Soil Science, Sofia 24, Shosse Bankya 5, Bulgaria

VÖRÖS, N. I. (Mrs) Research Institute for Soil Science and Agricultural Chemistry of the Hungarian Academy of Sciences, 1022 Budapest, Herman Ottó St. 15, Hungary

WEGRZYN, T. (Mrs) University of Agronomy, Institute of Soil Chemistry, Soil Science and Microbiology, 50—930 Wroclaw, Grunwaldzka St. 53, Poland

WILDMAN, A. Regional Laboratory of the Institute of Agricultural Quality Testing, 9200 Mosonmagyaróvár, Hungary

ZABAWSKI, J. University of Agronomy, Institute of Plant Physiology and Biophysics, Wroclaw, Cybulskiego St. 32, Poland

ZABAWSKA, L. (Mrs) University of Agronomy, Institute of Plant Biology and Biophysics 50—205 Wroclaw, Cybulskiego St. 32, Poland

ZUBKO, I. K. All-Union Research Institute of Agricultural Microbiology, Leningrad, Pushkin 6 Podbelshky St. 3 USSR

ŽUKOWSKA, Z. (Mrs) University of Agronomy, Institute of Soil Chemistry, Soil Science and Microbiology, 50—930 Wroclaw, Grunwaldzka St. 53, Poland

ŽURAWSKA, M. (Mrs) University of Agronomy, Institute of Plant Physiology and Biophysics, 50—205 Wroclaw, Cybulskiego St. 32, Poland

EDITOR'S PREFACE

This volume contains the papers presented at the VIIth Meeting on Soil Biology, held at Keszthely University of Agriculture between 2–4 September, 1975. The meeting was organized by the Soil Biology Section of the Hungarian Society for Soil Science of the Hungarian Association of Agricultural Sciences under the auspices of the Keszthely University of Agriculture. There were more than a hundred participants — and almost half came from abroad — to discuss soil biological problems. The 54 papers presented here were written by experts of 14 countries (Bulgaria, Canada, Chile, Czechoslovakia, Egypt, Federal Republic of Germany, France, German Democratic Republic, Poland, Cuba, Romania, Soviet Union, Spain and Hungary).

As it is usual with such multi-author volumes, subjects range over a wide field and there are considerable differences in their internal set up. This heterogeneity has only been diminished by division of the matter into six chapters outlined according to important trends in recent soil biology. Papers are arranged around a central theme: the protection and conservation of the human environment and the role of soil biology in this. Influence of up-to-date agricultural methods on our environment calls for permanent study and control of soil ecosystems. The discovery of interactions between biotic and abiotic processes could significantly contribute to a more extended involvement of environmental aspects in soil science and agricultural chemistry.

On behalf of the Organizing Committee, it is my privilege to express our appreciation to persons and organizations who contributed to making this meeting a success. We are particularly indebted to the authorities of the Keszthely University of Agriculture for providing the facilities and for invaluable help during the meeting.

The generous support of the Hungarian Academy of Sciences, especially that of the Department of Agricultural Sciences making the edition of this volume possible is gratefully acknowledged.

J. Szegi,
Chairman of the Organizing Committee

INTERACTION BETWEEN
CHEMICALS INTRODUCED IN AGRICULTURE
AND SOIL ORGANISMS

UTILIZATION OF CHEMICALS IN HUNGARIAN AGRICULTURE

by

I. KONKOLY
Supply Trust for Agriculture,
Budapest, Hungary

Hungarian agriculture in the last decade has arrived in that period of development in which chemicalization has become an indispensable, integral part of agricultural technology. Progress is illustrated by data on the value of chemicals used, which amounted to 5% in 1960, 12.6% in 1970 and to 23% in 1975 of the expenses of agricultural production (calculated without amortization of hardware).

This rapid increase of utilization is closely connected with the socialist re-organization of Hungarian agriculture. Before collectivization, the use of fertilizers as well as herbicides remained below the European standards. For example, in 1958, 18 kg fertilizer/ha arable land was used in Hungary. Use of herbicides was also at a low level, except for several (i.e. vine) cultures. Fungicides used were mostly copper- and sulphur-containing inorganic compounds while pesticides were dominated by chlorinated hydrocarbons.

Factors promoting the increased use of chemicals are rather complex; development of large-scale farming, industrialization of agriculture, increasing need for food and for improved products should be mentioned here. Progress was greatly encouraged by the system of subsidized prices. As a result of these circumstances, use of fertilizers increased sevenfold between 1961 and 1975. The corresponding figure for herbicides is even larger, the amount used in 1975 was almost eight times more than in 1961.

Intensified chemicalization has led to a significant increase of agricultural production. Wheat and maize — main crops of the Hungarian agriculture produced on about 55% of arable land of the country — yielded 18.6 q/ha and 26.1 q/ha on the average in the years of 1961—65. However, in 1974, the average yield of wheat was 37.5 q/ha and maize yielded 42.0 q/ha. Programmes designed for other, less-developed cultures are in progress and have given encouraging results.

The two main groups of chemicals used in Hungarian agriculture are fertilizers and herbicides. The use of *fertilizers* quickly spread especially in the late sixties due to increased production and partly to import. In 1975, 1.5 million tons of fertilizers were used, which is equal to 240 kg fertilizer/ha of arable land of the country. According to economical calculations, this increase counterbalanced the loss of some

0.6 million ha decrease of arable land between 1961 and 1975. Taking into consideration that the whole area of arable land of the country amounts to 6.7 million hectares, this result is not negligible.

The average value of 240 kg/ha covers a rather wide scattering of individual figures of counties or farms. For example, state farms use some 80% more fertilizer per unit of cultivated land than that used by smaller cooperatives. If counties are considered, the differences are even larger. In 1974, the figures for the largest users (Fejér, Baranya and Komárom counties) were larger by a factor of 2,2 than the figures of the least developed ones (Borsod, Nógrád and Hajdú counties). Differences existing between farms were further differentiated by introduction of new production systems. Use of 500—600 kg/ha (active ingredient) fertilizer is a common practice in a number of farms. On the other hand, especially in farms working under unfavourable natural conditions of Borsod and Nógrád counties, the utilization of fertilizers is much less, it is below 100 kg/ha. Governmental measures have been taken in order to resolve these difficulties, however, attaining significant results obviously needs more time.

In the early sixties, most of the fertilizers used were the simpler types. Multiple fertilizers were introduced in 1968 and recently about 20% of the amount utilized belongs to this group. Besides the 8—10 different kinds of complex fertilizers available in Hungary, 4—5 types of fertilizers amended with microelements are also available. Within the group of singular fertilizers the compounds containing more active ingredients (urea, triple-phosphate, etc.) increased considerably. It is noteworthy, that potassium sulphate is used in large amounts instead of potassium chloride. Potassium sulphate is extremely important in the cultivation of chloride-sensitive plants, such as tobacco, certain fruits, etc.

Concerning the structural development of Hungarian agriculture, the chemicalization of plant protection is at the highest level. The progress achieved in this field is clearly illustrated by data on volume and choice of herbicides used. In 1961, Hungarian agriculture utilized pesticides costing about 500 million Forints (on governmentally subsidized prices). This sum amounted to 3.8—3.9 billions in the year of 1975, which is about 60% of the value of fertilizers used. These figures are comparable to the corresponding figures of the most developed countries. Number of commercially available fertilizers was about 60 in 1961, while in 1975 this number increased to about 400. If use of pesticides is characterized by projection of prices to hectares of arable land, Hungarian agriculture used 2.3 US $ value of pesticide/ha in 1961 and 19 US $ in 1975. These figures are the highest in relation to the socialist countries and are at the 6th—7th place in statistics in all countries of the world.

It should be noted that these averages — without additional information — are somewhat misleading. Concerning various branches of agriculture, the figures are widely differentiated. In viticulture and in production of fruits chemicalization has been 100% for several years, however, concerning cereals or gardening, this level is much lower. Therefore, the average level of the chemical plant protection is around 60% if the whole country and all cultures are taken into account.

There are apparent shifts in the spectra of chemicals used. These changes were initiated by a critical survey of the chemicals available on the market followed by proper measures taken in due time by central organizations. The copper-containing inorganic fungicides — from the early sixties onwards — were gradually changed to organic, systemic compounds and to combined (copper + organic) types. Similarly, mercury-containing seed dressing compounds were changed to new, more effective and less dangerous types.

Until 1966, chlorinated hydrocarbon pesticides were predominant. Between 1966 and 1969 DDT was withdrawn from the market. The last type of chlorinated hydrocarbons which still is in use, is Lindane, but use of this compound is thoroughly restricted. Chlorinated hydrocarbons have been replaced by new types of carbamates and esters of phosphoric acid from 1972 onwards.

The most progress was achieved in the field of herbicide utilization, resulting in revolutionary changes in agricultural technologies. Till the early seventies triazines were the most widely used types. From 1973 their use has been restricted in Hungary and at present they may be used only in combinations. Instead of triazines the use of carbamates and chloracetanilides is encouraged because these compounds are quickly (within 4–6 months) decomposed in soils.

As far as the future trends of chemicalization are concerned, in the next five years qualitative aspects (correct, more effective application, etc.) will be stressed rather than quantitative increase of production and utilization. In 1975, 1.5 million tons (active ingredient) of fertilizers were used in Hungary. The planned yearly increase is 6–8%, i.e. the total amount used will be 2 million tons in 1980. At the end of the current Five Year Plan, 300 kg/ha fertilizer will be used in Hungary; 1 : 0.8 : 0.9 NPK ratio is planned. Approximately 35–40% of the total utilization will be provided in the form of complex fertilizers.

According to our intentions, liquid fertilizers will also be used on a broader scale than they were before. Experiments with liquid ammonia produced by high-pressure technology are in progress. However, because of the much less expensive production, mixibility with other chemicals, more easy handling and other advantages, liquid fertilizers not requiring high-pressure technology will be extensively used in the future.

Use of herbicides will increase by about 20% in this period; this planned increase is less than the 30% achieved between 1971 and 1975. Value of pesticides utilized in Hungary in 1980 will be about 7.7–7.8 billion Forints. The expected number of available herbicides will be approximately 800 in 1980; important changes are planned in the use or withdrawal of certain groups.

These developments must be based on the intensive development of the Hungarian chemical industry. At present, almost 40% of herbicides used in Hungary are imported from capitalist countries. Import of certain special compounds (or several common products in order to provide proper choice) is necessary, but compounds indispensable for the most important cultures must be produced in Hungary or imported from the socialist countries. The Olefin Project of the Hungarian chemical industry will help considerably in this respect making the production of precursors, intermediers and final products possible independently from import.

Quantitative and qualitative development of chemicalization demands continuous improvement in efficiency of utilization which is one of the major factors of feasibility in agricultural production. From this complex problem only the most actual aspects will be discussed here.

Except for recent years, it was a common practice in many farms that every available method of plant protection was involved in the technology of agricultural production. Only one point was taken into consideration: whether that particular method was suitable for large-scale farming or not. Pesticides were used indiscriminately, which resulted in an unreasonably high level of utilization. The only way to abandon this is a reliable prognosis. For these purposes a central organization was established, which provides prognoses on the 10 most important parasites of apple, vine and potato. This centre sends prognoses to every farm producing vine on more than 10 hectares or potato on more than 20 ha. In the following years a further ten cultivated plants will be involved in this system; we expect that the network of this service system will help to reduce the use of herbicides to a reasonable level. At the same time, a number of experts and modern equipment are also needed.

Particular attention is being paid to scientific and practical problems of soil fertility. In the framework of a governmental programme, long-term experiments are in progress. Among them, one of the most important is the series of fertilization experiments started in 1966. The aim of this work is the study of systematic, continuous use of fertilizers in various doses and rations of nutrient elements. Data obtained in these experiments are evaluated according to the different soil types and are utilized in advisory work.

Distribution and storage of chemicals are also crucial factors in improvement of effectiveness. The future trend is the organization of chemicalization centres for every 20 000–50 000 hectares. These centres (common interests of chemical works and commercial units) will organize the storage and distribution of chemicals and will help the users with advisory work based on scientific research. Several centres of this type are functioning now and extension of this system is planned.

INTENSIVE CHEMIZATION OF LAND FARMING AND NEW PROBLEMS OF SOIL MICROBIOLOGY

by

G. S. MUROMTSEV
All-Union Research Institute of
Agricultural Microbiology
Leningrad, USSR

Under natural conditions soil fertility is closely connected with the activity of saprophytic microflora. In this case, microbes perform two very important functions: first — mineralization of organic matter of plant and animal origin, and secondly — atmospheric nitrogen fixation. Until recently (to be more exact, before the beginning of the large-scale production of nitrogenous fertilizers) almost the entire biospheric nitrogen was of microbial origin and the process of atmospheric nitrogen fixation could be considered equal in importance to that of photosynthesis.

Under natural conditions there is a sort of symbiosis between autotrophic plants and heterotrophic microbes. The former produce organic matter during the photosynthetic process while the latter, consuming the organic matter, release nutrients required by the plants.

As a result of microbial activity not only nitrogen but also considerable amounts of available phosphorus and potassium are accumulated in the soil.

Such is the role played by micro-organisms in natural fertility of the soil.

As can be seen, the evolution has made microbes be the most important links of the nutrient cycle in the biosphere: decomposition and mineralization of a large amount of organic matter continuously entering the soil and the water bodies, and synthesis of nitrogenous compounds from atmospheric nitrogen. However, nowadays this situation is undergoing radical changes.

The above-described natural processes occurring in the soil cannot any longer ensure high yields of crops corresponding to intensive growth of the world's population. And now natural fertility of the soil is being replaced by the artificial one, made by man. Producing and applying artificial fertilizers on a still larger scale, man, so to say, has taken upon himself the most important function of soil microbes, i.e. supply of plants with mineral nutrients. Large-scale application of mineral fertilizers is a new factor formerly unknown to the evolution process. An equally new factor is removal from the soil of big quantities of nitrogen, phosphorus, potassium and other elements at the expense of rapidly growing yields. Such removals cannot be compensated by the useful activity of microbes alone, without the application of fertilizers at high rates.

The scale of the described processes can be characterized by the following figures. According to the approximate calculation (apparently, an exact count cannot be made in this case) the amount of atmospheric nitrogen annually fixed by nitrogen-fixing microbes is measured in scores of millions of tons. At present in the world about 40 million tons of nitrogen are manufactured annually in the form of mineral fertilizers, and by 1980 this figure may reach 60 to 70 million tons. Thus, nowadays the scales of industrial and natural production of fixed nitrogen have practically become equal.

And, of course, one should not forget that microbial mineralization of organic matter, as it is, continues to be the most essential link in the nutrient cycle on our planet, while nitrogen fixation by microbes is the most inexpensive and safe method of supplying plants with nitrogen.

Until recently the main task faced by soil microbiologists was to study the part played by microbes in root feeding of plants. Under the conditions of natural soil fertility this part is actually the key one. However, as it was mentioned above, in the majority of cases the formation of sufficiently high yields of crops due to natural fertility alone is not possible. Big removals of nutrients from the soil must be made up for, and today, and the more so tomorrow, mankind will not do without the application of high rates of fertilizers.

What new problems are put before microbiologists by intensification of arable farming, by changing over to the artificial fertility of the soil?

In connection with the large-scale application of mineral fertilizers a very acute problem arises which is enhancing the efficiency of fertilizers. The efficiency of utilization of nitrogen from mineral fertilizers ranges from 50 to 60 per cent, and that of phosphorus – still less: 20 to 25 per cent. Understanding the "destiny" of nutrients applied to the soil in the form of fertilizers is a question of the utmost importance. And the part played by micro-organisms in the transformation of these nutrients in the soil is great.

Now we are well aware of the actual scale of denitrification and harm which it causes – as is known up to 20 per cent of nitrogen applied to the soil in the form of fertilizers goes to the air.

Another process – consumption of fertilizer nitrogen and phosphorus by soil microbes during their multiplication has been studied to a lesser extent. The tests with nitrogen isotope ^{15}N show that in the well-managed soil having big and active microbial population, micro-organisms assimilate over 1/4 of mineral fertilizer nitrogen. How should we evaluate this phenomenon? On the one hand, mineral nitrate nitrogen is very mobile; as a result of denitrification it goes to the air in the gaseous form, that is why its partial fixation in the form of microbial protein can be regarded as a positive phenomenon. On the other hand, mineral fertilizers are intended for plants rather than for microbes. So a thorough study of the part played by microbes in the "destiny" of mineral fertilizers in the soil is the most important question which has arisen in soil microbiology in connection with chemization of land farming.

The activity of soil microflora is closely connected with organic matter. Any transformations of organic matter in nature are, primarily, a result of the life activity of microbes. Until recently organic material, farmyard manure in particular, was actually the only form of fertilizers, and livestock farms supplied not only meat and milk but also performed one more important function — they were a factory of organic fertilizers. Nowadays due to intensive application of mineral fertilizers the function of organic fertilizers, to be more exact — organic matter, as a source of nutrients for plants, is gradually decreasing. This does not mean, of course, that the application of organic fertilizers should be reduced. On the contrary, alongside with the growth of livestock population, the amount of organic fertilizer application will also increase. However, the rates of growth of mineral fertilizer production and application are so much higher that the share of organic fertilizers in the total amount of fertilizers applied, is continuously going down.

May one conclude from this that organic fertilizers will gradually become unnecessary? No, on no account. Organic matter has two functions to perform in the soil — a chemical one (a source of nutrients for plants) and a physical one (an improver of soil structure). And whereas its chemical function may become less important, its physical function, on the contrary, is enhanced. To a considerable extent it is associated with the spreading of soil erosion. And in this capacity mineral fertilizers can in no way replace the organic ones.

Traditional methods of land cultivation, which commonly are being used now include methods aimed at maximum utilization of natural fertility of the soil. For example, active loosening of the soil considerably intensifies the activity of aerobic micro-organisms, as well as the decomposition of organic matter and release of mineral nutrients from it. When high rates of mineral fertilizers are applied, this may lead to such a situation in which it would be more important to preserve the organic matter of the soil for the purpose of improving its physical condition rather than to use this organic matter as a source of nutrients for plants. Thus the spreading of the so-called minimum-tillage of the soil, which means loosening of the soil reduced to the minimum, is a progressive development from the point of view of not only soil physics but also that of soil microbiology.

Under the conditions of intensification and specialization of agricultural production the development of methods of plant soil infections control is becoming of great importance. One of the main methods of soil sanitation from plant pathogens is a traditional one, i.e. crop rotations. It should be noted that existing systems of crop rotation were formed mainly under the conditions of multibranch farming. Specialization of agricultural production requires maximum "saturation" of the crop rotation system with the main crop.

Regular applications of pesticides make it possible in a number of cases to change over even to a monoculture, i.e. growing the same valuable crop on the same field year after year. While in the past this resulted in accumulation of parasites and pests: insects, weeds and microbes specific to a particular crop, now it is possible to control them with pesticides. Thus, while specialization of agricultural production requires maximum "saturation" of the crop rotation system with the main crop, chemization of agriculture makes it possible to fulfil this requirement.

But though, on the whole, pesticides can control weeds, pests and pathogenic microbes affecting the above-ground parts of plants, the chemical control of root infections is not a big success for the time being. It is difficult and unprofitable economically to saturate the soil with pesticides to such an extent as to destroy pathogenic microflora in the soil. Besides, a great deal of useful microbes are eliminated too. At the same time for a pesticide sprayed over a plant it is much more difficult to penetrate into the root system than into the leaves.

Cotton wilt and gramen root rots are typical examples of root infections causing big losses. Annually their pathogens get accumulated in the soil. Under such conditions in case of cotton the main factor determining the yield is not the level of nutrients in the soil (which is normally very high) and even not the water supply level (which is ensured by irrigation), but the degree of wilt infection development. Thus, under the conditions of intensive land farming when plants are fully supplied with mineral nutrients and water, problem No. 1 is the soil microbiological factor, i.e. accumulation of plant pathogenic fungi in the soil.

In the complex of agrotechnical measures aimed at clearing the soil from plant pathogens a greater place is being given to enriching the soil with available organic matter. And this is another, I would call it, sanitary function of organic matter whose importance is noticeably increasing under the conditions of land farming intensification. The significance of this agrotechnical practice will become still greater after the number of crops in the crop rotation system is reduced and other crops of the rotation system are replaced to a greater extent by the main crop.

Of certain interest is the mechanism of the sanitating effect produced by organic matter on the soil.

Research carried out in our Laboratory showed that after green manuring the number of antagonistic micro-organisms increases in the soil to a greater level than the total number of microbes. This phenomenon (which at first sight seems paradoxical) may be explained by the fact that when there is sufficient amount of available organic matter, antagonistic microflora, while multiplying, inhibit the development of other microbes including plant pathogenic ones.

On the other hand, the application of available organic matter provokes the germination of resistant dormant forms of plant pathogenic fungi, for example microsclerotia of *Verticillium dahliae,* which expedite their subsequent destruction in the soil.

And still another, very important and actually new function of saprophyte microflora should be mentioned. This is the part they play in protection of the environment from pollution. The main items of the rapid process of environmental pollution are industrial and domestic sewage, wastes from large-scale livestock farms, water soluble fertilizers and pesticides. The latter, despite the insignificant share they have in the total volume of polluters, play an important role due to their high biological activity.

A large-scale pig breeding alone gives annually hundreds of thousands of tons of liquid manure. Rational utilization of big quantities of this substrate is one of the most acute problems of today. Several solutions of this problem are being outlined. The simplest and most realistic one is the use of liquid manure for soil fertilization. In this case, we make use of an efficient natural filter, *i.e.* the soil with its numerous microbial populations. However, here we also encounter difficulties. Liquid manure transportation for a rather long distance as a rule, is not justified economically. That is why fields located not far from a big livestock farm get even surplus manure for several years while agricultural land far away from such a farm may get no manure at all.

Methods of methane fermentation of liquid manure are rather well worked out. Their application may help to supply the countryside with large quantities of burning gas. And finally, methods are being developed for growing fodder yeasts on liquid manure.

A considerable part of organic matter carried out with industrial and domestic sewage is represented by products of non-fermentative, artificial synthesis. And the problem of their microbial decomposition (though a very complicated one from the scientific point of view) is of utmost economic significance. It is highly desirable that pesticides, phosphorus organic compounds and mineral fertilizers are fully decomposed and assimilated in the soil and that they should not enter water bodies, including the world ocean. The entry of some of these substances (herbicides in particular) into the world's ocean may result in the inhibition of algae development, not to mention the direct danger of the pollution of water bodies and groundwater. And this, alongside with a considerable reduction of areas under forests, would lead to the weakening of photosynthesis on a global scale. Figuratively speaking, the earth's biosphere may be compared to an engine using the solar energy as a source of power. And photosynthesis is the main mechanism transforming and using this energy. That is why processes leading to the photosynthesis inhibition are very dangerous.

In this connection, it should be mentioned that while in modern industrial technologies, measures are provided to prevent environmental pollution, in agricultural technologies insufficient attention is being paid to these measures. It is sufficient to mention unsolved problems of manure utilization on large-scale livestock farms, washing a big amount of mineral fertilizers out of the soil into water bodies as well as badly managed and controlled application of pesticides.

As for the acceleration of microbial decomposition of these substances, in the environment it can be achieved by two principally different ways. The first one is the creation of conditions beneficial for their decomposition in the soil by following appropriate agrotechnical practices. For instance, it has been established that the DDT decay is sharply accelerated under anaerobic conditions. Ploughing of fresh plant residues into the soil expedites the decomposition of such herbicides as atrazine and diuron. The other way is guided synthesis of unstable compounds easily undergoing the fermentative hydrolysis. A very insignificant change of the pesticide molecule infrequently converts it from the stable molecule into the one easily destructed by microbial enzymes.

Nowadays "classical" biological science — ecology is undergoing, so to say, an intensive period of renaissance. We owe this considerably to the fact that mankind has realized the danger of crucial meddling with the environment. It is precisely what Frederick Engels warned us about. In "Dialektik der Natur" he wrote: "Schmeicheln wir uns nicht zu sehr mit unsern menschlichen Siegen über die Natur. Für jeden solchen Sieg rächt sie sich an uns. Jeder hat in erster Linie zwar die Folgen, auf die wir gerechnet, aber in zweiter und dritter Linie hat er ganz andre, unvorhergesehene Wirkungen, die nur zu oft jene ersten Folgen wieder aufheben."

Let us hope that rapid extension of research in the field of soil microbial ecology will help in the near future to answer complicated questions put before our science by intensive development of industrial and agricultural production.

REPRODUCTION OF SOIL FERTILITY BY THE REGULATION ACTIVITY OF SAPROPHYTE MICRO-ORGANISMS AFTER APPLYING PHYTOPHARMACEUTICALS

by

G. MÜLLER
Martin Luther University,
Department of Soil Science and Microbiology
Halle, GDR

Nowadays, when industrial plant protection systems have become usual, in the course of regeneration of the soil fertility, great attention has been paid to the introduction of highly effective chemicals and scientific methods. The question arises, how are we supported by the widespread scientific knowledge, when applying chemicals.

Scientific knowledge about the effect of fertilizers on the reproduction of soil fertility is satisfactory. Much is known about the conducive activities (*i.e.* dynamics of the microbiological activity in the soil, mineralization, humification, soil respiration, enzyme activity, root exudate decomposition, and suppression of the soil-borne phytopathogenic organisms) of the autochthonous soil micro-organisms.

However, much less is known about the effect of different phyto-pharmaceuticals, such as pesticides, herbicides, growth regulators, urease, and nitrification inhibitors.

The main effects of these chemicals have been rather well elucidated but the side-effects on the mentioned soil biological criteria of the soil fertility regeneration have not been clarified. Generally, in the permission standards for these chemicals only, human toxicological tests are required but the effect of phytopharmaceuticals on the soil micro-organisms is not assayed.

For planning industrial plant production systems, we must study the side-effects of chemicals in order to prevent their accumulation, while they are applied continuously, in increasing dosages.

To make my exposition more clear a diagram of the different types of the biological regulation dynamics in the soil is presented (Fig. 1. Abscissa: time, ordinate: activity. Control is taken as 100).

After applying different chemicals the microbial activity in the soil shows three basic types of trends. As can be seen from curve No. 1 (Fig. 1) most chemicals stimulate the microbial activies (soil respiration, enzyme activity, population density, etc.) in the soil.

— After a short lag-period this effect turns into the exponential phase, then comes up to the culmination. A short stagnancy is followed by a decreasing period, which is a relatively long one and often turns into negative values.

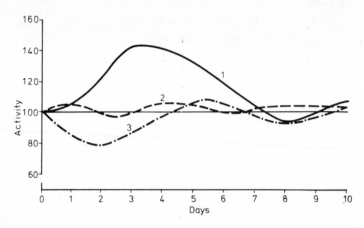

Fig. 1. The types of soil biological regulation dynamics

— This is followed by a shorter exponential phase, then the curve approaches that of the untreated control.

Many other chemicals — as is presented by curve No. 3 — show the inversion of curve No. 1. In this case, chemicals inhibit the microbiological activity in the first period and this is followed by an attenuated renewal of the activity and finally, this curve also approaches the control.

— There are only a few chemicals not showing significant changes in microbial activity (curve No. 2).

— For example, when the effect of different herbicides on soil respiration, enzyme activity, and population density was investigated, Hedolit, Gramoxone, Wonuk, Betanil, Betanal, Defenuron, Tribunil, Omnidel, and Agrosan showed a curve similar to No. 1, curves obtained after Bi 3411, Azaplant, Thiram and Sys 67 MEB treatments were compared to curve No. 3, and only two herbicides, Simazine and Spritzhormit proved to be indifferent (curve No. 2 type).

— Additionally, when treatments with different urease and nitrification inhibitors, bactericides, fungicides, growth regulators as well as disinfectants are carried out similar effects can be observed.

Most phytopharmaceuticals produce not only the desired, main effect but several side-effects also. At present, these side-effects are not well-known. Many investigations are needed in order to achieve a better knowledge of this problem.

The above-mentioned three main types of biological regulation dynamics in the soil are detailed as follows.

Chemicals (curve No. 1) found to be stimulators of the microbial activity (soil respiration, enzyme activity, population density) at the early stage, usually increase the mineralization in the soil and this effect results in an increased nutrient supply.

This increased mineralization is advantageous only, if the nutrients released may be, utilized and will not be leached out. Erosion frequently occurs in spring and autumn and when winter is mild. The intensive plant production together with the permanent application of those phytopharmaceuticals, which are able to increase the mineralization result in undesirable humus losses and leaching out of the nitrogen released.

If a given chemical is applied before the balancing regulation is completed, the stimulation effect will be much less expressed. A weak exponential phase is followed by a very short stagnation then by a decreasing period. In most cases this decline turns into negative activity values and the regeneration of the autochthonous soil microflora needs longer time.

Phytopharmaceuticals included in the third group (curve No. 3) show the following characteristics.

After application, the soil respiration, the enzyme activity, and the population density are depressed almost immediately. This effect is manifest by the inhibition of the mineralization, accumulation of the root-extracts, and the phytopharmaceuticals. When these chemicals are repeatedly applied in high dosages, the yield and the soil fertility will decrease.

The degree of these negative influences depends on the range and duration of the action of the chemical. Although, soil micro-organisms have a wide adoptive capacity, the negative influences may lead to a serious damage of soil fertility.

From a soil biologist's viewpoint the most suitable phytopharmaceuticals are those which have a good main effect and are free from undesired side-effects on the soil micro-organisms.

Urease and nitrification inhibitors as well as fungicides, bactericides, nematicides applied against soil-borne pathogens are required to have a highly selective effect.

As it was shown before, only a very few phytopharmaceuticals do not have deleterious side-effects. During this complicated and highly responsible work soil biologists must co-operate with the pesticide industry and with practical agriculture more effectively, and must help the. until advisory institutions for soil fertility control are not organised.

A research group under my direction is now working on organization of a similar counter-examination, which would serve the preservation of soil fertility. According to our conceptions, during the examination two steps can be distinguished: the permission and the application of a given chemical. In the course of permission, which must be very critical and extensive, over the main effect a great number of side-effects must be thoroughly investigated too.

It is well-known, that a soil of high sorption capacity has a higher buffer capacity towards chemicals. However, the permission examinations must be extended to sandy, loamy, and clay soils also.

Several other environmental factors, such as temperature, humidity, soil reaction, structure, etc. must also be taken into account in the course of a permission procedure. It is especially important to study the physiological mode of action of the chemicals (*e.g.* fungicidal or fungistatical action), and to investigate the action spectra.

The second controlling step should be done only after a longer practical application. In this step, investigations on some general characters of production biology in soil life (*i.e.*, soil respiration, enzyme activity as well as the enumeration of a representative and sensitive, but easily detectable organism, e.g. *Azotobacter* or algae test) are suggested.

SUMMARY

The socialist transformation of agriculture demands the introduction of new scientific knowledge in the course of the increased utilization of high-efficiency chemicals.

Such highly effective chemicals are the phytopharmaceuticals.

Because of the excellent main effect of these chemicals their application is essential. However, in order to promote reproduction of soil fertility, greater attention must be paid to their soil biological side-effects.

The effect of phytopharmaceuticals can be classified into one of the three types of soil biological regulation dynamics.

Chemicals in the first group stimulate, in the third group inhibit the saprophytic soil micro-organisms. Phytopharmaceuticals of the second group are indifferent.

Every type shows a specific activity on the soil fertility regeneration. Recognition, evaluation and modification of this activity are urgently needed.

In this report different aspects of the specific regulation dynamics are exposed.

GENETIC EFFECT OF PESTICIDES
ON A *RHIZOBIUM* POPULATION

by

K. SZENDE
Research Institute for Soil Science and Agricultural Chemistry
of the Hungarian Academy of Sciences
Budapest, Hungary

The use of different chemicals, viz. pesticides, fertilizers etc. in our environment raises the question how these substances influence the biotic communities genetically. These communities are composed of genetically determined populations with diverse fitness traits and these diversities render them to adapt to the changing environment.

In a model system we tried to simulate the changes of our environment and followed the shift of fitness traits in a population of the N_2-fixing, symbiotic soil bacterium, the *Rhizobium* after the effects of different mutagens in a selective environment containing a pesticide. The results provide some insight into the changes of the genetic structure of this bacterial population after raising the mutational pressure in a strong selective stress environment.

MATERIAL AND METHODS

Bacteria. In the experiments an *R. meliloti* strain (N^O 41–222–21) was used. This is a temperature-tolerant clone of the original strain isolated by us (Ördögh and Szende, 1961).

Scheme of the experiments. At the start of the experiments the *Rhizobium* strain was cloned from a single cell. The clone was divided into 6 lines. Four of them were treated by mutagens: N-methyl-N'-nitro-N-nitrosoguanidine (NG), ethyl-methane-sulphonate (EMS), and Captan (the latter in two concentrations). One line received no mutagen treatment and the last line served as overall control, and was stored in a refrigerator. After mutagenesis each line was subdivided into two parts, one of them was submitted to the effect of the herbicide Gramoxon as a selective agent, the other part was grown in normal yeast-mannitol-medium without Gramoxon.

Five ml media was inoculated approximately with 10^6 cells. The growth continued at 37 °C in a microfermentor up to saturation. This lasted for 48–72 hours in normal yeast-mannitol-broth; in Gramoxon supplemented one for 5 days.

When the cultures reached the stationary phase the number of viable cells was calculated. Then the next subcultures were inoculated in the same manner and the selection followed over 7 subcultures: hence in the Gramoxon-containing broths till the 50th generation.

From the 10 parallel growing sublines 5 subclones each were isolated randomly at the end of 0, 3, 7 subcultures (at 0, 20th and 50th generations in the selective media) for growth rate experiments.

Growth rate experiments. The growth rate was followed in a normal environment viz. yeast-mannitol-broth and in Gramoxon-supplemented yeast-mannitol-broth, in the stress environment in side-armed Erlenmeyer flasks at 37 °C on a horizontal shaker in waterbath. The changes in optical densities were followed with a Magnephot II densitometer. Then the data were graphically recorded and from the curves obtained the time necessary for doubling was calculated during the logarithmic growth. The doubling times were given in minutes. Occasionally, from a subclone we made two growth rate experiments for the calculations of the reproducibility (for the calculation of the within media correlation).

Statistical calculations. Since for each growth rate experiment an overall control was included (the original subclone) it was possible to express the growth rates as per cent of the overall control and then submit them to analysis of variance. The overall controls were stable during the course of the experiments and this points to the stable environmental conditions applied in these. Beside the analysis of variance, the correlation coefficients of growth rates in normal and stress media were also calculated to determine the degree of expressivity of the genotype in the different environmental conditions. The works of Li (1964) and Sváb (1967) were used for the calculations.

Nodulation experiments. One possible measure of fitness in Rhizobia is the effectiveness to produce a symbiotic relationship with the host plant. Therefore, the mutagenized or non-mutagenized bacteria were used in nodulation experiments also. *Medicago sativa* seeds were germinated in test tubes under sterile conditions and after germination they were infected with the treated bacteria after different degrees of selection and the effectiveness in nodulation were calculated on the basis of the number of nodules per plant formed in greenhouse conditions (Ördögh and Szende, 1961).

Chemicals. NG and EMS were a product of Koch-Light, England and were purchased commercially. Captan was a gift of Dr. Gy. Ficsor (Kalamazoo, U.S.A.). The herbicide Gramoxon a 1, 1'-dimethyl-4,4'-bipyrridylium-bichlorid (paraquat) was a gift of Dr. J. Szegi, Budapest and was used in the stress media in 30 μg/ml concentration.

Mutagenesis. *NG treatment.* The washed logarithmic phase cells were treated with the mutagen in 5 μg/ml concentration for 240 minutes in yeast-mannitol-broth.

EMS treatment. The cells were washed and then treated with 2 per cent concentration of EMS for 60 minutes at 37 °C in M9 buffer at pH 7.0. At the end the cells were diluted in cold yeast-mannitol-broth.

Captan treatment. The mutagen was used in 10 μg and 30 μg/ml concentrations respectively, for 90 minutes.

After mutagen treatments the cells were washed (except EMS) and plated for calculation of viables and inoculated for the selection experiments.

RESULTS

The aim of the experiments was the demonstration of the fitness ($w = r_1/r_2$) changes in a haploid population after single mutagen treatment. How does the increased genetic variability in the viability and multiplication of the treated cells become expressed? One of the best ways in bacterial populations to denote these in numerical terms is to express them in time necessary for the doubling of the cell number or the biomass. The less time is necessary for the doubling the more likely that in a given system those cells will proliferate themselves rapidly and will compose the largest part of the population which have a shorter doubling time relative to the rest.

Therefore, the growth rate of the different treated subclones (r_1) was measured and compared to those of the overall controls (r_2).

An additional purpose was to follow the changes of the increased genetic variability in normal and stress environment during the sequence of generations and evaluate the effect of these selective environments on the composition of the populations.

The mutagenic treatments were performed with two potent mutagens: NG and EMS and with Captan a widespread mutagenic fungicide (Ficsor, 1972; Bridges *et al.*, 1972).

The analysis of variance of the obtained w values are seen in Table 1. The w values are relative values: if they are lower than 1.0, then the growth rate is faster compared to the overall control. If higher, the growth rate is slower, therefore the growth is retarded. The data of the 0. generation denote the growth of those cells which were not subjected to selection and were obtained after more generations elapsed. This time is necessary for the propagation of cells for the growth measurements. Methodically this was inevitable and had a benefit viz. the cells recovered from the physiological damages obtained during the mutagen treatment. The shift between the mutagen treatment and the start of selection was about 5–6 generations.

The *measurements of growth* were carried out in two different media. One of them was the common yeast-mannitol-broth, the normal environment; the other was the Gramoxon-supplemented medium, the stress environment.

In the 0. generation, after the start of the experiments the growth of non-mutagenized cells was slower than the overall control in normal and stress environment as compared to the mutagen-treated cells. The latter were faster but not significantly. At the 20th and 50th generations the rate of growth of the non-

Table 1
The analysis of variance of fitness data in the growth experiments

At zero generation		Growth				
		in normal environment			in stress environment	
Treatment	n	$\bar{x}$	S. D.	n	$\bar{x}$	S. D.
None	30	126.68±	17.43**	30	110.07±	23.61
NG		107.48	13.81		94.93	19.46
EMS		101.02	9.62		94.27	30.28
Captan 1		105.86	30.22		91.90	21.95***
Captan 2		113.49	13.70		93.22	16.47
At the 20th generation						
		$\bar{x}$	S. D.	n	$\bar{x}$	S. D.
Treatment	n					
None	30	130.41	24.96***	30	147.71	89.69
NG		108.44	22.49		78.43	6.50
EMS		112.92	28.43		144.12	47.66
Captan 1		146.31	47.54**		163.21	100.75
Captan 2		94.59	12.22		94.47	21.23
At the 50th generation						
		$\bar{x}$	S. D.	n	$\bar{x}$	S. D.
Treatment	n					
None	25	216.29	81.32*	25	224.03	132.25**
NG		144.19	54.55		106.72	41.29
EMS		151.13	55.42		86.17	7.63
Captan 1		137.58	13.30		91.73	32.60

The data are expressed in relative values $w = r_1/r_2$. Where r_1 is the growth rates of treated subclones; r_2 = the growth rate of the overall control; $\bar{x}$ = means of relative growth rates; n = number of observations; S. D. = standard deviations; * significant at 1 per cent level; ** significant at 5 per cent level; *** the significance approached the 5 per cent level.

mutagenized cells decreased. This decrease was significant in the normal and in the stress environment too.

The growth of the mutagenized cells in a normal environment decreased also. This is noticeable at 50th generation, but is not significant, however. In the stress environment the rate of growth of the mutagenized cells does not differ from the overall control.

The variance increased in a normal environment and in the case of non-mutagenized cells. This became definite in the stress environment too at advanced selection (50th generation). The variance of cells treated by mutagens increased also and this was sometimes high.

From the relative values of the mutagen-treated *versus* non-mutagenized cells (Table 2) it can be seen that after mutagen treatment the relative growth rates increase

Table 2
The growth of mutagen-treated *versus* non-mutagenized cells in normal
and in stress environment

	Growth in	
	normal	stress
	environment	
At zero generation treatments		
NG/none	0.8484***	0.8624
EMS/none	0.7975***	0.8465
Captan 1/none	0.8357***	0.8349
Captan 2/none	0.8559***	0.8469
At 20th generation treatments		
NG/none	0.8292	0.5533***
EMS/none	0.8658	1.0168
Captan 1/none	1.1222	1.1518
Captan 2/none	0.7253**	0.6806
At 50th generation treatments		
NG/none	0.6667**	0.4764**
EMS/none	0.6987	0.3845**
Captan 1/none	0.6361**	0.4095**

The data are compiled from the analysis of variance of Table 1. *Significant
at 1 per cent level;** at 5 per cent level;*** approaches 5 per cent level.

and mainly in the stress environment they grow significantly faster than the non-mutagenized cells.

On the calculations of the between media correlations it is possible to draw a picture of the evolutionarily interesting flexible or rigid genetical changes of populations (Blatherwick and Wills, 1971).

The growth correlations of some subclones (in correlation coefficients, *r*) in normal and stress environment are seen in Table 3. While the within media correlations were strongly positive (not seen here and tested only from time to time) the between media correlations (normal *versus* stress environment) were different. At zero time the values of the correlation coefficients were positive, significant in the case of EMS treated cells. The effect of this decreased at 50th generation. The non-mutagenized cells show increasing correlation coefficients. By the Captan treated cells this increased first then decreased but not significantly.

As the Rhizobia are symbiotic bacteria, the ability to develop the symbiotic relation between bacterium and host is a fitness trait also. In preliminary tests

Table 3
Correlation coefficients (r values)

Durations of selection	Treatments		
	none	EMS	Captan
0 generation	+0.3059	+0.9944**	+0.3153
20 generations	+0.1590	+0.4930	+0.8168
50 generations	+0.8587	+0.0217	−0.7628

**Significant at 5 per cent level.

Table 4
The data of nodulation experiments with different mutagen treatments

A	Relative number of nodules per seedlings	
	with selection at the 35th generation	no selection at the 50th generation
Mutagen-treated (average) per no treatment	0.88	1.01
NG/none	0.79	0.98
EMS/none	1.16	0.78
C2/none	0.68	1.30

B	Changes of nodulation during selection		
	at 20th	at 35th	at 50th
	generation		
None	1.00	1.00	1.00
NG	0.84	0.81	1.34
EMS	1.03	1.47	3.10
Captan 2	0.93	0.52	2.10
Mutagen-treated (average)	1.02	1.11	2.18

(Table 4) the bacteria from the selection experiments (± mutagen-treated and submitted to selection in stress environment) were inoculated into alfalfa seedlings and the nodulations were checked in a given period, at 35th viz. 50th generations (Table 4, part A). In the same experiments the effect of selection on the nodulation was followed also (Table 4, part B). The data varied significantly, from technical reasons, therefore a statistical treatment of these does not have any meaning.

It is noteworthy, that the nodulation increases in the stress (selective) environment in the mutagen-treated cells compared to the non-mutagenized bacteria. This was definite at 20th, 35th, and 50th generations. It seems that, as in the case of growth experiments, the number of evolutionary adaptive mutations increases.

DISCUSSION

To demonstrate the genetic effect of our changing environments it seems useful to follow these changes in model systems with bacterial populations. The advantages of these systems are the following:

1. The rapid proliferation of bacteria allows the observation of many generations within a short period.
2. The mutational change of the bacterial genome expresses itself rapidly in the phenotype.
3. Therefore the shifts in the composition of a genetical population and the stabilization of the changes in the new environment can be easily observed.

In such types of experiments, the effects of mutations and selection from the evolutionary forces, can be analysed. In the new era of chemization the genetic effects of the chemicals used are not wholly known. Research is mainly anthropocentric, the investigations extend only to the damages caused in the human genetical heritage. The biosphere is composed of many more organisms too, and therefore it is not indifferent to investigate the genetic changes and the evolutionary trends of those organisms also, which live in our environment.

The increasing mutation and selection pressure speed up the rate of evolution and in the case of the lower organisms as bacteria, these changes are enormous even after a short period, as a human generation.

In our experiments the effects of mutagens were followed on the genetical fitness of a *Rhizobium meliloti* population. The best expression of the fitness in bacteria is the rate of their growth or the time necessary for the doubling of cells or biomass.

Our system allowed us to analyse the effect of a single increase of the mutation pressure on the growth rates during selection in a stress medium. It was very surprising, that the growth rate of the non-mutagenized cells, measured in normal and stress environment, decreases during the selection. This means that there is an increased accumulation of genetical damages in such a population also.

The growth rate of the mutagen-treated cells decreases in normal environment and this becomes expressed mainly at the 50th generation. In stress environment, however, the growth rate was the same as of the overall control. An exception was the effect of Captan at 20th generation; however, in the 50th generation the growth was the same as earlier.

We found an essential difference therefore between the mutagen-treated or non-mutagenized cells, namely, that the accumulation of the spontaneous variability is more deleterious to the population and remains so during the selection period. In contrast with this, the mutagen treatment induces a different class of variability in the genotypes and these have a higher adaptibility to the stress environment. The situation that the growth of the mutagenized subclones in normal environment is slower at 50th generation points to the accumulation of spontaneous variability in such populations also. During the experimental period, however, the accumulation of this type of mutations cannot counter balance the effects of induced variability in the stress environment.

Blatherwick and Wills (1971) proposed two types in genetical changes, namely the formation of rigid and flexible genotypes. The former ones are sensitive to environmental changes and sorted out rapidly, whereas the latter have higher adaptive flexibility and remain in the population. Rigid types show higher degrees of positive correlations in their reactions to different environments. If the similarity of reactions is small the correlations in different environments are low, therefore the genotype on this basis is flexible. In our experiments this rigidity in the non-mutagenized subclones could be demonstrated but not significantly. In EMS treated cells at 0. generation the rigidity was significant. The damaged genotypes diluted out from the populations and so the correlation decreased also. The EMS is a drastic mutagen and the strongly damaged cells are sorted out during the first 20 generations. The spontaneously formed deleterious genotypes produce possibly at most, inferior but functioning proteins and therefore the sorting out of this type of cells is slower and they accumulate in the population.

Captan and NG increased the variability. This variability is flexible however. It may be assumed that in the conditions of increased variability the probability of forming new adaptively "valuable" clones with changed permeability, detoxication systems, etc. is higher and counter balances the effects of the stress environment.

The *fitness measured in growth* is based on many changes in genetical traits, not on a simple one, and therefore it can be attributed to the *gross* assimilatory capacity.

The results indicated that in a new stress environment the variability of cells increases to a greater extent after being subjected to mutagens. As a result of this increased variability the adaptively useful mutations accumulate. As an effect of these the populations shift to a higher degree of adaptibility in the new environment.

SUMMARY

The use of enormous quantities of different chemicals in our environment raises the question how these substances influence genetically the biotic communities of our ecosystems. These communities are composed of genetically determined populations of which diverse fitness traits render them to adapt to the changing environment.

In model experiments we followed the changes in the fitness of a *Rhizobium* population after treatment with different mutagens — pesticides and controls — increasing the genetic variability. Then the population was submitted to the effect of another pesticide as a selective agent. The changes of the fitness — expressed in the relative growth rate — were followed during more than 50 generations. The results — treated statistically — allow some insight into the changes of the genetic structure of this population after raising the mutational load in a strongly selective environment.

REFERENCES

Blatherwick, C. and Wills, C. (1971): *Genetics.* **68**, 547–557.
Bridges, B. A. *et al.* (1972): *Newsletter of the Environmental Mutagen Society.* **6**, 9.
Ficsor, Gy. (1972): *Newsletter of the Environmental Mutagen Society.* **6**, 6–8.
Li, C. C. (1964): *Introduction to experimental statistics.* McGraw-Hill, New York.
Ördögh, F. and Szende, K. (1961): *Acta Microbiologica Hungarica.* **8**, 65–71.
Sváb, J. (1967): *Biometriai módszerek a mezőgazdaságban.* Mezőgazdasági Kiadó, Budapest.

INTERACTIONS OF MICRO-ORGANISMS
WITH VENZAR AND CIPC*

by

Natalia BALICKA, Jadwiga LUBCZYNSKA and Teresa WEGRZYN
Agricultural University of Wroclaw,
Department of Microbiology,
Wroclaw, Poland

The various mechanisms of interactions between micro-organisms and herbicides (Bartha 1975; Johnston *et al.* 1972; Kaufman 1975a, b; Kearney and Kaufman 1969; Kosinkiewicz 1975; Wolf *et. al.* 1975) have been pointed out by many. Biodegradation and metabolization of herbicides leads to the formation of new compounds (Frear and Swanson 1975; Lamoureux *et al.* 1972, 1973; Menzie 1974; Tsung-Shin Hsu and Bartha 1974). Some of them, like conjugated and bound pesticide residues may be of great importance to living organisms and the soil because of their different toxicity and persistence.

The aim of the present study was to examine the interactions between some bacterial metabolites and herbicides.

MATERIAL AND METHODS

The interactions of CIPC (isopropyl-N-(3-chlorphenyl)carbamate) and Venzar (3-cyclohexyl-5,6-trimethylenuracil) with 50 strains of micro-organisms isolated from soil and rhizosphere of sugar beet were examined. They were: *Azotobacter chroococcum, Rhodotorula glutinis, Bacillus subtilis, Pseudomonas* sp. and some unidentified bacterial strains.

The change in herbicide phytotoxicity induced by bacterial metabolites was tested biologically. For this purpose *Sinapis alba* was used; the germination test was applied. Seeds were saturated with: a) solution of herbicide in the water or in the cultural medium for bacteria, b) solution of herbicide in the liquid bacterial culture or its filtrate, c) liquid bacterial culture or its filtrate, d) sterile cultural medium for bacteria. Herbicides in doses of 10, 50 and 100 ppm were used. After 20 hours of saturation, seeds were washed with water, germinated and grown for 3 weeks in the sand. Sand contained neither herbicide nor bacterial metabolites. Death rate of the plants showed the effect of herbicides.

* The work was supported financially by the Grant No. FG-Po-335 from the U.S. Department of Agriculture

RESULTS

The effect of micro-organisms on the phytotoxicity of herbicides varied. The phytotoxicity of CIPC was not affected in the presence of bacteria (Fig. 1); the actions of the herbicide and bacterial culture on plants were independent of each other. Whereas the interactions between Venzar and micro-organisms could be observed (Fig. 2). About 25% of examined strains increased the phytotoxicity of Venzar and about 10% decreased it.

The effect of interaction depended on the dose of Venzar (Fig. 3) and the concentration of bacterial culture. The culture of *Rhodotorula glutinis* could suppress the germination of test plants, but after dilution of 1 : 10 this property was lost (Fig. 4). The effect of decreasing and increasing Venzar phytotoxicity by micro-organisms is presented in Figures 5 and 6.

DISCUSSION

The increased phytotoxicity of Venzar by micro-organisms may be attributed to two reasons: formation of conjugated compounds with bacterial metabolites, or synergistic effect of herbicide and bacterial metabolites on the physiological processes in the plant. The culture of these bacteria showed the presence of phenolic metabolites, which might have interfered with Venzar (Balicka *et al.* 1975).

As it is already known, Venzar is an inhibitor of the respiratory process in plants and certain phenols inhibit the electron transport, photophosphorylation and CO_2-fixation (Sikka *et al.* 1972), which makes the synergistic effect of Venzar and bacterial metabolites possible.

The interaction between bacteria and Venzar which leads to a decrease in the toxicity of the latter may be caused by the production of growth promoting substances (Sobieszczanski 1975) and their physiological antagonisms with herbicides, competitive mode of action of both agents. The strains used for the study did not degrade Venzar because its contact with bacteria was very short; therefore such explanation of the decreasing activity of herbicide was not possible.

SUMMARY

Interaction between CIPC and Venzar with 50 bacterial strains was studied. Changes in the phytotoxicity of the herbicides were determined by means of biological tests with *Sinapis alba*.

It was found that the CIPC action was not affected by the contact with bacterial cultures, whereas the toxicity of Venzar was increased or decreased depending on the strain combined with the herbicide.

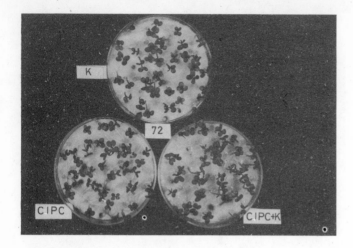

Fig. 1. Interaction of bacterial culture with CIPC
Seeds soaked with: K – bacterial culture; CIPC – 10 ppm of CIPC suspended in the water; CIPC + K – 10 ppm of CIPC suspended in the bacterial culture

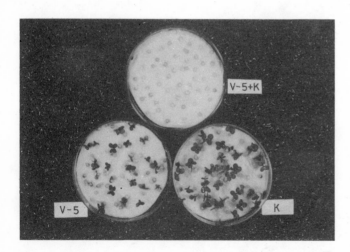

Fig. 2. Interaction of bacterial culture with Venzar
Seeds soaked with: K – bacterial culture; V–5 – 50 ppm of Venzar suspended in the water; V–5 + K – 50 ppm of Venzar suspended in the bacterial culture

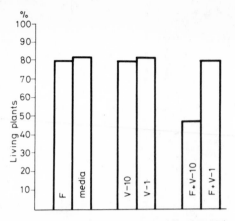

Fig. 3. Interaction of *Azotobacter chroococ-*
cum with Venzar
F – filtrate of bacterial culture; V–10
– 100 ppm of Venzar; V–1 – 10 ppm
of Venzar

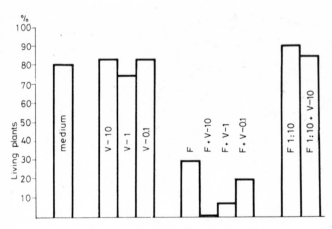

Fig. 4. Interaction of *Rhodotorula glutinis* with Venzar
F – filtrate of the culture; V–10 – 100 ppm of Venzar;
V–1 – 10 ppm of Venzar

50

Fig. 5. Increase of Venzar phytotoxicity in presence of bacterial culture
Seeds soaked with: V–10 – 100 ppm of Venzar suspended in the water, K + V – 100 ppm of Venzar suspended in the bacterial culture; K – bacterial culture

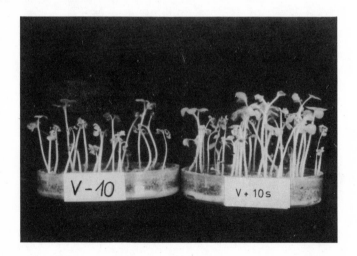

Fig. 6. Decrease of Venzar phytotoxicity in presence of bacterial culture
Seeds soaked with: V–10 – 100 ppm of Venzar suspended in the water; V + 10s – 100 ppm of Venzar suspended in the bacterial culture

REFERENCES

Balicka, N., Wegrzyn, T. and Lubczynska, J. (1975): *Rocz. Glebozn.* **26**, 65–71.

Bartha, R. (1975): *Rocz. Glebozn.* **26**, 17–22.

Frear, D. S. and Swanson, H. R. (1975): *Pest. Biochem. and Physiol.* **5**, 73–80.

Johnston, M. W. Briggs, G. G. and Alexander, M. (1972): *Soil Biol. and Biochem.* **4**, 187–190.

Kaufman, D. D. (1975a): *Rocz. Glebozn.* **26**, 5–15.

Kaufman, D. D. (1975b): *Rocz, Glebozn.* **26**, 55–64.

Kearney, P. C. and Kaufman D. D. (1969): *Degradation of herbicides.* M. Dekker Inc. New-York.

Kosinkiewicz, B. (1975): *Acta Microbiol. Polon.* 7/**24**, 16–23.

Lamoureux, G. L., Stafford L. E. and Shimabukuru R. H. (1972): *Agric. Food Chem.* **20**, 1004–1010.

Lamoureux, G. L. Stafford L. E., Shimabukuro R. H. and Zaylskie R. G. (1973): *Agric. Food. Chem.* **21**, 1020–1030.

Menzie, C. M. (1974): *Metabolism of pesticides an update.* Special Scientific Report Wildlife. N^O 184, Washington D. C.

Sikka, H. C., Shimabukuro, R. H. and Zweig, G. (1972): *Plant physiol.* **49**, 381–384.

Tsung-Shin Hsu, and Bartha R. (1974): *Soil Sci.* **118**, 213–220.

Sobieszczanski J. (1975): *Rocz. Glebozn.* **26**, 79–88.

Wolf, D. Bakalivanov, D. I. and Martin, J. P. (1975): *Rocz. Glebozn.* **26**, 35–48.

ENZYME DECOMPOSITION OF SOME AMIDE HERBICIDES BY SOIL FUNGI

by

D. BAKALIVANOV
"N. Poushkarov" Institute for Soil Science
Sofia, Bulgaria

The decomposition of pesticides in soil is, to a large extent, caused by biological factors and is partly related to the physical and chemical reactions in it (Lyubenov 1970, Bailey and White 1965). Soil microflora is one of the basic agents for detoxication of pesticides and a barrier to their harmful accumulation in soil (Kearney and Kaufman 1965), but the data for the part that microflora and respectively the different types of micro-organisms play in that decomposition are scarce (Bakalivanov 1972a, b; Kaufman *et al.* 1965; Voinova and Bakalivanov 1970).

The present paper aims to clarify in certain details the enzymatic decomposition of some amido-herbicides by certain fungi isolated from different regions in Bulgaria.

MATERIAL AND METHODS

The isolation of enzymes by certain types of soil fungi has been studied as well as the decomposition of amide herbicides under their action such as alidochlor ($C_8H_{12}ClNO$, CDAA, Randox), alachlor ($C_{14}H_{20}ClNO$, Lasso), and propachlor ($C_{11}H_{14}ClNO$, Ramrod). Isolation of micro-organisms has been made from various soil types in Bulgaria on Kaufman's nutrient media (Kaufman *et al.* 1965) each one containing 5 mg/l of the above-mentioned herbicides used as a source of carbon. The isolated fungi were incubated in Kaufman's liquid medium (without herbicides) for 10 days at 26 °C and the enzymes formed were purified by dialysis.

The decomposition of herbicides under the action of enzymes in the studied fungi is determined by the quantity of chloride ions liberated from their molecule by the method of Iwasaki *et al.* (1952).

RESULTS

In Table 1 some fungi liberating enzymes which decompose the amide herbicides such as alidochlor (Randox), alachlor (Lasso) and propachlor (Ramrod) are presented. Thus, some species of *Fusarium* display a certain activity towards the decomposition of the alachlor herbicide. For instance, the decomposition of the preparation by *Fusarium oxysporum* is about 13%, by *Fusarium moniliforme* – 10%, *Fusarium solani* – 9%. The decomposition of this herbicide by some species of *Penicillium* is similar, e.g. *P. frequentans* – 12%, *P. lilacinum* – 8%. We have found that *Trichoderma viride*, which often occurs in our soils also decomposes the alidochlor herbicide but to a lesser degree, e.g. the isolated *Aspergillus flavus* and *A. fonsecaeus* decomposing respectively 6% and 2% of alidochlor. The fact that some of those fungi commonly occurring in our soils are also able to decompose it, is a premise for speeding up its deactivation in the soil. This fact is of particular importance, bearing in mind that the preparation differs in its greater toxicity compared to the remaining herbicides studied. According to Lyubenov (1970) LD_{50} of the alidochlor is 750 mg/kg, while for alachlor and propachlor this value is 1200 mg/kg. Therefore, when using alidochlor as a herbicide, its quick decomposition is indispensable for preventing the harmful effect of increasing soil toxicity. According to some authors (Lyubenov 1970, Herbicide handbook 1970) this preparation is deactivated in the soil within 3–6 weeks; the microbiological factors having a prevalent importance in its decomposition. Unfortunately, there are no data on the actual soil and climatic conditions in Bulgaria. There are no data on the specific influence of certain soil micro-organisms as well. That is why we should be very careful when using alidochlor, especially under the conditions of irrigation, bearing in mind the high water-solubility of the preparation and the possibility of its passing into the ground waters. As the data in Table 1 shows some species of *Penicillium* are more active in the decomposition of the alachlor herbicide decomposing 8–10% of that preparation. Certain fungi of some other genera (*Aspergillus, Cephalosporium*, etc.) have been found, which can also deactivate alachlor, but these possess weak enzyme activity in this respect and the decomposition is only around 1–3%. From the investigations carried out we could judge that comparing the alidochlor, the isolated species of fungi decomposing the alachlor (Lasso) are fewer and their activity is weaker. This conclusion can be supported by other investigations, according to these, the alachlor is decomposed to a lesser degree by the micro-organisms; its period of action in the soil is longer (6–10) weeks.

The data of the investigation carried out (Table 1) shows that the isolated fungi taking part in the enzymatic decomposition of the propachlor herbicide (Ramrod) are even rarer, the species variety and the quantity of decomposed preparation is minimal. Thus, some of the isolated strains of *P. funiculosum* and *Trichoderma viride* decompose 3.5–4% of the preparation, while other strains of the same species decompose only 2% of it. These results correspond to some investigations carried

Table 1
Decomposition of some amide herbicides by enzymes from soil microscopic fungi

No	Micro-organisms	Soil	Places %	decomposed herbicide
A.	Alidochlor			
1.	*Fusarium oxysporum*	Calcareous chernozem	Viniza	13
2.	*Fusarium moniliforme*	Leached cinnamonic	Grigorevo	10
3.	*Fusarium solani*	Leached cinnamonic	Grigorevo	9
4.	*Penicillium frequentans*	Typical cinnamonic	Slivnitza	12
5.	*Penicillium lilacinum*	Leached chernozem	G. Toshevo	8
6.	*Penicillium funiculosum*	Podzolised chernozem	Rakovski	3
7.	*Trichoderma viride*	Leached cinnamonic	Grigorevo	7
8.	*Trichoderma viride*	Podzolised chernozem	Rakovski	7
9.	*Trichoderma viride*	Chernozem-smolnitza	Bojoriste	8
10.	*Aspergillus flavus*	Chernozem-smolnitza	Bojoriste	6
11.	*Aspergillus fonsecaeus*	Grey forest	Nikolaevo	2
B.	Alachlor			
1.	*Penicillium cyclopium*	Deluvial	Pestera	10.8
2.	*Penicillium funiculosum*	Brown forest	Borovetz	8.5
3.	*Penicillium funiculosum*	Grey forest	Nikolaevo	3
4.	*Penicillium sp.*	Typical cinnamonic	Slivnitza	3
5.	*Aspergillus fumigatus*	Podzolised chernozem	Rakovski	3
6.	*Cephalosporium sp.*	Meadow-cinnamonic	Plovdiv	1
C.	Propachlor			
1.	*Penicillium funiculosum*	Grey forest	Nikolaevo	4
2.	*Penicillium funiculosum*	Podzolised chernozem	Rakovski	2
3.	*Trichoderma viride*	Meadow-cinnamonic	Plovdiv	3.5
4.	*Trichoderma viride*	Rendzina (Humus-calcareous)	Chirpan	3.5
5.	*Trichoderma viride*	Leached cinnamonic	Grigorevo	2.3

out in the USA, according to these, the microbiological decomposition of the propachlor herbicide is considerably restricted (up to 20%). At the expense of this the share of decomposition under the influence of chemical factors in the soil is greater. According to the same data the propachlor herbicide eliminates its toxic effect in the soil in the course of 4–6 weeks.

The enzyme decomposition of pesticides depends on various factors (temperature, pH, duration of action of the enzymes – exposition, etc.). Exposition, as the data in Figure 1 show, has a certain influence on the quantity of the preparation decomposed. In this relation we studied the decomposition of alidochlor herbicide (Randox) under the action of enzymes of three soil fungi isolated from various regions in Bulgaria. These fungi exhibit different capacities for decomposing that preparation. As shown in Figure 1, *Fusarium osysporum* is a more active deactivator in comparison to the other two strains *(P. frequentans* and

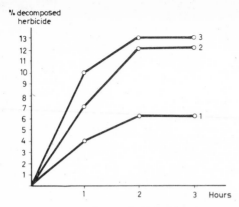

Fig. 1. Decomposition of Alidochlor by enzymes from soil fungi
1 – *Aspergillus flavus;* 2 – *Penicillium
frequentans;* 3 – *Fusarium oxysporum*

A. flavus) studied. Under the action of the enzymes isolated from *F. oxysporum,*
decomposition was 3% which was determined by the quantity of chlorine liberated.
When using enzymes from *P. frequentans* and *A. flavus* this quantity is 12% and 6%
respectively. The duration of enzyme action has a lesser influence on the decomposition than the species of the fungus which produces the enzyme. The data show
that the enzymes used exhibit considerable activity in the first 60 minutes. This
action increases during the next 60 minutes. Then the process of enzymatic
decomposition ceases.

CONCLUSIONS

1. The enzymes obtained by dialysis of preparations from soil fungi decompose
the studied herbicides as follows: alidochlor 2–13%, alachlor – 1–12%,
propachlor – 2–4%.
2. Active enzyme producers decomposing the herbicides studied are the following
species of soil fungi: *Fusarium oxysporum, F. moniliforme, Penicillium frequentans,
P. cyclopium, P. funiculosum, P. lilacinum, Aspergillus flavus.*

SUMMARY

The decomposition of some amido herbicides, such as alidochlor ($C_8H_{12}CINO$,
CDAA, Randox), alachlor ($C_{14}H_{20}CINO_2$, Lasso), propachlor ($C_{11}H_{14}CINO$,
Ramrod) by dialysed enzymes of soil fungi (isolated from various soil types in

Bulgaria) has been studied. It has been established that the decomposition of the studied herbicides depends on both the type of micro-organisms and on the chemical composition of the preparation. The degree of decomposition was determined by the quantity of chloride ions separated from the herbicide molecule. It has also been established that under these conditions of investigation the preparations are decomposed as follows: alidochlor − 2−13%, alachlor − 1−10.8%, propachlor − 2−4%.

Soil fungi displaying activity in their enzyme decomposition are the following ones: *Fusarium oxysporum, F. moniliforme, Penicillium frequentans, P. cyclopium, P. funiculosum, P. lilacinum, Aspergillus flavus,* etc.

REFERENCES

Bailey, G. and White G. (1965): *Residue Reviews.* 10, 97−122.
(Bakalivanov, D.) Бакаливанов, Д. (1972a): *Втори конгрес по микробиол.* № 4.
(Bakalivanov, D.) Бакаливанов, Д. (1972b): *Влияние на химизацията в селското стопанство върху микробиологичните процеси в почвата.* Сб. АСН Болгария, 60−64.
Herbicide Handbook of the Weed Society of America, (1970): Humphrey Press Genova− New York.
Iwasaki, I. Utsumi S. and Ozawa T. (1951): *Bull. Chem Soc. Japan,* 25, 226.
Kaufman, D. D., Kearney P. C. and Sheets T. J. (1965): *Agric. and Food Chem.* 13, 238−242.
Kearney, P. C. and Kaufman D. D. (1965): *Degradation of herbicides.* Dekker, New-York.
(Ljubenov, J.) Любенов Я. (1970) : *Справочник по хербицидите,* Земиздат, София.
Voinova, J. and Bakalivanov, D. (1970): *Détoxication de certaines aminotriazines herbicides par les bacteries du sol.* Mat. In: Symp. Action des pesticides et herbicides sur la microflora et la faunule du sol. Mededelingen Faculteit Landb. Wetenschappen Gent, 1970.

DECOMPOSITION OF DIAZINON IN DIFFERENT SOIL TYPES*

by

KECSKÉS, M.[1], HARGITAI, L.[2], FARKAS, Edit[2] and TÓTH, Á.[2]
[1] Research Institute for Soil Science and Agricultural Chemistry
of the Hungarian Academy of Sciences, Budapest,
[2] University for Horticulture, Budapest.

In the course of our studies on microbe-pesticide-soil relations (Kecskés 1973a; 1973b; Kecskés 1975; Kecskés, Balázs and Schmidt 1975; Kecskés, Szűcs and 1976; Kecskés and Schmidt 1976, etc.) we also dealt with the microbe inhibitory effect and the degradation of diazinon due to the lack of information on these and contradictory data.

The ability of diazinon to hydrolyse in an acidic medium compared to Parathion, one of the oldest phosphoric acid esthers, as it is well-known, is twelve times faster and its choline estherase inhibitory effect is stronger. Its toxical effect on haematothermals is nevertheless weaker because of its peroral toxicity. As the most common active ingredient containing Basudin it is used as a soil "disinfectant" but is applied as an insecticide in Hungary too (e.g. Diazinon-Phenkapton).

The "non-biological" decomposition of diazinon proceeds by chemical hydrolysis (Konrad et. al. 1967) and a mechanism of sorption-catalyzed hydrolysis (Mortland and Ramand 1967).

As regards the persistence of diazinon in soils Getzin and Rosefield (1966) established that half of the diazinon was lost in 2—4 weeks and 8% remained after 20 weeks in a laboratory experiment and in the field when 4.93 kg/ha were applied to silt loam soil. Rapid loss of the insecticide in the first eight weeks was followed by a slow decline. Degradation curves for field and laboratory tests were similar. At the same time Gunner et al. (1966) found that if they applied 2.96 kg/ha diazinon it persisted in the soil under non-sterile conditions for 180 days but decomposed after 10 weeks when it was used at a rate of 0.29 kg/ha.

Getzin (1967) observed that after five months 10—15% of the insecticide remained in silt loam soil. Greater amounts of hydrolyzed compounds were recovered from fumigated soil than from non-fumigated soil.

According to Kearney, Nash and Tsensee (1969) the persistence of diazinon in soil was 12 weeks while Alexander (Kunz 1975) found it to be 9 days. The half-life of diazinon was determined by Stathopoulos et al. (1971) to be 25 days. Sethunathan (1972) reported that in a flooded soil (rice field, pH 6.6) previously

* Connected with "Sikfőkút Project" No. 36 .

treated with diazinon it persisted only for 15 days and 60 days in soil which had never been exposed to this insecticide.

Using insects for bioassays in laboratory investigations Harris (1969a) found that diazinon disappeared within two weeks from the soils (sandy and muck) and according to Read (1969) diazinon proved to be highly toxic within 1–2 days and became steadily less toxic for the next months. Sethunathan and McRae (1969) observed that it rapidly disappeared in sterilized samples of an acid clay (pH 4.7) due to its instability under acid conditions. Sethunathan and Yoshida (1969) observed that the less toxic hydrolysis product (2 isopropyl-6-methyl-4-hydroxy pyrimidine) resisted further degradation in rice soil (pH 6.6) under submerged conditions. Concerning the metabolism of other pesticides Menzie (1969) has reported some data on diazinon too.

In pot experiments Bro-Rasmussen, Noddegard and Voldum-Clausen (1968) established using 1 and 10 kg/ha active ingredient of diazinon that non-steam-treated soil, moist soil and loam soil had faster degradation rates than steam treated soil, dry soil and sandy loam soil respectively. Diazinon concentration had the least effect on the degradation rate. According to Getzin (1968) the degradation of the insecticide increased with the rise in temperature and soil moisture (the water solubility of diazinon is 40 ppm, Weber 1972).

Harris (1964) found bioactivity of diazinon to be much greater in moist soils than in dry soils and the bioactivity decreased with increased organic matter content of moist soils, but the relationship did not hold for dry soils. In mineral soils the insecticides were more effective when the soil was moist than dry. In muck soils the insecticides were tightly adsorbed and released so slowly as to be ineffective when the moisture content was high.

Diazinon in muck soil was depressed by the presence of marl, degrading twice as fast in marl muck soil as in marl-free muck, moreover the chemical persistence in the marl muck was greater in the autoclaved soil than in non-autoclaved one (Kageyama, Rawlins and Getzin 1972). Among the organophosphoric insecticides diazinon has a relatively high mobility in soil systems (Harris 1969b).

Diazinon degraded by isolated soil micro-organisms was reported by Gunner et al. (1966) as the predominant bacterial isolate utilizing it as a source of S, P, C, N in this order of preference. Boush and Matsumura (1967) dealing with *Pseudomonas melaphora* the bacterial symbiont of apple maggot, Matsumura and Boush (1968) concerned with *Trichoderma viride* isolated from insecticide decontaminated soil and also Trela, Ralston and Gunner (1968) observed that the chemical hydrolysis of diazinon to pyrimidine and phosphorthioate was greatly stimulated in the presence of micro-organisms isolated from diazinon-treated soils. According to Gunner (1967) the strains belonging to the *Pseudomonas, Arthrobacter,* and *Streptomyces* species rather decompose the hydrolysis product but diazinon remains intact. The synergism of the last two species is possibly manifest in the degradation of the pyrimidine ring (Gunner, Zuckermann, Langely, 1967; Gunner and Zuckerman, 1968). Sethunathan and McRae (1969) isolated a *Streptomyces sp.* from diazinon-treated submerged soils which could degrade the insecticide in shaken cultures in the presence of glucose. Sethunathan (1972) isolated from the water of a diazinon-treated rice field a Flavobacterium strain which could metabolize diazinon exceptionally well as a sole C-source, hydrolysing it to 2-isopropyl-6-methyl-4-hydroxypyridine (Sethunathan and Yoshida, 1969). Nasim Baig and Lord (1972) also reported on soil microorganisms, which readily decomposed diazinon from Dacca rice fields.

The effect of diazinon on the micro-organisms of the rhizosphere applied to the soil or directly to the leaves of beans was reported by Gunner et al (1966). Sethunathan and Pathak (1972) published data on the diazinon-degrading activity which was paddy soil > rhizosphere soil < non-rhizosphere soil.

As regards the microbial ecosystem stress induced by diazinon the work of Gunner should be mentioned (1970).

Salem (1971) reported on the susceptibility of rhizobia to organophosphorus insecticides. He observed that diazinon firstly inhibited and in the latter periods of the experiments stimulated the effective strains of *Rhizobium trifolii*. The ineffective strains were stimulated by this preparation.

On the uptake of diazinon residues from soils treated or contaminated with this insecticide, Onsager and Rusk (1967) found less insect damage to the leaves in the field and 0.032 ppm leaves from potted soil in sugarbeet. For bean, Kansouh and Hopkins (1968) found that ^{14}C concentration in terminal and primary leaves increased with time while root concentration slowly decreased in solution treatment. For rice Sethunathan, Caballa and Pathak (1971) 0.06 – 0.26 ppm in stem and leaf blade reached a maximum in 5 days after first application in potted plants. Total diazinon and diazinon concentration decreased after second field application.

In cherry fruits five days after 0.02% active compound was applied no diazinon was found (Mitic-Muzina et al. 1971).

Comparing the data of the above-cited literature it seemed to be advisable to investigate some aspects of the interaction of diazinon and some micro-organisms, especially with respect to the sensitivity of different soil bacteria to diazinon and the effect of pH, temperature, humic acid on the decomposition in different soils in model experiments in natural and agrar-ecosystems, as well as in "rocks" and spoil banks (open-cut mining banks) representing the different degrees of recultivation.

A) DIAZINON SENSITIVITY OF SEVERAL SOIL BACTERIA

In the course of the investigations of more than 200 pesticides (e.g. Kecskés, 1972) we could make comparisons when we tested the numerous representatives of the *Rhizobium* species fixing the atmospheric nitrogen in symbiosis with legumes but living freely in the soil too or the spore-forming *Bacillus* species which could survive the unfavourable conditions in the soil as well as the non-spore-forming rod-shaped motile *Pseudomonas* species. A few data on these results are shown in

Table 1
Diazinon sensitivity of some soil bacteria

PESTICIDE		Bac. cereus var. mycoides Ö 1	Bac. cereus	Bac. megaterium	Bac. substilis	Pseudomonas stutzeri	Rhizobium leguminosarum 245/A	AVERAGE of INHIBITION
		STRAINS						
INSECTI-CIDE	BASUDIN 10 (DIAZINON)	10.3	11.3	–	10.0	–	–	6.4
	EKATOX 20	12.0	14.3	13.3	12.6	10.3	13.6	12.6
	METASYSTOX-I	28.3	36.3	37.0	35.3	27.3	34.6	32.8
HERBI-CIDE	ARESIN	12.6	24.0	12.6	12.6	15.3	26.6	15.4
	BALAN	34.6	40.6	40.0	44.0	14.3	44.6	34.8
	KREZONIT E	59.3	61.3	45.0	58.0	52.6	46.6	55.2
FUNGI-CIDE	BERCEMA FERBAM 50	44.6	38.0	40.0	51.3	43.6	20.0	43.6

Inhibition: in m/m ϕ

Table 1. As it can be seen, diazinon (applied in excess using paper disc method) proved to be only slightly inhibitory to the examined strains of the important and frequent soil microbe genera compared with the fungicides Bercema-Ferbam, Aresin, Balen and Krezonit E, herbicides and other zoocides like Ekatox and Metasystox.

B) DECOMPOSITION OF DIAZINON RELATED TO TEMPERATURE AND pH

First of all the decomposition of diazinon and preparation containing diazinon was determined in aqueous solutions. In Figure 1 the formation of diazinon content of aqueous solutions can be seen buffered to the same values at different temperatures as a function of time. It should be noted (Fig. 2) that the decomposition rate became faster above 30 °C than at 20 °C and the half-life was 70 days, at 30 °C only 20 days and, at 40 °C already only 6–7 days.

The decomposition rate of diazinon solutions adjusted to different pH values as a function of time at constant temperature can be seen in Figure 3. The greatest stability of the insecticide was measured not far from the neutral pH.

C) DECOMPOSITION OF DIAZINON IN QUARTZ SAND, WIND BLOWN SAND AND ALLUVIAL SOIL AFFECTED BY HUMIC ACID

Continuing our investigation systematically before field trials we conducted model experiment series too, with at least three replications. Peat humic acid was used prepared by NaOH extraction from peat of Osli, according to the Flaig procedure (Hargitai 1974). The 1 and 5 percentage weight of peat humic acid was added to the pure quartz sand as well as wind blown sand (Kecskés and Szűcs 1974) and the alluvial soil of Csepel besides 500 ppm diazinon active ingredient containing Basudin. The materials of the model experiment prepared in this way were incubated at 28 °C in the thermostat in quartz sand and soils having 60% relative moisture content of the maximal water holding capacity which is optimal for the microbe activity. Samples were taken after 5, 18 and 30 days and the diazinon content was determined.

In Figure 4 the concentration of diazinon residues of quartz sand as a function of temperature and humic acid concentration in a three-dimensional coordinate system is presented. In the presence of 1% humic acid the amount of diazinon was decreased only slightly but when 5% humic acid was applied the quantity of the active ingredient was decreased markedly.

In the case of wind blown sand (Fig. 5) the same tendency was observed but the decreasing effect of the humic acid was not so expressed leaving more residues than in the quartz sand.

The effect of humic acid was similar but smaller in the alluvial soil (Fig. 6) in which more diazinon residues were detected than in the wind blown sand and more than in quartz sand.

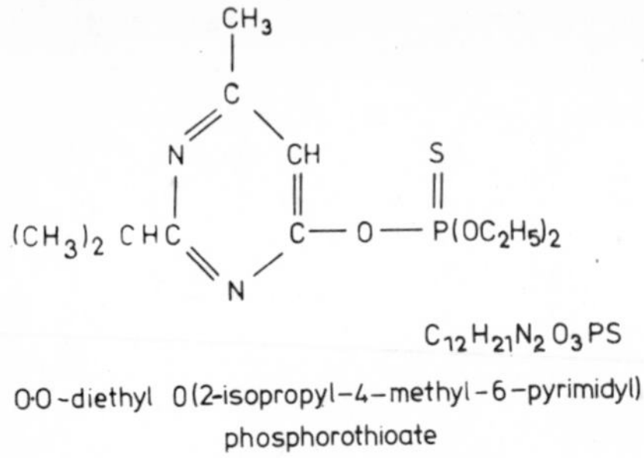

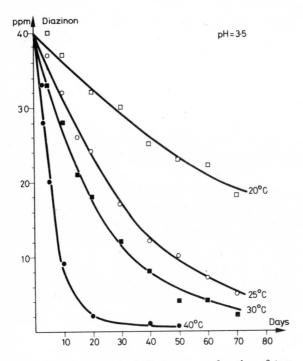

CH3
C
N
CH
S
(CH3)2 CHC
C— O — P(OC2H5)2
N
C12H21N2O3PS
O-O-diethyl O(2-isopropyl-4-methyl-6-pyrimidyl)
phosphorothioate

Fig. 1. Chemical structure of diazinon

ppm
Diazinon
pH=3·5
40
30
20
10
20°C
25°C
30°C
40°C
Days
10
20
30
40
50
60
70
80

Fig. 2. Decomposition of diazinon as a function of temperature

Comparing the three substrates it is obvious that the half-life of diazinon in quartz sand was the same as in the aqueous solution measured at neutral pH. In the case of the wind-blown sand and alluvial soil the rate of decomposition is a little faster due to the pH deviating from the neutral and besides other factors, as a consequence of the microbial activity too.

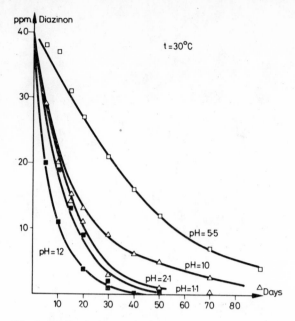

Fig. 3. Decomposition of diazinon as a function of
pH

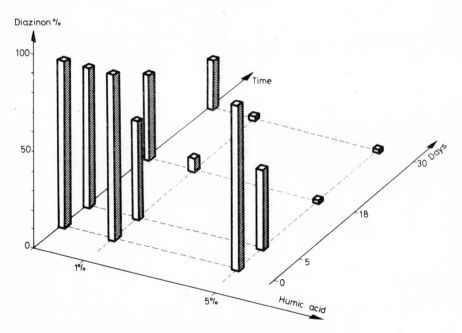

Fig. 4. Effect of humic acid on decomposition of diazinon in quartz sand

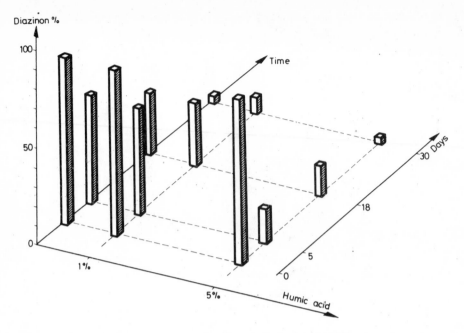

Fig. 5. Effect of humic acid on decomposition of diazinon in wind-blown sand

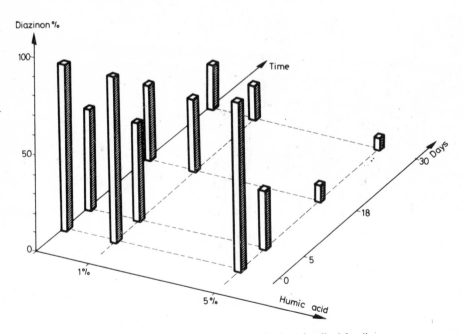

Fig. 6. Effect of humic acid on decomposition of diazinon in alluvial soil

D) DECOMPOSITION OF DIAZINON IN "NATURAL" ("SÍKFŐKÚT PROJECT") AND CONNECTED AGRO-ECOSYSTEMS

After these laboratory investigations we started to study the decomposition rate of diazinon under natural conditions too. As the site a *Querceto petraeae-cerris* (brown forest soil) ecosystem of the "Síkfőkút Project" was chosen where the natural life world of the soil is not disturbed by the agricultural activity (agro-technique or chemicalization). For the characterization besides the description of Jakucs (1973) we used also the organic matter content and the Hargitai (1955) humus stability coefficients presented in Figure 7.

In the *Querceto petraeae-cerris* site we isolated two parts a) brown forest soil with shrubs and b) brown forest soil covered with grass. The raw organic matter percent of the brown forest soil with shrubs is recorded as a function of depth measured from the surface, as can be seen in Figure 7. One half of this experimental part was left intact covered with litter (left diagram) from the other half the litter and the upper two centimeter layer was removed. Mini plots ($2m^2$) were formed and granulated Basudin equivalent to 75 kg/ha and 15 kg/ha doses were sprinkled equally over those. After 41 days in the case of 75 kg/ha diazinon treatments 17.1 ppm residue was detected in the intact plots and 8.6 ppm in the plots where the litter was removed and the upper two centimeter layer. In the plots treated with 15 kg/ha insecticide (as disinfectant) the amounts of diazinon were 5.4 and 3.4 ppm respectively. These data show that the diazinon transformation is greater, that is, the residue is smaller when the insecticide instead of raw litter was in contact with layers containing more real humic acids. This is demonstrated by the greatly increased values of the humus stability coefficients (characterizing the humification state) just in this soil layer. The "K" values express the humus quality according to the method of Hargitai (1955). The higher "K" values indicate a higher rate of real humic substances compared to raw organic matter.

Figure 8 contains also the raw organic material percentages and the values of the humus stability coefficients in the intact and dug grass covered plots. In the samples taken after 41 days the measured diazinon concentrations were 8.1 ppm (75 kg/ha Basudin in the intact plots and in the dug plots 2.4 ppm). In the case of 15 kg Basudin/ha treatments the residue values were 1.5 and 11.1 ppm respectively. These data proved that more diazinon remained in the dug plots. The sprinkled diazinon in contact with the deeper soil layers had much less organic matter and moreover had less microflora poor in quality.

Diazinon transformation was observed also in the same soil type of an oat *(Avena sativa)* culture having the same culture ecosystems connected to the natural one, not far from the area (about 150 meters) of "Síkfőkút Project".

This site has the same exposition, climatic conditions, soil types etc. but has been cultivated for a long time. The transformation of diazinon in this agro-ecosystem was 20–30% slower than in the above discussed natural one (intact brown forest soil covered with grass of (*Querceto petraeae-cerris*).

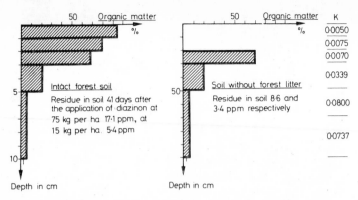

Fig. 7. Decomposition of diazinon in natural ecosystem of Sikfőkút forest soil as a function of organic matter of soil
(Brown forest soil/with shrubs)

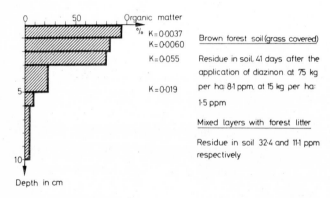

Fig. 8. Decomposition of diazinon in natural ecosystem of
Sikfőkút forest soil as a function of organic matter
of soil

E) TRANSFORMATION OF DIAZINON IN THE OPEN-CUT MINE BANK REPRESENTING DIFFERENT DEGREES OF RECULTIVATION.

In connection with our earlier microbiological investigations carried out in the recultivation area of Visonta (Kecskés and Gulyás 1972) the studies of diazinon transformation were extended to such rocks and open-cut mine banks in which we could not speak about organized or entirely any soil life yet. We used the different rocks (raw open-cut mine banks) from the different layers of a 30 meter profile of an open-cut mine and more or less recultivated open-cut mine banks as well as the original fertile soil (chernozem brown forest soil) see Figure 9. In the first group

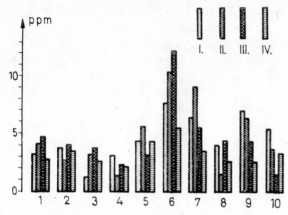

Fig. 9. Effect of lignite and fertilizers on decomposition of diazinon in different spoil banks and recultivated earths

numbered 1—4 are the rocks of the raw open-cut mine bank samples prepared from the 30 meter wall of different geological origin. 1) yellow clay; 2) sandy gray clay; 3) and 4) gray sand. The second group number 5—7 consists of mixed secondary and alluvial open-cut mine banks: 5) Quaternary sediment 6) a mixture of secondary tuff, fluviatile deposit Quaternary sediment, 7) secondary solidified tuff.

The third group: 8) Original fertile soil of Visonta 9) so-called yellow clay recultivated earth open-cut mine banks 10) Recultivated tuff-mixture. The 10 kg samples from the rocks, recultivated earth and original soil were put into pots treated with

1) 6 t/ha lignite — NPK 50 t/ha lignite
2) 6 t/ha lignite — NPK
3) 3 t/ha NPK
4) No treatment.

The initial diazinon concentration was 37.5 ppm added to the above samples in the form of granulated Basudin and soybean *(Glycine soya)* was used as the test plant.

After 41 days the samples were examined and the following results were obtained:

Diazinon residues were found of 1.5—4.5 ppm in the samples No 1—5, 5—12 ppm in the samples of No 6 and 7, and 2—7 ppm in the samples of 8, 9 and 10.

As it can be seen, the raw open-cut mine banks had relatively the smallest measurable diazinon. The highest amount of residues was determined in the second group of which soils were compact with high plasticity:

As regards the effect of the treatments it was established that in the open-cut mine banks treated with fertilizers and lignite, in most cases the transformation of diazinon was relatively slower. The degradation of diazinon could be explained by the physical-chemical properties of the investigated samples: the mobility of diazinon, aeration, pH of the soil and the chemical and biological ratio of its transformation. In the pots treated with diazinon the soybean grew more intensively compared to the control. The biggest amount of diazinon was determined after 41 days in the No 7 raw open-cut mine banks treatment, one-third of the initial active ingredient and the smallest amount of residues in the original fertile soil samples (No 8). On the basis of these data it seems that the diazinon can be used during the recultivation process as an insecticide or soil disinfectant.

SUMMARY

The sensitivity of some soil bacteria (*Bacillus, Pseudomonas* and *Rhizobium* strains) to diazinon was tested and it was established that diazinon compared to other pesticides proved to be slightly inhibitory.

The transformation of diazinon (as insecticide and "disinfectant") was also investigated in a laboratory model, pot and small plot field experiments in natural and culture ecosystems added to different layers of a 30 meter profile of open-cut mines and open-cut mine banks which represented different degrees of recultivation. It was found that the transformation of diazinon was realized by the total effect of the organic material content by humus quality characterized by the K stability coefficients according to Hargitai, pH, temperature of the substrate, as well as the activity of the soil microflora. The transformation rate of the insecticide used as soil "disinfectant" was increased in "natural" ecosystems rather than in culture ecosystems connected with the former.

The peat humic acid decreased the persistence of diazinon in model experiments, which was confirmed by the data received in natural ecosystems of brown forest soil ("Síkfőkút Project", *Querceto petraeae-cerris*). From the investigation results it may be supposed that diazinon could be applied in the course of recultivation without danger of persistence.

REFERENCES

Boush, G. M. and Matsumura F. (1967): *J. Econ. Entomol.* **60**, 918–920.
Bro-Rasmussen, F., Noddegaard, E. and Voldum-Clausen, K. (1968): *J. Sci. Food Agr.* **19**, 278–281.
Getzin, L. W. (1967): *J. Econ. Entomol.* **60**, 505–508.
Getzin, L. W. (1968): *J. Econ. Entomol.* **61**, 1560–1565.
Getzin, L. W. and Rosefield, I. (1966): *J. Econ. Entomol.* **59**, 512–516.
Gunner, H. B. (1967): In: *Coop. Reg. Proj. NE-53. CSRS, U. S. Dep.* Washington, D. C. pp. 1–14.
Gunner, H. B. (1970): *Mededelingen Faculteit Landbouwwetenschappen Gent.* **35**, No. 2, 581–597.

Gunner, H. B. and Zuckerman, B. M. (1968): *Nature (London).* 217, 1183–1184.

Gunner, H. B., Zuckerman, B. M. and Longley, R. E. (1967): *Bacteriol. Proc.* 67, 7.

Gunner, H. B., Zuckerman, B. M., Walker, R. W., Miller, C. W., Deubert, K. H. and Longley, R. E. (1966): *Plant and Soil.* 25, 249–264.

Hargitai, L. (1955): *Összehasonlítható szervesanyag vizsgálatok különböző talajtípusokon optikai módszerekkel* (Investigation of comparable organic matter in different soil types with optical methods.) (Agrártud. Egy. kiadványa). Mezőgazdasági Kiadó, Budapest.

Hargitai, L. (1974): *International Peat Symposium.* Gdansk, 124–130.

Harris, C. R. (1964)' *Econ. Entomol.* 57, 946–950.

Harris, C. R. (1969a)' *J. Agr. Food Chem.* 17, 80–82.

Harris, C. R. (1969b)' *J. Econ. Entomol.* 62, 1437–1441.

Jakucs, P. (1973): *MTA Biol. Oszt. Közl.* 16, 11–25.

Kageyama, M. E., Rawlins, W. A. and Getzin, L. W. (1972): *J. Econ. Entomol.* 65, 873–874.

Kansouh, A. S. H. and Hopkins, T. L. (1968): *J. Agr. Food Chem.* 16, 446–450.

Kearney, P. C., Nash, R. G. and Isensee, A. K. (1969): In: Miller, M. W. and Berg, G. G. (ed.) *Chemical fallout.* Current researches on persistent pesticides, Cherles C. Thomas Publ. Springfield III.

Kecskés, M. (1972): *Symposia biologica Hungarica,* 11, 405–416.

Kecskés, M. (1973a): *Rhizobium Newsletter.* 18, 74–75.

Kecskés, M. (1973b): *„ Víz–Levegő–Élet 73".* Környezetvédelmi szakmai napok előadásai. Táj és környezet. (The effect of pesticides on soil and its living world "Water–Air–Life" Professional days of Biosphere, Region and Environment). METESZ. Budapest. IV. 117–121.

Kecskés, M. (1975): *A mezőgazdaság kemizálása.* NEVIKI-KAE. Veszprém–Keszthely II, 53–59.

Kecskés, M., Balázs, E. and Schmidt, K. (1975): *Roczniki Gleboznawcze.* XXV, 185–190.

Kecskés, M. and Gulyás, F. (1972): *Ásványi humuszhordozók, humuszvegyületek kutatása és hasznosítása.* (Research and utilization of humus mineral carriers and humus compounds). Monográfia. 179–192.

Kecskés, M. and Schmidt, K. (1976): *Agrokémia és Talajtan* 25, 145–162.

Kecskés, M. and Szűcs, L. (1974): *Agrártud. Közl.* 33, 25–32.

Kecskés, M., Szűcs, L. and Balázs, E. (1976): *Agrártud. Közl.* 36, 305–315.

Konrad, J. G. Armstrong, D. E. and Chesters, G. (1967): *Agron. J.* 59, 591–594.

Kunz, F. (1975): *Zbl. Bakt. Abt. II,* 130, 82–103.

Matsumura, F. and Boush, G. M. (1968): *J. Econ. Entomol.* 61, 610–612.

Menzie, C. M. (1969): *Metabolism of pesticides.* U.S. Fish. Wildl. Serv., Spec. Sci. Rep. pp. 127.

Mitic-Muzina, N. et al. (1971): *Zast. Bilja.* 22, 43–51.

Mortland, M. M. and Ramand, K. V. (1967): *J. Agr. Food Chem.* 15, 163–167.

Nasim, A. J., Baig, M. M. and Lord, K. A. (1972): *Pak. J. Sci. Ind. Res.* 15, 330–332.

Onsager, J. A. and Rusk, H. W. (1967): *J. Econ. Entomol.* 60, 586–588.

Read, D. C. (1969): *J. Econ. Entomol.* 62, 1338–1342.

Salem, S. H. (1971): *Agrokémia és Talajtan* 20, 368–376.

Sethunathan, N. (1972): *Advan. Chem. Ser.* 111, 244–255.

Sethunathan, N., Caballa, S. and Pathak, M. D. (1971): *J. Econ. Entomol.* 64, 571–576.

Sethunathan, N. and Mc Rae, I. C. (1969): *J. Agric. Food Chem.* 17, 221–225.

Sethunathan, N. and Pathak, M. D. (1972): *J. Agric. Food Chem.* 20, 386–389.

Sethunathan, N. and Yoshida, T. (1969): *J. Agric. Food Chem.* 17, 1192–1195.

Stathopoulos, D. G., Zenon-Roland, L., Biernaux, J. and Seutin, E. (1971): *Meded. Fac. Landbouwwetenschapen, Gent,* 36, 410–418.

Trela, J. M., Ralston, W. J. and Gunner, H. B. (1968): *Bact. Proc. 1968,* 6.

Weber, J. B. (1972): In: Gould, R. F. (ed.) *Advan, Chem. Ser.* 111, 55–120. Amer. Chem. Soc. Washington, D. C.

INTERACTION OF METRIBUZIN HERBICIDE WITH SOIL MICRO-ORGANISMS AT DIFFERENT LEVELS OF MINERAL FERTILIZATION

by

RANKOV, V. and VELEV, B.
"Maritsa" Vegetable Crops Research Institute,
Plovdiv, Bulgaria

In recent years the effect of herbicides on the microbiological processes and their detoxication in soil has been a subject of many investigations (Kruglov 1970, Rankov 1967, Mishustin 1964, McLaren and Peterson 1976). A great number of studies show that the interaction of herbicides with soil micro-organisms exerts a considerable influence on the cultivation practices, fertilization, soil cultivation, irrigation, etc. It is interesting to know the effect of fertilization on these interactions, especially for regions of intensive farming, where high rates of fertilizers are used (Dimitrov and Rankov 1973a, b). The investigations of Nepomiluev, Grechin and Kuzyakina (1967) show that fertilization decreases the inhibitory effect of herbicides on soil micro-organisms. Our investigations (Rankov and Velev 1975) showed also, that organic (FYM or peat) or organo-mineral fertilization decreases the inhibitory effect of Metribuzin on micro-organisms and accelerates its detoxication.

To elucidate the effect of single mineral fertilization on the interaction of the herbicide Metribuzin (4-amino-6-t-butyl-3-(methylthio)-triazin-5-(4H)-one) with soil micro-organisms, during 1972—1974, an investigation was conducted in a field trial and container trials under a controlled environment.

The field trial was carried out on alluvial meadow soil with direct-seeded tomato (variety "Druzhba") using Metribuzin in a rate of 525 g/ha. Different levels of mineral fertilization: 120, 240 and 360 kg/ha at a ratio of $N : P : K = 1 : 1 : 1$ were used in the trial. Adjacent, untreated plots were used as control.

The alluvial-meadow soil physically is a sandy loam with humus content of 1.8 per cent, neutral to slightly alkaline (pH in water 7.0—7.4). Soil samples for microbiological analysis and an analysis for herbicide residues were taken on the 20th, 50th, and 100th day after the treatment with Metribuzin from the layers of 0—10 and 10—20 cm.

The container trial was carried out on the same soil under controlled environmental conditions (temperature — 20—22 °C and soil moisture content — 60—65% of the water holding capacity). The herbicide was applied in a rate of 525 g/ha; the fertilizer rates for single fertilization with N, P, K were the same as in the previous

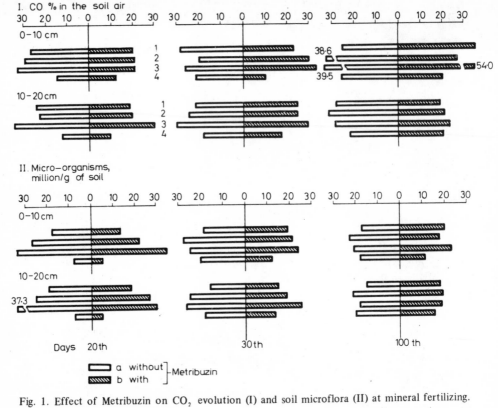

I. CO % in the soil air

0–10 cm

1
2
3
4

38·6

39·5

54·0

10–20 cm

1
2
3
4

II. Micro–organisms, million/g of soil

0–10 cm

10–20 cm

37·3

Days   20th   30th   100 th

☐ a without ⎫
▨ b with   ⎬ Metribuzin

Fig. 1. Effect of Metribuzin on CO_2 evolution (I) and soil microflora (II) at mineral fertilizing.
a) Mineral fertilizing
b) mineral fertilizing + herbicide
Variants: 1. $N_{120}P_{120}K_{120}$; 2. $N_{240}P_{240}K_{240}$; 3. $N_{360}P_{360}K_{360}$; 4. $N_0P_0K_0$ (the same refer to Fig. 2.)

experiment. The soil samples for analysis were taken on the 20th, 45th, and 75th day after starting the experiment by application of fertilizers and the herbicide.

The microbiological analysis was done as described by Rankov (1972), while CO_2-evolution (soil respiration) was measured interferometrically at 28 °C for 20 hours. The Metribuzin residues were determined by the biological method of Reisler with brewing barley as a test crop.

The results from field experiment show that the mineral fertilization has an influence on the interaction of Metribuzin with soil micro-organisms. The rate of Metribuzin (525 g/ha) initially (up to 20th day after treatment) slightly inhibits the development of soil micro-organisms, similarly to our former investigations (Velev et Rankov 1975). After application of mineral fertilizer, the inhibitory effect of Metribuzin on soil microflora was diminished (Fig. 1). This effect increases with the dose of mineral fertilizers and it is the most pronounced at $N_{360}P_{360}K_{360}$.

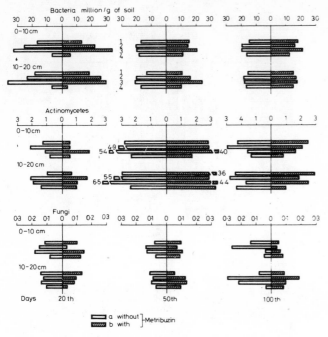

Fig. 2. Effect of Metribuzin on different soil micro-organisms at
mineral fertilizing

In Figure 1 it can be seen, that the results for CO_2 evolved and total biomass of soil micro-organisms are in correlation.

On the 50th day after the treatment the inhibitory effect of Metribuzin decreases and is retained in non-fertilized soil. At the highest rate of mineral fertilization even some stimulation is observed in the development of soil micro-organisms and an increase of CO_2 concentration in soil air.

On the 100th day, the inhibitory effect of Metribuzin is detectable only in the non-fertilized area and it is stronger in the 0—10 cm layer.

The decrease of inhibitory action of Metribuzin on application of mineral fertilizers is more pronounced for bacterial flora and less so (after a more prolonged period) — for actinomycetes. In microscopic fungi changes in this direction at the different levels of fertilization (Fig. 2) were not detected.

Analysis for Metribuzin residues in soil of the field experiment show that with increasing rates of mineral fertilizers, the detoxication of the herbicide is accelerated (Fig. 3). On the 20th day of the experiment, larger amounts of Metribuzin residues were found in the 0—10 cm layer, especially at the lowest rate of mineral fertilization $(N_{120}P_{120}K_{120})$, where Metribuzin is present in a concentration of 0.175 ppm. At higher fertilizer rates there was a trend for more accelerated detoxication.

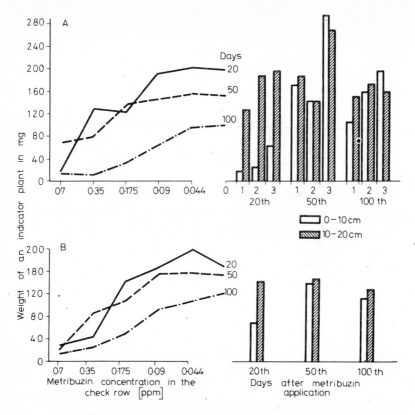

Fig. 3. Metribuzin residues, determined through test plants (brewing barley)
A. Mineral fertilizing: 1. $N_{120}P_{120}K_{120}$; 2. $N_{240}P_{240}K_{240}$;
3. $N_{360}P_{360}K_{360}$.
B. Non-fertilized – ($N_0P_0K_0$)

On the 50th day (and particularly on the 100th day after the application) traces of the herbicide 0.044 ppm) were still found in the 0–10 cm layer of the un-fertilized soil, while at mineral fertilization, no Metribuzin residues were found, either in the 0–10, or in the 10–20 cm layer.

The detoxication of the herbicide was accelerated by nitrogen fertilization under the conditions of container trial (Fig. 4). This effect is less pronounced in the case of single fertilization with phosphorus or potassium. On the 20th day of the experiment with an increasing rate of phosphorus the herbicide detoxication was retarded. On the 45th day, however, on single fertilization with phosphorus and potassium, no Metribuzin residues were found. By that time there were still traces of the herbicide in the control (non-fertilized) soil.

The results from these experiments show that mineral fertilization decreases the inhibitory effect of Metribuzin on soil microflora, reduces the "lag-phase" and

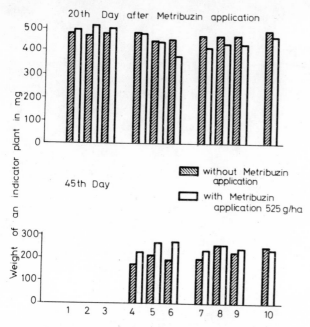

Fig. 4. Effect of Metribuzin residues on the development of the test plants, brewing barley, at mineral fertilizing.
Variants: 1. N_{120}; 2. N_{240}; 3. N_{360}; 4. P_{120}; 5. P_{240}; 6. P_{360}; 7. K_{120}; 8. K_{240}; 9. K_{360}; 10. – non-fertilized

accelerates its detoxication. This is explained primarily by improving the nutritive regime of the soil as a result of fertilization. The investigations we have made with Trifluralin (Rankov 1971) also show that its inhibitory effect on different soil micro-organisms decreases in nutritive media with richer mineral or organic composition.

CONCLUSIONS

With increasing rates of mineral fertilizers, up to $N_{360}P_{360}K_{360}$, the mineral fertilization diminishes the inhibitory effect of Metribuzin on soil microflora, reduces the "lag-phase", and accelerates its detoxication in soil.

On single fertilization with nitrogen, phosphorus or potassium, accelerated detoxication of the herbicide was observed after application of nitrogen, while weaker detoxication was observed when potassium and phosphorus were applied.

SUMMARY

The interaction of soil micro-organisms with the herbicide Metribuzin (applied in a rate of 525 g/ha) was investigated for three years in field and model trials on alluvial meadow soil. Different levels of fertilizers were used: 0, 120, 240, and 360 kg/ha. — combined as N : P : K = 1 : 1 : 1, or in single application. The changes in the development of soil microflora and the herbicide residues were studied.

The results show that with increasing fertilizer rates the mineral fertilization decreases the inhibitory effect of Metribuzin, reduces the "lag-phase" and accelerates its detoxication in the soil.

Single application of nitrogen, phosphorus or potassium accelerated detoxication of the herbicide.

REFERENCES

(Dimitrov, G. and Rankov, V.) Димитров, Г., Ранков В. (1973a): *Градинарска и лозарска наука.* **2**, 55—61.

(Dimitrov, G. and Rankov, V.) Димитров, Г., Ранков, В. (1973b): *Градинарска и лозарска наука.* **6**, 97—103.

(Kruglov, Yu. V. and Gulidov, A. M.) Круглов, Ю. В., Гулидов, А. М. (1970): *Микробиология на службе сельского хозяйства.* ВИНИТИ 104—106.

McLaren, A. D. and Peterson, G. H. (1976): *Soil Biochemistry* New York.

(Mishustin, E. N.) Мишустин, Е. Н., (1964): *Изв. АН СССР* сер. биол. **2**, 197—209.

(Nepomiluev, V. F., Grechin, I. P. and Kuzyakina, T. I.) Непомелуев, В. Ф., Гречин, И. П., Кузякина, Т. И. (1967): *Изв. ТСХА,* **2**, 128—136.

(Rankov, V.) Ранков, В. (1967): *Селскостопанка наука.* **4**, 37—46.

(Rankov, V.) Ранков, В. (1971): *Почвознание и агрохимия* **1**, 113—120.

(Rankov, V.) Ранков, В. (1972): *Почвознание и агрохимия* **6**, 109—114.

(Rankov, V., Velev, B.) Ранков, В. Велев, Б. (1975): Симпозиум *Механизм действия гербицидов и синтетических регуляторов роста и их судьба в биосфере.* Пущино IV, 14—19.

Velev, B. and Rankov, V. (1975): *Rock. Glebozn.* **26**, 223—232.

THE BEHAVIOUR OF HERBICIDE HUNGAZIN PK
IN TWO DIFFERENT SOILS

by

E. MANNINGER[1], Ágota GÄRTNER-BÁNFALVI[2], Éva BAKONDI-ZÁMORY[2] and T. SOÓS[3]
[1] Research Institute for Soil Science and Agricultural Chemistry
of the Hungarian Academy of Sciences,
Budapest, Hungary
[2] National Institute for Agricultural Quality Testing,
Budapest, Hungary
[3] Phylaxia Veterinary Biologicals and Feedstuff,
Budapest, Hungary

Hungazin PK is a herbicide widely used in Hungarian agriculture. The possible accumulation of this compound (or toxic products of its decomposition) in soils was studied in long-term experiments. One part of our results has been reported in the course of the conference on "Chemical processing of Agriculture" held in 1975. (Manninger et al. 1975) In our present work an account will be given on our further experiments, and summarizing the results of the former.

MATERIAL AND METHODS

Two types of soils have been used in our studies: sandy-soil and calcareous chernozem. The soils were collected (in order to avoid structure deformation) into plastic cylinders of 12 cm height and of 10 cm diameter, open at both ends. In the sterile variants the structure deformation was inevitable.

Hungazin PK in a quantity equivalent to 10 kg/ha herbicide was applied to the surface of the soil, and the soil was moistened with distilled water according to the average distribution of rainfall registered during the last 5 years from March till August. The layers of the soil were studied separately in depths of 0 to 6 and 6 to 12 cm.

For determination of biological activity, the carbon-dioxide production of the soils (soil respiration) was measured and the total number of bacteria was determined on bean-, Czapek- and nutrient agars. In addition the presence and effects of the pesticide or of its accidental catabolites was tested by biotests.

The biological activity was tested four times, on the 5th, 40th, 100th and 180th days following the treatment. The results were compared to the untreated control soils moistened only during the experiments.

For gas-chromatographic analysis soils were air-dried, then from the homogenized material 40 g were extracted with hot chloroform in Soxhlet-apparatus for 2 hours. After evaporation, the solvents were stored in rubber-stopped glass vials till gas-chromatographic analysis.

A Packard 7400 Series gas-chromatograph apparatus with electron capture detector was used applying 40 ml/min N_2 as carrier gas. 180 cm long glass column (bore diameter 4 mm) was filled with 1.5% NPGS Chromosorb W, 60 to 80 mesh carrier column temperature was 190 °C.

RESULTS AND DISCUSSION

Carbon dioxide production of the 200 g soil in a closed space was insignificant and pesticide effect was not detectable with this method.

On the basis of the average bacterial count of the 3 applied media, the total number of bacteria (determined at the 5th day following the treatment) showed a stimulating effect of the herbicide at a depth of 6 to 12 cm of the chernozem soil (Figs 1—4).

The herbicide treatment resulted in a marked drop in the bacterial numbers of samples taken after 40 days from both depths of the sandy soil. The depressive effect of the herbicide on the number of micro-organisms was not observed on the 100th and 180th days.

The biotest was carried out using soils in pots in which seeds of *Sinapis alba* had been sown. The decay of the plants was observed and the data are presented in Figures 5—8.

From Figure 5 it is apparent that at the first observation (after 5 days) due to 4 mm rainfall, the plants decayed by 100% on the 10th to 11th days in the upper layer of the calcareous chernozem soil. By this time, the herbicide had not reached the 6 to 12 cm depth in chernozem soil. The herbicide could be demonstrated by the test plants of the sandy soil both in layers of 0 to 6 and 6 to 12 cm.

The samples taken at the 40th day (Fig. 6) indicated that the herbicide appeared in the layers of 6 to 12 cm of the calcareous chernozem, because 93% of the plants decayed by the 11th day following the sowing. In the sandy soil the effect of the herbicide became apparent in about the same way, in both layers about 90 to 100% of the test plants decayed on the 10th and 11th days. Upto this time, water equivalent to 126 mm rainfall was applied to the soils.

Both layers of the sandy soil samples contained about the same amount of herbicide according to the biotest carried out on the 100th day (Fig. 7) following the treatment, while 240 mm moisture was applied (decay of 97% and 86% after 11 days).

The 0 to 6 cm of soil layer having a denser consistency had contained herbicides only in a quantity which was decayed by every plant to the 11th day, while the degree of decay was slightly above 40% in the layer of 6 to 12 cm. The reason for this is unknown.

According to Figure 8, on the 180th day (413 mm moisture) 100% decay of the test plants was detected after 24 days only in the upper layers of both soils, viz., the effect of herbicide diminished. For gas-chromatography, samples were prepared

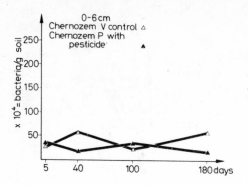

Fig. 1. Total number of bacteria in chernozem soils (0—6 cm)

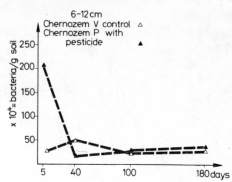

Fig. 2. Total number of bacteria in chernozem soils (6—12 cm)

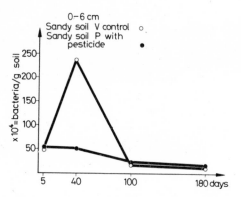

Fig. 3. Total number of bacteria in sandy
soils (0—6 cm)

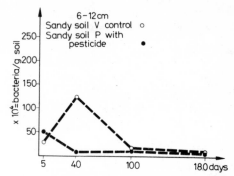

Fig. 4. Total number of bacteria in sandy
soils (6—12 cm)

according to the method described by Ramsteiner *et al.* (1971). This method was
slightly modified; the aluminium oxide proposed by the authors was replaced by
alumina according to Brockman, Grade II. Dry residues of the aforementioned
chloroform extracts were redissolved in 2 × 5 ml benzene and this solution was
applied to a 14 cm high column filled with alumina. The column was washed with
100 ml n-hexene, then the herbicide was eluted with 100 ml of n-hexene/ether
2 : 1 mixture followed by 100 ml of ether (methanol) water 20 : 9 : 1 to obtain its
catabolic products.

Each eluate was dissolved in n-hexane and these samples were analysed in a gas-
chromatograph. The results obtained are presented in Table 1.

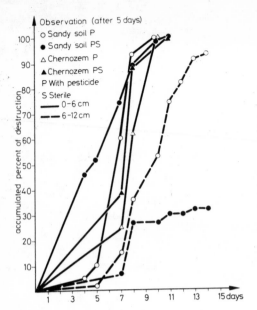

Fig. 5. Detection of Hungazin PK with biotest after 5 days

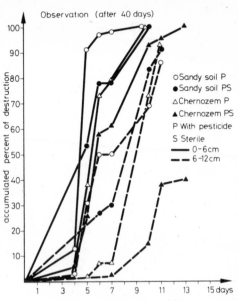

Fig. 6. Detection of Hungazin PK with biotest after 40 days

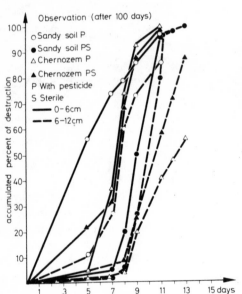

Fig. 7. Detection of Hungazin PK with biotest after 100 days

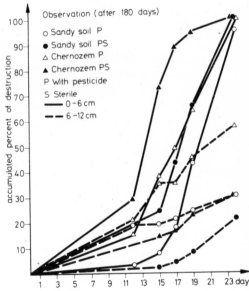

Fig. 8. Detection of Hungazin PK with biotest
after 180 days

Table 1
Atrazine content (ppm) of fractions containing effective agent and metabolite

Sample	Fraction	I.	II.	III.	IV.
		a f t e r			
		5	40	100	180
		d a y s			
CP a	c	1.9	2.2	<0.1	<0.1
	d	44.0	0.8	<0.1	0.2
SP a	c	3.4	0.1	<0.1	0.0
	d	28.0	0.1	<0.1	0.0
CP b	c		<0.1	<0.1	<0.1
	d		<0.1	<0.1	0.1
SP b	c		0.2	<0.1	<0.1
	d		0.0	<0.1	0.0

C = chernozem soil
S = sandy soil
P = Pesticide treatment
a = 0 to 6 cm
b = 6 to 12 cm
c = agent-fraction
d = metabolite-fraction

At the first sampling atrazine content proved to be higher in that fraction, which had to actually contain the metabolites. It is also remarkable, that from the second sampling atrazine could be detected in less than 0.1 ppm amounts, while agents could be found in test plants even after 180 days.

None of the metabolites detected by us was identical with the three dealkylated metabolites found with the original method (4-amino-2-chlor-6-isopropyl-amino-1,3,5-triazine; 6-ethyl-amino-4-amino-2-chlor-1,3,5-triazine; 4,6-diamino-2-chlor-1,3,5-triazine) because their characteristics are not similar. However, the previous paper reports that atrazine may have 9 metabolites.

The data determined from the peaks of the chromatograms of the four metabolites (α, β, γ, δ) found by us are shown in Table 2.

From the data it can be seen that these metabolites are present in every sample. One of the chromatograms is shown in Figure 9.

Summarizing, it can be established that the presence of Hungazin PK and its metabolites can be detected after 180 days by determination of total bacterial count and by decay of *Sinapis alba,* as well as by gas-chromatography. Thus, it can be concluded that Hungazin PK may persist for a long time in the soil and in the case of repeated application, we have to reckon with its accumulation.

Table 2
Height of the peaks of 4 metabolites (α, β, γ, δ)
(mm)

Term	Sample	Fraction	Metabolites			
I. after 5 days	CP a	c	–	17	–	17
		d	15	12	26	26
	SP a	c	6	–	–	48
		d	–	5	–	–
II. after 40 days	CP a	c	12	9	19	45
		d	8	–	5	–
	CP b	c	–	12	–	39
		d	–	–	2	26
	SP a	c	20	–	16	–
		d	–	–	–	–
	SP a	c	8	12	19	18
		d	–	–	–	–
III. after 100 days	CP a	c	120	21	–	–
		d	–	..	–	–
	CP b	c	39	22	12	45
		d	–	–	3	5
	SP a	c	38	23	34	24
		d	–	–	4	3
	SP b	c	21	30	35	40
		d	–	–	9	6
IV. after 180 days	CP a	c	32	17	–	21
		d	–	–	8	–
	CP b	c	27	–	–	9
		d	–	–	5	4
	SP a	c	10	11	–	5
		d	–	–	–	–
	SP b	c	38	26	33	15
		d	–	–	–	–

C = chernozem soil
S = sandy soil
P = pesticide treatment
a = 0 to 6 cm
b = 6 to 12 cm
c = agent-fraction
d = metabolite-fraction

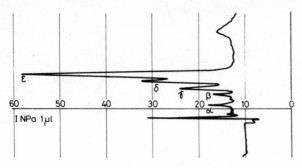

Fig. 9. Chromatogram of metabolities of chernozem soil
treated with Hungazin PK (0–6 cm, I. observation)

SUMMARY

In undisturbed samples (kept in greenhouse) of a calcareous chernozem and in a
sandy soil the behaviour of Hungazin PK was investigated for six month.

At the first sampling time, the treatment resulted in a small increase in the total
number of bacteria in the lower layer of the chernozem soil. At the second
sampling time, the treatment resulted in a marked decrease in the total number of
bacteria in each soil, in both layers. The third and fourth samplings did not show
any significant effect of the herbicide.

In the upper layer of the chernozem soil and in both layers of the sandy soil the
indicator plants died out by 100 per cent till the first sampling. After re-sowing of
the indicator plant, at the second sampling a toxic effect was found even in the
lower layer of the chernozem soil. At the third and fourth samplings, the effect of
the herbicide was measurable by biotest. The residues of the herbicide were
measured by gas-chromatography.

According to these experiments, Hungazin PK – or products of its decomposition – may remain in the soil for considerably long periods of time. Therefore,
effects resulting from accumulation of Hungazin PK may cause environmental
problems.

REFERENCES

Manninger, E., Gärtner-Bánfalvi A. and Bakondi-Zámbory, É., (1975): A mezőgazdaság kemizálása
(Ankét) NEVIKI Veszprém (Keszthely) 111–118.
Ramsteiner, K. A., Hörmann, W. D. and Eberle, D. O. (1971): *Mededelingen Fakulteit Land-
bouwwetenschappen.* Gent, 36, 1119–1131.

SYMBIOTIC NITROGEN FIXATION BY BROAD BEAN AND GROWTH OF *RHIZOBIUM LEGUMINOSARUM* STRAINS AS INFLUENCED BY CERTAIN HERBICIDES

by

A. N. IBRAHIM[1], M. S. TEWFIK[2] and K. G. SALEM[2]
Botany Department
[1] Al Azhar University, Faculty of Agriculture,
Cairo, Egypt
[2] Agricultural Research Centre, Weed control Department,
Cairo, Egypt

The effect of Linuron, DNBP, Nitralin, Terbutol and Chlorothal Dimethyl was studied on nodule formation and symbiotic nitrogen fixation by broad bean. Only the highest rate of Linuron and Nitralin showed an adverse effect on the growth, nodulation and nitrogen content of plants. The lower rates of these herbicides and all rates of the other herbicides tested did not have any harmful effect; on the contrary, they caused some stimulation, especially in the dry weights of roots, nodules and nitrogen content.

The growth of 14 strains of *Rh. leguminosarum in vitro* was not inhibited except by concentrations higher than 10 000 ppm active ingredient of Nitralin, Terbutol and Chlorothal Dimethyl. DNBP and Linuron were not toxic in this respect; thus they caused inhibition at lower concentrations, i.e. 500 and 1 000 ppm respectively.

The application of pre-emergent herbicides is becoming widespread in practice in legume plantations, especially those cultivated for fodder or vegetables. As the application of herbicides may affect the symbiotic system and consequently nitrogen fixation in plants, it was of interest to study the effect of these chemicals on the growth of rhizobia *in vitro,* and their efficiencies *in vivo,* and to determine the best herbicide and the most suitable rate for recommendation. Broad bean, as one of the most important legumes in Egypt for human consumption, was chosen for this study.

MATERIAL AND METHODS

Strains of Rhizobium

Fourteen strains of *R. leguminosarum* locally isolated and obtained from the Department of Soil Microbiology, Ministry of Agriculture were used for testing the toxicity of the herbicides. For pot experiment, the commercial inoculum of *Rh. leguminosarum,* locally known as "Okadin", produced by the above Department was used for inoculating broad been seeds before cultivation.

Herbicides

For the pot experiment, the following herbicides were used at the rates mentioned below: 1-Linuron 50% (N-3,4-dichlorophenyl N-methoxy-N-methyl urea) at the rates of 0.5, 0.75 and 1.0 kg/feddan, as a pre-emergence treatment, 2-DNBP 50% (2,4-dinitro-o-butylphenol) at the rates of 0.5, 1.0 and 2.0 L/feddan, as a pre-emergence treatment, 3-Nitralin 75% (4-methylsulphanyl-2,4-dinitro-N,N-dipropyl-anitine) at the rates of 1.0, 2.0 and 3.0 kg/feddan incorporated into the top ten centimetres of the soil before planting, 4-Terbutol 80% (2,6-di-tert-buty-p-tolyl-methylcarbamate) at the rates of 8.0, 10.0 and 12.0 kg/feddan mixed all over the soil before planting, and 5-Chlorothal Dimethyl 75% (tetrachlorophthalic acid) at the rates of 8.0, 10.0 and 12.0 kg/feddan incorporated into the soil before planting.

The same herbicides were used also for the *in vitro* studies, but at the following rates: 100, 500, 1 000, 10 000, and 100 000 ppm calculated as active ingredients.

Pot experiment

Earthenware pots (25 cl diameter) each filled with 5 kg of clay loam soil (total N 0.11%, organic matter 1.28%, T.S.S. 0.18%, $CaCO_3$ 2.74%, and pH 8.1) mixed with 1.0 g superphosphate were used. Eight broad bean seeds; var. Giza 2 inoculated with "Okadin" were planted in each pot after the respective herbicide treatment. Inoculation was carried out by thoroughly mixing the inoculum with the seeds (10 : 100 w/w). Four replicates were prepared for each treatment, and pots were completely randomized in the wire greenhouse. Moisture was kept up to 60% of Whc during the experimental period, and plants were thinned to leave 4/pot after 2 weeks from planting. After 60 days from planting, plants were taken up carefully from the soil, divided to shoots, roots and nodules, weighed after drying (70 °C overnight) and kept for total nitrogen determination.

Sensitivity experiment

The strains of *Rh leguminosarum* were grown in yeast extract-mannitol agar medium known as medium 79 (Allen, 1961) for five days. One ml of every strain culture 3 days-old was used as an inoculum for each seeded agar medium plate. Filter paper discs of 7 mm diameter were soaked in the solutions of herbicides dissolved in acetone and calculated according to the required final concentration then drained and dried at 35 °C for 15 minutes under sterile conditions. The discs were then placed on the surface of the inoculated agar plates. Discs soaked in acetone served as control. Inhibition zones were recorded in mm after 5 days' incubation at 28 °C.

Effect of herbicides on:

a) *dry matter yield and nitrogen content*

As shown in Table 1, dry weight of shoots generally decreased as the herbicide rate increased. These reductions, however, were not significant except with the highest rates of Linuron and Nitralin, where that of Nitralin (3 kg/feddan) caused dwarfing of the shoots and slight chlorosis.

The weight of the roots was not affected by all the rates of herbicides used, except again in the case of the highest rate of Nitralin, which caused a significant inhibition. Otherwise, all the rates of the other herbicides caused some stimulation in the weight of roots, especially in the middle rate of DNBP and Terbutol (1.0 and 10.0 kg per feddan, respectively), where the increase was significantly above the control.

Unexpectedly, the weight of nodules was significantly higher than that of the control in all treatments, except with the highest rate of Linuron (1 kg/feddan). The

Table 1

Mean dry weights of shoots, roots, and nodules of broad bean plants, and their nitrogen contents per one plant, as affected by herbicides

Herbicides and rate of application		shoots		roots		nodules	
		dry wt. g	total N, mg	dry wt. g	total N, mg	dry wt. g	total N, mg
Linuron, kg/feddan	0.50	3.67	133.6	1.16	32.7	0.23	11.5
	0.75	3.38	136.9	1.21	36.4	0.19	10.6
	1.00	2.71	102.9	1.20	42.4	0.09	5.6
DNBP, Lt./feddan	0.50	3.42	98.3	1.23	35.2	0.16	8.9
	1.00	3.86	113.8	1.71	47.1	0.18	8.9
	2.00	4.15	120.9	1.48	42.6	0.21	11.7
Nitralin, kg/feddan	1.00	3.05	122.8	1.16	34.6	0.17	8.6
	2.00	3.39	146.4	1.10	34.7	0.12	7.2
	3.00	1.10	49.7	0.54	14.9	0.05	2.9
Terbutol, kg/feddan	8.00	3.93	142.4	1.82	59.9	0.16	9.1
	10.00	3.55	149.1	1.81	51.1	0.15	8.7
	12.00	4.11	174.0	1.41	41.7	0.10	6.6
Chlorothal Dimethyl, kg/feddan	8.00	4.07	140.7	1.42	42.8	0.17	9.9
	10.00	3.65	140.1	1.35	42.6	0.18	10.4
	12.00	3.49	138.1	1.23	35.1	0.14	8.5
Control		4.22	152.6	1.08	34.0	0.13	6.1
L. S. D.	0.05	0.94	38.3	0.52	10.4	0.04	2.3

Table 2
Mean diameters in mm of the inhibition zones around discs treated with the different herbicides

Herbicides, ppm active ingredient	*Rh. leguminosarum* strains													
	300	310	329	384	3LE	3LEA	A1/2	A3/1	A3/2	B3/2	C3/1	C3/2	H3/2	O3/2
Linuron														
100	–	–	–	–	–	–	–	–	–	–	–	–	–	–
500	–	–	–	–	–	–	–	–	–	–	–	–	–	–
1 000	6	6	6	6	6	6	7	7	7	6	6	6	6	6
10 000	6	6	6	6	6	6	7	8	7	6	6	6	6	6
100 000	6	12	6	10	7	10	7	8	7	7	7	6	7	7
DNBP														
100	–	–	–	–	–	–	–	–	–	–	–	–	–	–
500	13	14	6	11	11	13	14	9	12	9	9	12	12	9
1 000	15	16	13	17	12	15	18	11	17	14	18	17	15	14
10 000	29	30	25	28	28	28	25	33	28	25	28	28	25	25
100 000	40	41	40	41	38	40	39	41	41	41	41	40	41	41

Nitralin

Terbutol

Chlorothal Dimethyl

	100	500	1 000	10 000	100 000
Nitralin					6
					6
					—
					6
					—
					7
				6	
				12	
				7	
				6	
				—	

	100	500	1 000	10 000	100 000
Terbutol					—
				14	
				6	
				7	
				14	
				6	
				7	

	100	500	1 000	10 000	100 000
Chlorothal Dimethyl				14	
				6	
				7	
				7	

91

two highest rates however, and that of Terbutol (12 kg/feddan) caused a significant decrease in nodule weight, resulting in the inhibition of nodule initiation and development.

As for nitrogen content in shoots, only Linuron and Nitralin at the highest rates, and DNBP at the first two rates caused a significant decrease, otherwise all the other treatments showed no effect. Total nitrogen in roots was generally increased by the herbicide treatments, especially by Terbutol and DNBP. Most of the herbicide treatments caused also a significant increase in the nitrogen content of nodules. In one case only, (i.e. Nitralin at the highest rate) significantly decreased the nitrogen content of nodules.

b) *Growth of Rh. leguminosarum* (Table 2)

Nitralin, Terbutol and Chlorothal Dimethyl did not inhibit the growth of *Rh leguminosarum* strains, except at concentrations of 10 000 or even 100 000 ppm active ingredient. The inhibition zones started to appear at a concentration of 1000 ppm in Linuron and 500 ppm in DNBP, where the inhibition zones increased in size as the concentrations increased. It must be noted here, however, that even in the last case, the inhibitory concentration is much higher than that recommended and used in the field (500 ppm active ingredient, DNBP is equal to the application of 200 lb per acre according to Fletcher (1956)).

DISCUSSION

Dry weight of plants or their nitrogen contents did not significantly decrease on the application of lower rates of the tested herbicides. On the contrary, some treatments caused an increase, especially in the dry weight of roots, nodules and in the nitrogen content in general. Nitralin, at 3 kg/feddan, was the most toxic from the point of view of dry weight and nitrogen content. These results are in agreement with those obtained with Trifluralin, which has a very similar structure to Nitralin. Thus, Gafar *et al.* (1969) showed that the application of 0.5, 1.0 and 2.0 l Trifluralin per feddan at planting time inhibited nodulation and caused root deformation. Similarly, nodulation and growth of cowpea plants were inhibited upon the application of 1.0, 3.0 and 6.0 L/feddan of Trifluralin at the time of planting (Hamdi and Tewfik 1969). The yield of broad bean was also significantly reduced by the herbicide Methazol and Dinitramine (Tewfik *et al.* 1974).

Resistance of rhizobia to certain herbicides may be due to the ability of these organisms to degrade such chemicals. Thus, DNOC was degraded by certain strains of rhizobia and *Azotobacter* (Hamdi and Tewfik 1970). In the present study, the nature of resistance of some strains of *Rh leguminosarum* to certain herbicides awaits further investigation; this aspect is now receiving attention.

Results reveal that rhizobial strains tolerated very high rates of the herbicides tested. DNBP, which proved to be the most toxic to the growth of *Rh leguminosarum in vitro,* did not inhibit the growth except at 500 ppm active ingredient which is much more than that used in the field. In the case of Nitralin, however, although it did not cause inhibition except at 100 000 ppm level in the *in vitro* investigation, a rate of 3 kg/feddan adversely affected nodulation, growth of plants and nitrogen content. These contradictory results can be explained by the fact that the growth of pure strains of *Rh leguminosarum* were tested in a very rich medium; in which the nitro group serves as a hydrogen acceptor for many enzyme-systems oxidizing their substrates and reducing the nitro group to amino group which is much less toxic (Tewfik 1966). In the soil, however, especially under Egyptian conditions, the organic matter-content is very low and therefore detoxication of the nitro-compounds is much slower. Thus, a concentration which is non-toxic in rich medium can be toxic in the soil.

Hence, it can be concluded that the high rates of the herbicides used in this study, especially Nitralin should not be used, to avoid any adverse effects on the growth and nitrogen fixation in broad beans.

REFERENCES

Allen, O. N. (1961): *Experiments in soil bacteriology.* Burgess Pub. Co., Minneapolis.
Fletcher, W. W. (1956): *Nature. (London)* 177, 1244.
Gafar, A. Z., Hamdi, Y. A. and Tewfik, M. S. (1969): *Effect of trifluralin on the nitrogen fixed in broad beans.* The 1st. Arab Conf. of Physiological Sciences, Cairo.
Hamdi, Y. A., and Tewfik, M. S. (1969): *Acta Microbiol. Polon.* 1, (18) No 2, 53–58.
Hamdi, Y. A., and Tewfik, M. S. (1970): *Soil Biochem.* 2, 163–166.
Tewfik, M. S. (1966): *The metabolism of certain aromatic nitroherbicides by soil micro-organisms.* Ph. D. Thesis, Univ. of Wales.
Tewfik, M. S., Embabi, M. S. and Hamdi, Y. A. (1974): *Ztbl. Bakt. Abt. II.* 122, 528–532.

STUDIES ON THE SIMULTANEOUS FUNGICIDE TREATMENT AND *RHIZOBIUM* INOCULATION OF SOYBEAN SEEDS

by

Éva BAKONDI-ZÁMORY[1], Ágota GÄRTNER-BÁNFALVI[1], GY. KISS[2] and I. PAPP[2]
[1] National Institue for Agricultural Quality Testing, Budapest, Hungary
[2] Plant Protection Centre of the Ministry of Agriculture and Food

Efforts to increase the protein production has resulted in a great extension of the soybean growing area in Hungary, accompanied by the adaption of a complex technology. Besides introducing intensive varieties *Rhizobium* inoculation of the seeds as well as plant protection have played an important role in this process.

The efficiency of *Rhizobium* inoculation of the soybean has already been verified by several experiments in Hungary. Thus, Kerpely (1958) in his *Rhizobium* inoculation experiments, which were carried out during 1935–43 at 20 different localities, found 21% average increase in the yield, as compared to the uninoculated control. On the basis of the average data of an experiment conducted over 10 years Kurnik (1962) stated, that owing to the *Rhizobium* inoculation, the soybean seed yield increased by 20.3%.

Recently, fungicide treatments of the seeds have been introduced in the practice of the large-scale soybean production and these treatments may influence the efficiency of the *Rhizobium* seed inoculation.

In the literature there are several contradictory results on the effect of the different fungicides on *Rhizobium* bacteria. In a series of pot experiments using soybean and pea as test plants Appleman (1941) found, that the positive or negative effects of Ceresan, Semesan and Cuprocide treatments depends on the duration of storage of the inoculated seeds. According to Golebiowska and Kaszubiak (1965) organic mercury preparations (Ceresan, Fungitox OR, and Phenylmercury – acetate) strongly inhibited the growth of the different *Rhizobium* species. The Thiram preparations were less toxic. Studying the compatibility of fungicide treatment and *Rhizobium* inoculation of vetch Kecskés and Vincent (1969) concluded, that among the seven fungicides tested, Thiram did not inhibit the rhizobia and the *Rhizobium* inoculation, while Ceresan proved to be a strong inhibitor. Kapusta and Rouwenhorst (1973) investigated the effect of 24 different pesticides on *Rhizobium japonicum* in pure culture and in field trials. Among the chemicals tested only two preparations inhibited the nodulation. Experiments on the compatibility of red clover led to the conclusion, that Thiram and Dexon at a concentration of 0.2 and 0.06%, respectively did not inhibit the nodulation (Diatloff, 1970). When they investigated the interaction between different fungicides and certain papilionaceous plants Hamdi et al. (1974) found, that Orthocid was toxic to soybean at a concentration of 0.3%. Nery and Dobereiner (1975) studied the simultaneous effect of the fungicide seed treatment on the *Rhizobium* inoculation of soybean in field experiments. According to their results, Captan inhibited the nodulation, while Dithane had no such effect.

In the present work, laboratory and pot experiments were carried out in order to study the effect of fungicides generally applied or to be introduced for soybean in Hungary, on *Rhizobium* bacteria.

MATERIAL AND METHODS

In the laboratory tests, fungicides listed in Table 1 were used at a concentration of 1.0, 0.1, 0.01 and 0.001%. In practice a concentration of 0.1% is generally applied. Strains of *Rhizobium japonicum* (G3 and G6) were supplied by the Department of Agricultural Biology, Serum and Food-preparation Production Factory, "Phylaxia", Budapest. Before use, strains were tested on virulence and on effectivity. The bacteria were maintained on yeast extract mannitol agar (YMA).

The effect of fungicides on the two strains of *Rhizobium japonicum* was tested by the agar-diffusion method. 20 ml of the YMA medium were poured into Petri-dishes of 10 cm in diameter. After congealing, 4 ml of YMA media containing 0.5 ml bacterium suspension and kept at 45 °C was evenly dispersed over the agar. The bacterium suspension was prepared by washing off a 24 hours' culture. Its concentration was adjusted according to the density of the 7th degree of Braun's scale. In each of the Petri-dishes five reservoirs were made by means of a sterilized metal borer of 16 mm in diam. 0.4 ml of fungicide suspensions at different concentrations as well as the same volumes of sterilized water were pipetted into the holes. Inhibition zones were measured after 48 hours' incubation at 28 °C. Results are given as an average of five replications.

The phytotoxicity of the fungicides used in the pot trials was tested in laboratory experiments. Fifty seeds from each treatment were germinated on moistened filter paper. The germinating capacity was expressed in the germinating per cent of the control, which was counted to be 100.

Experiments with plants were carried out in glass-house. Plastic pots of 13 cm in diameter and 12 cm in height were used for the planting. The field trials in three replications were conducted on a calcareous chernozem soil, using the variety "Merit". Treatments and dosages applied are given in Table 3. Fungicide treatments from Nos 1 to 12 were completed at the Plant Protection Station, Velence under farm conditions, those from Nos 14 to 19 were carried out in the laboratory. Before sowing, treated soybean seeds were inoculated with a mixture of *Rhizobium japonicum* strains G3 and G6. The sowing time was July 16, 1975. On August 16,

Table 1
Fungicides tested during the experiments

Number	Trade name	Active ingredient	Manufacturer
1	Orthocid 50 WP	Captan 50%	BMV, from the active ingredient of the Chevron CO
2	Quinolate 15	Copper oxyquinolate 15%	BMV
3	Quinolate V-4-X	Copper oxyquinolate 15% + Carboxin 50%	BMV
4	TMTD 50 seed dresser	TMTD 50%	BMV
5	A-115	BCM 50%	Chinoin
6	Fundazol 50 seed dresser (B-115)	Benomyl 50%	Chinoin
7	Fundazol 50 WP	Benomyl 50%	Chinoin
8	Dithane M-45	Mancozeb 80%	Rhom and Haas, France
9	Terra-Coat L-205	PCNB 50% + ETMT 50%	Olin Co., USA
10	BAS 3302 F	N-cyclohexyl-2,5-dimethyl-furan-3-carbonamid 50% + + Maneb 32%	BASF, BRD
11	Evershield Mc	Methoxychlor 38% + + not known carrier	Gustafson Inc., USA

Table 2
The effect of fungicides on two strains of *Rhizobium japonicum* as determined by the gel diffusion method.
(Inhibition zones are given in mm)

Fungicides	*R. japonicum* G3			*R. japonicum* G6		
	Fungicide concentration					
	1%	0.1%	0.01%	1.0%	0.1%	0.01%
Orthocid 50 WP	–	–	–	–	–	–
Quinolate 15	–	–	–	–	–	–
Quinolate V-4-X	10	3	–	7	4	–
TMTD 50 seed dresser	–	–	–	–	–	–
A-115	–	–	–	–	–	–
Fundazol 50 seed dresser (B-115)	–	–	–	–	–	–
Fundazol 50 WP	–	–	–	–	–	–
Dithane M-45	4	3	–	4	3	–
Terra-Coat L-205	–	–	–	–	–	–
BAS 3302 F	6	–	–	6	–	–
Evershield Mc	–	–	–	–	–	–

Table 3

Evaluation of the simultaneous fungicide treatment and *Rhizobium* inoculation. Results of pot test with soybean

| Treatments[1] | Dosage | | Per cent of germination as compared to the control | Average values for 1 plant | | | | | |
| | Preparation g/q | Seed dresser solution ml/q | | Plant height | | Number of nodules | | Pod yield | |
				cm	per cent in untreated control	number	per cent in inoculated control	in fresh condition g	per cent in inoculated control
1 Orthocid 50 WP	300	—	120	45.5	97	5.9	50.4	0.334	66.5
2 Evershield Mc + Orthocid 50 WP	—	530	150	43.0	91	6.7	57.3	0.575	114.5
3 A 115 + Quinolate V-4-X	100 + 200	—	130	48.0	102	3.6	30.8	0.573	114.1
4 Evershield Mc + A 115 + Quinolate 15	—	530	150	51.0	108	5.8	50.0	0.468	93.2
5 Quinolate V-4-X	200	—	130	49.5	105	2.7	23.1	0.491	97.8
6 Evershield Mc + Quinolate V-4-X	—	530	140	45.0	96	6.3	53.8	0.401	79.9
7 A 115 + Orthocid 50 WP	100 + 200	—	120	48.6	103	11.7	100.0	0.393	78.3
8 Evershield Mc + A 115 + Orthocid 50 WP	—	530	110	51.0	108	10.3	88.0	0.494	98.4
9 Fundazol (B-115) seed dresser	200	—	140	54.1	114	9.4	80.0	0.476	94.8
10 Evershield Mc + Fundazol (B-115) seed dresser	—	530	110	45.6	97	7.5	64.0	0.440	87.6

Treatment									
11 TMTD 50 seed dresser	200	—	120	46.0	98	8.8	75.2	0.637	126.9
12 Evershield Mc + + TMTD 50	—	530	110	50.1	106	9.1	77.7	0.603	120.1
13 F-319 70 WP	—	—	investigated in field experiment only						
14 Fundazol 50 WP	200	—	80	43.5	92	12.3	105.1	0.677	134.9
15 A 115	200	—	130	51.8	110	9.3	79.5	0.579	115.3
16 Quinolate 15	300	—	150	42.8	91	10.7	91.5	0.701	139.9
17 Quinolate V-4-X + + Fundazol 50 WP	100 + 100	—	140	58.2	124	8.2	70.1	0.487	97.0
18 Quinolate V-4-X + + Orthocid 50 WP	100 + 200	—	130	51.2	109	7.7	65.8	0.353	70.3
19 Dithane M 45	250	—	100	46.0	98	4.1	35.1	0.411	81.9
Inoculated with Rhizobium only	—	—	140	41.6	88	11.7	100.0	0.502	100.0
Control (absolute)	—	—	100	47.1	100	4.9	100.0	0.434	86.4

Remarks: [1] In tests from Nos. 1 to 19, fungicide treatment and Rhizobium inoculation were given simultaneously. Experiments from 14 to 19 were performed in glass-house only.

1975 plants were sprayed with Bi 58 at a concentration of 0.2% against spider mites and worms. The evaluation of the pot experiment was carried out on August 26, 1975. Plant height, pod harvest and nodulation were measured.

RESULTS AND CONCLUSIONS

The results obtained from the gel diffusion tests are given in Table 2. As can be seen, among the fungicides tested Quinolate V-4-X, Dithane M-45 and BAS 3302 F inhibited both strains of *Rhizobium japonicum*. Quinolate V-4-X proved to be the strongest inhibitor, followed by BAS 3302 F and Dithane M-45 in a decreasing order.

Small differences were only observed in the sensitivity of the two rhizobia strains. Concerning the total number of nodules and the pod yield, results obtained in pot tests were similar to those of laboratory tests. In the Quinolate V-4-X treatment only 23.1% nodulation was observed as compared to the untreated, *Rhizobium-inoculated* control. Similarly, a depressed nodulation (30.8%) was found when combined application of Quinolate V-4-X and A 115 was performed. In the other combinations such depression was not observed.

The inhibition effect of Dithane M-45 on rhizobia was supported by the glass-house experiments too, where Dithane M-45 treatment resulted in poor nodulation (35.1%).

An apparent increase (105.1%) in the nodulation was found, when seeds were treated with Fundazol 50 WP.

Orthocid 50 WP did not prove to be toxic to the *Rhizobium japonicum* strains in laboratory experiments. However, in the field trials seed treatment with this fungicide resulted in the strongest inhibition of the nodulation and in the poorest pod yield.

In pot experiments with soybean as can be seen from Table 3, the best yields were obtained when Fundazol 50 WP treatment was combined with TMTD 50 and Evershildes, or when Quinolate 15 treatment was applied. Although Quinolate V-4-X inhibited the nodulation strongly, this negative effect was not manifest in the yield.

Fungicide treatments had no significant influence on the plant height. In general, plants inoculated with rhizobia showed a stubby form as compared to the uninoculated plants.

Since there were no significant differences in the germinating capacities of the treated seeds, the fungicides tested are not phytotoxic to soybean.

SUMMARY

The simultaneous fungicide treatment and *Rhizobium* inoculation of soybean seeds were investigated in order to determine the effect of the different fungicides on *Rhizobium* bacteria and on their activity. Laboratory gel diffusion tests and glass-house trials using natural soil were performed.

1. In laboratory tests, Quinolate V-4-X, BAS 3302 F and Dithane M-45 fungicides applied at a concentration of 1.0 and 0.1% inhibited the growth of rhizobia.

2. Fundazol 50 WP did not inhibit the bacteria in vitro, and increased the nodulation and the yield in pot tests.

3. Quinolate V-4-X strongly inhibits both the *in vitro* growth of the *Rhizobium japonicum* strains and the nodulation. However, inhibition of nodulation did not result in decrease of the yield.

4. Although, Orthocid 50 WP did not inhibit the rhizobia *in vitro,* the seed treatment with this fungicide resulted in a strong inhibition of the nodulation and in a greatly depressed yield.

REFERENCES

Appleman, M. D. (1941): *Soil. Sci. Amer. Proc.* 6, 200–203.

Diatloff. A. (1970): *J. Aust. Inst. Agric. Sci.,* Melbourne 36, 4. 293–294.

Golebiowska, J. and Kaszubiak, H. (1965): *Ann. Inst. Pasteur Supl.* 3, 153–160.

Kecskés, M. and J. M. Vincent (1969): *Agrokémia és Talajtan.* 18, 3–4. 461–472.

Kapusta, G. and Rouwenhorst, D. L. (1973): *Agron. J. Madison.* 65, 1. 112–115.

Kerpely, A. (1958): Talajoltásra szolgáló baktérium-készítmények ismertetése. *Mezőgazdák talaj-ismereti és trágyázási útmutatója.* Ed. di Gleria J. Mezőgazdasági Kiadó, Budapest,

Kurnik, E. (1962): *A szója.* Akadémiai Kiadó, Budapest.

Nery, M. and Dobereiner, J.: (1975): *Rhizobium Newsletter.* 20, No. 2 104.

EFFECT OF SOME PESTICIDES ON THE GROWTH
OF *RHIZOBIUM LEGUMINOSARUM* IN LIQUID CULTURE MEDIA

by

A. S. HAMED and S. H. SALEM
Soil Department of the National Research Centre,
Cairo, Egypt
Anatomy Department of the Faculty of Agriculture, Zagazig University, Dokki
Egypt

Pesticides are organic compounds used in great amounts to combat certain pests. When these chemicals are introduced into the soil, as seed dressing or soil application in agricultural practice they either stimulate or inhibit the growth and activities of the most important group of soil microflora such as the symbiotic nitrogen fixers. The continuous application of these toxicants to the soil may injure the *Rhizobium* inoculum on the inoculated leguminous seeds. Many investigations have studied the harmful effect of these pesticides on rhizobia. Among them Henry (1974), who found that some pesticides were liable to kill legume bacteria on inoculated seeds. Goss and Shipton (1965) and Hamed (1968) found that systemic organophosphorus insecticides were very harmful to the inoculated *Rhizobium* on leguminous seeds. Wilson and Choudhri (1948) found that some pesticides had no effect on rhizobia. While Taha *et al.* (1966), Selim *et al.* (1970) and Diatloff (1970) observed that different pesticides had a stimulatory effect on rhizobia.

From the aforementioned investigations, it was clear that most of the researchers dealt with the symbiotic relationship between rhizobia and the plants, while few studies were made on the growth behaviour of *Rhizobium* when subjected directly to the action of pesticides in liquid culture media. Therefore, an experiment was conducted to study the effect of some pesticides (Endrin, Sevin and Dipterex as insecticides, copper oxychloride, Dithane Z 78 and Phygon XL DDT as fungicides and CIPC as herbicide) on the growth of two strains of *Rhizobium leguminosarum* in liquid culture media.

MATERIAL AND METHODS

The turbidity caused by the growth in liquid medium was taken as an index to reflect the influence of the application of the pesticides on *Rhizobium leguminosarum.*

A batch of Pyrex test tubes was filled with 15 ml liquid medium of yeast extract-mannitol medium (after Allen, 1961), in each and autoclaved. The tubes were then inoculated with either of the following strains of *R. leguminosarum:*

a) *R. leguminosarum* isolated from nodules of broad bean (R_v)
b) *R. leguminosarum* isolated from nodules of lentil (R_L)

The following pesticides were applied, after inoculation by the rhizobial cultures, in a concentration of 0, 0.5, 1.0, 2.0, 4.0 and 8.0 ppm.

I. Insecticides:
  1) Dipterex (Organophosphorus compound)   0,0-Dimethyl-hydroxy-2,2,2-trichloro-ethyl-phosphanale
  2) Endrin (Hexa-chloro-phenoxy-octahydron)
  3) Sevin (1-Naphthyl-N-monomethyl carbamate)
II. Fungicides:
  1) Copper oxychloride   metal compound
  2) Dithane Z 78   carbamate compound
  3) Phygon XL DDT   Fungicide + insecticide
III. Herbicide:
  CIPC N-(m chlorophenyl)-0-isopropyl carbamate.

The treated cultures were then incubated at 30 °C. The growth of the organisms were measured periodically by a turbidimeter apparatus 24, 48, 72, 120 and 144 hours after inoculation. The blank treatment was carried out at the same time without inoculation of the organisms. The blank figures were substracted from each treatment in order to avoid any turbidity attributable to the pesticides or to the ingredients of the medium. The control treatment was also carried out at the same time without pesticide applications. All these treatments were done in five replicates.

RESULTS AND DISCUSSION

Application of insecticides represented by Dipterex, Endrin and Sevin, generally inhibited the growth of both rhizobial strains (R_v and R_L), belonging to one group, *R. leguminosarum*. The inhibitory effect was different according to the concentration of the insecticides. These results were in accordance with those obtained by Taha *et al.* (1966), Hamed (1968), Salem (1971) and Taha *et al.* (1972).

However, in this work a stimulatory effect in the rhizobium growth was observed due to addition of certain concentrations of insecticides. This was especially clear in the case of Endrin when (Fig. 1b) it was added to the culture of *R. leguminosarum* (R_L). Similar stimulatory effect on *Rhizobium* inoculation and on symbiotic relationship due to addition of insecticides was also recorded by Salem *et al.* (1971), and Taha *et al.* (1972).

This work showed also that the inhibitory effect of the insecticides on the *Rhizobium* growth was different from one *Rhizobium* strain to another. For example, Endrin application inhibited the growth of *R. leguminosarum* (R_v) in almost all the concentrations, while it caused a relatively stimulatory effect on the

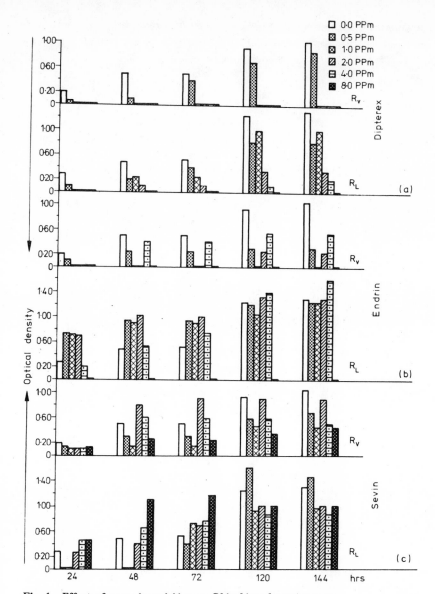

Fig. 1. Effect of some insecticides on *Rhizobium leguminosarum*

growth of the strain of *R. leguminosarum* (R_L) in certain concentrations. Gillberg (1971) also found different responses between *Rhizobium* plant groups on application of pesticides.

In this investigation, it was found that Dipterex was the most inhibitory to the rhizobial growth among the insecticides under investigation, followed by Endrin and

Sevin. This could be attributed to the fact that *Rhizobium* strain R_v absorbed Dipterex more easily than Sevin and Endrin, since Dipterex is considered to be a semi-systemic insecticide. This is in accordance with the finding of Goss and Shipton (1965) who found that systemic organophosphorus insecticides were very harmful to rhizobia.

In this work, it was found that fungicides represented by copper oxychloride caused almost complete inhibition of the growth of the rhizobium strain (R_v) especially when higher concentrations were applied and during the whole experimental period (Fig. 2). This might be due to the toxic action of Cu^{++} or the Cl^- ions on the growth of rhizobia. This result was in harmony with the findings of Henry (1974), Banling and Linn (1974), Taha *et al.* (1966), Hamed (1968), Kecskés and Vincent (1969a) and Gillberg (1971). Meanwhile, the toxic action of copper oxychloride was not so clear on the growth of the *Rhizobium* strain R_L than that found in the strain R_v. This was another example in which the differences were found in the susceptibility of the rhizobial strains towards the toxic action of the pesticides. This also confirmed the work of Gillberg (1971).

The addition of Dithane Z 78 to the media, in this investigation resulted in lower figures than that of the control. In one case, however, a stimulatory effect was recorded with strain R_L addition of Dithane Z 78 in the concentration of 8 ppm. This could be explained by considering that the fungicide in its high concentration might act as a mutagenic chemical causing selection of mutants capable of resisting the high toxicity of the fungicide and showing normal growth. Gillberg (1971) also came to the same conclusion.

Phygon XL DDT, was found to cause a stimulatory effect in the first period of the experiment on the growth of the *Rhizobium* strain R_v. This may be explained by the fact that the stimulatory effect of DDT on the *Rhizobium* strain R_v masked the detrimental effect of Phygon XL at these levels. This explanation is also supported by Afifi *et al.* (1969) and Kecskés and Vincent (1969a and b), who found that Phygon inhibited the growth of *R. leguminosarum.*

Moreover, application of CIPC (herbicide) at different concentrations, generally had a detrimental effect on the growth of the rhizobial strains (Fig. 3). Such data confirmed those recorded by Skrdleta *et al.* (1964), Taha *et al.* (1966) and Hamed (1968), who studied the effect of CIPC on the symbiotic relationship. They found that CIPC prevented the nodule formation of broad bean plants.

From the above discussion, it can be concluded that the susceptibility to certain pesticides of rhizobia isolated from different plants in the pea group and belonging to *R. leguminosarum* (R_v and R_L), varied with the strain and the group of the pesticide from complete toxicity to negative effect. Sometimes it caused a stimulatory effect.

The growth of the rhizobial strains after a slight inhibition may be attributed to the fact that the organisms were adapted to the new medium, probably by excreting some extracellular (induced) enzymes to decompose the chemical to compounds

106

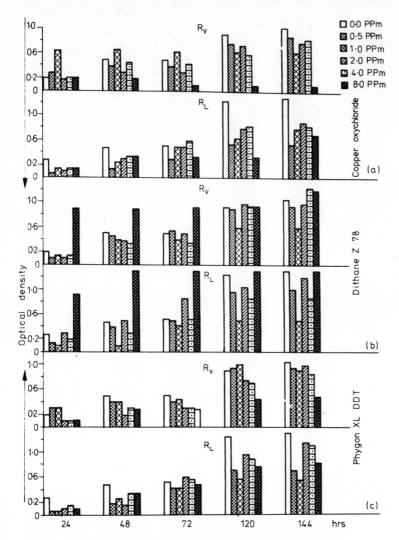

Fig. 2. Effect of some fungicides on *Rhizobium leguminosraum*

stimulatory for the organisms. This was especially true for the organophosphorus compounds.

Dipterex was found to be the most inhibitory among the pesticides under investigation for strains R_v and R_L.

The inhibitory effect of the pesticides on the growth of *R. leguminosarum* in liquid media could be arranged in this investigation as follows: Insecticides > Fungicides > Herbicides.

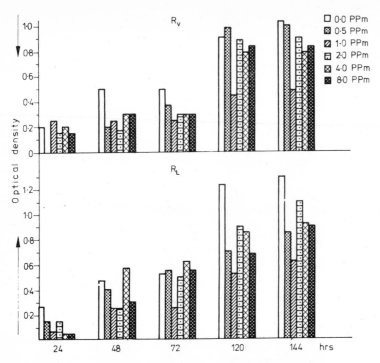

Fig. 3. Effect of herbicide "CIPC" on *Rhizobium leguminosarum*

SUMMARY

The effect of certain pesticides, belonging to different chemical groups (such as Dipterex, Endrin, Sevin – as insecticides), copper oxychloride, Dithane Z 78, Phygon XL DDT (as fungicides) and CIPC (as herbicide) on the growth of two strains of *Rhizobium leguminosarum* were studied in liquid culture media. The first strain of *Rhizobium* was isolated from broad bean nodules (R_V) while the second was isolated from lentil nodules (R_V).

This investigation showed that the susceptibility of R_V and R_L towards the added pesticides differed from one strain to another according to the nature (toxicity) of the chemical.

The effect varied from complete toxicity to a negative effect. Sometimes, the chemical behaved as a stimulant for the growth of the bacteria. When insecticides were used, Dipterex was found to be the most inhibitory for the growth of both rhizobial strains (r_V and R_L), followed by Endrin and Sevin. However, the strain R_L tolerated the application of the insecticides better than strain R_V did.

In the case of the fungicide applications, strain R_V tolerated the toxicant better than R_L. It was also found that copper oxychloride was highly inhibitory, minimizing the growth of both strains (R_V and R_L), stronger than Dithane Z 78 and Phygon XL DDT.

In general, Dipterex was found to be the most inhibitory among the pesticides under investigation. The inhibitory effect of the pesticides on the growth of *R. leguminosarum* could be arranged as follows: Insecticides > Fungicides > Herbicides.

REFERENCES

Afifi, N. M., Moharram, A. A., Hamdi, Y. A. and Abd El-Malek, Y. (1969): *Arch. Mikrobiol.* **66,** 121—128.

Allen, O. N. (1961): *Experiments on soil microbiology.* Burgess Publishing Co. Minnesota.

Banling, J. A.. and Linn, M. B. (1964): *Phytopath.,* **54,**

Diatloff, A. (1970): *Aust J. Exp. Agric. Anim. Husb.* 9, 357.

Gillberg, B. O. (1971): *Arch. Microbiol.* **75,** 203—208.

Goss, O. M. and Shipton, W. A. (1965): *J. West. Aust.* 6, 663—664.

Hamed, A. S. (1968): *Effect of some pesticides on microflora and some important biological processes in soil.* Thesis, Ain Shams University, Cairo, Egypt.

Henry, A. W. (1974): *Bull. Univ. Alberta.* **10.**

Kecskés, M. and Vincent, J. M. (1969a): *Agrokémia és Talajtan.* **18,** 57—70.

Kecskés, M. and Vincent, J. M. (1969b): *Agrokém. és Talajtan* **18,** 461—472.

Salem. S. H. (1971): *Agrokémia és Talajtan* **20,** 368—376.

Salem, S. H., Szegi, J. and Gulyás, F. (1971): *Agrokém. és Talajtan* **20,** 581—589.

Selim, K. G., Mahmoud, S. A. Z. and Mokadem, A. T. (1970): *Plant and Soil* **33,**

Skrdleta, V., Vintikova, H. and Strogl, M. (1964): *Rostl. Vyroba,* **37,** 824—837.

Taha, S. M., Mahmoud, S. A. Z. and Hamed, A. S. (1966): *Scientific Conference Book,* Baghdad, 409.

Taha, S. M., Mahmoud, S. A. Z. and Salem, S. H. (1972): *Symp. Biol. Hung.,* Akadémiai Kiadó, Budapest, 423—429.

Wilson, J. K. and Choudhri, R. S. (1948): *J. Agric. Res.* 77.

INVESTIGATIONS ON THE EFFECT OF HERBICIDES
ON SOME *NOCARDIA* STRAINS

by

Z ., GERGELY, F., BUDAY, and Mária KISS
University for Agricultural Sciences,
Gödöllő, Hungary

In the last decades, a great number of scientific papers have appeared on the effect of pesticides on the micro-organisms. Mickovski (1955), Klyutshnikov and Petrova (1960), Mastakov *et al.* (1962), Pochon *et al.* (1960) studied the effect of several herbicides on the soil. Others such as Ilyaletdinov and Zharokova (1963), Worsham and Giddnes (1957), Burschel (1963), Hale *et al.* (1957), Gamble *et al.* (1962), Fletcher (1956), Szegi and Gulyás (1971), Hauke-Paczewiczowa (1971) dealt with the effect of the herbicides on several groups of bacteria. (Magee and Colmer (1960), Voderberg (1961), Pántos *et al.* (1962) and others, carried out investigations on *Actinomycetes.*

Earlier research involving chemicals was limited to the numerical correlations of the micro-organisms, or to the study of single physiological groups, and they did not deal with the possible genetic effects of the pesticides. It was Kiss (1966) who first drew attention to the fact that certain chemicals produced permanent changes in certain *Actinomycetes.*

The first part of our investigations – the influence of pesticides on *Actinomycetes* – was published previously (Buday, Kiss and Gergely, 1973). In the present paper, we wish to discuss the effect of certain herbicides on the members of the *Nocardia* genus, which play an important role in the micro-organisms of the soil.

MATERIAL AND METHODS

The following strains of *Nocardia* were used: *Nocardia erythropolis* CBS 4277, *N. corallina* CBS 14347, *N. rubropertincta* CBS 14352, *N. opaca* CBS 4276, *N. blackwellii* CBS 27253, *N. salmonicolor* CBS 19657, *N. rosea* AEMT.

In this study the Sabouraud nutrient medium was used: 19 g peptone, 40 g maltose, 20 g agar and 1000 ml distilled water, pH = 7.0, sterilized at 1 atm for 15 minutes.

The herbicides applied were the following: simazine (2-chloro-4,6-bis-ethylamino-s-triazine), atrazine (2-chlor-4-ethylamino-6-isopropylamino-s-triazine) and 2,4-D-sodium

111

salt (2,4-dichlorophenoxyacetic-acid Na-salt). The herbicides were sterilized with ethylether, and they were added aseptically to the pre-sterilized medium.

For testing the effect of the chemical in question, 50 ppm was placed under aseptic conditions into an 500 ml Erlenmayer flask containing 100 ml of nutrient medium, then inoculated with 1 ml inoculum from a shaken culture of the examined strain. After inoculation the flasks were shaken for 5 days at 30 °C, on a horizontal shaker (n = 400/min.).

The effect of chemicals on growth of strains was characterized by measurement of dry weight of mycelium or by counting the number of viable propagules after 5 days' incubation. Dehydrogenase activity was determined from 5 day-old shaken cultures. The reaction mixture contained 70 mg (fresh weight) cells, 1.0 ml 0.01 M TTC solution, 1.0 ml 0.1 M succinic acid and 4.0 ml distilled water. After 24 hours of incubation at 30 °C in the dark, the reaction was stopped by boiling the mixture for 3 minutes. Then the cells were extracted with 10 ml of 96% ethanol for 24 hours in a cool, dark place. The extracted formazan was measured at extracted 500 mm on a "Spekol" spectrophotometer.

Decomposition of hydrocarbons was investigated in media containing 2.0 ml mineral oil. On the 5th day of incubation the liquid cultures were extracted with equal volume of ether; after distillation of ether the residues were dried at 105 °C for 30 min, then weighed.

The electronmicroscopic photographs were made using a "Tesla BS 242 A" apparatus.

RESULTS AND DISCUSSION

Results of investigations are presented in Tables 1—3. Some morphological changes caused by the different herbicides are shown in Figures 1 and 2. As it is shown in Table 1, the tested chemicals resulted in various effects on the different strains. As a rule, the mycelial weights were decreased except in the case of *Nocardia corallina* and *Nocardia rubropertincta* treated with simazine and atrazine. *Nocardia opaca* was stimulated by simazine as indicated by the increased mycelial weight. Data on the formation of living propagules also correlate well with data of the mycelium weights.

As it is proved by the data of Table 2, herbicides inhibited the dehydrogenase activity of most of the strains tested. On the other hand, *Nocardia corallina*, *Nocardia erythropolis* and *Nocardia rubropertincta* were stimulated by simazine and atrazine.

Generally, decomposition of hydrocarbons by the strains was decreased under the influence of chemicals tested, except in the case of *N. rubropertincta* which was stimulated by simazine and atrazine. It should be noted that under the circumstances of our experiments the maximal amount of decomposed hydrocarbon was only 56.5% but infrared spectroscopy revealed radical changes in the apparently

Table 1
The influence of the applied chemicals on the growth of the studied strains

Strains tested	Simazine		Atrazine		2.4-D		Control	
	Myc. weight g/100 ml	Germ. number %/ml	Myc. weight g/100 ml	Germ. number %/ml	Myc. weight g/100 ml	Germ. number %/ml	Myc. weight g/100 ml	Germ. number %/ml
Nocardia rosea	0.4472	$7.0 \cdot 10^6$	0.3805	$6.0 \cdot 10^6$	0.3756	$5.5 \cdot 10^6$	0.6071	$8.2 \cdot 10^6$
Nocardia corallina	0.3771	$5.9 \cdot 10^6$	0.3766	$5.8 \cdot 10^6$	0.2166	$3.7 \cdot 10^6$	0.3433	$4.9 \cdot 10^6$
Nocardia erythropolis	1.0500	$12.4 \cdot 10^6$	0.9929	$11.0 \cdot 10^6$	0.5393	$8.6 \cdot 10^6$	0.2765	$4.9 \cdot 10^6$
Nocardia opaca	0.2935	$4.8 \cdot 10^6$	0.2734	$4.6 \cdot 10^6$	0.2615	$4.2 \cdot 10^6$	0.2765	$4.9 \cdot 10^6$
Nocardia rubropertincta	0.3303	$4.7 \cdot 10^6$	0.3406	$4.9 \cdot 10^6$	0.2535	$3.5 \cdot 10^6$	0.3149	$4.0 \cdot 10^6$
Nocardia blackwellii	0.5948	$9.2 \cdot 10^6$	0.5820	$8.8 \cdot 10^6$	0.3179	$4.2 \cdot 10^6$	0.6577	$10.2 \cdot 10^6$
Nocardia salmonicolor	0.7598	$10.3 \cdot 10^6$	0.7562	$10.0 \cdot 10^6$	0.3212	$3.9 \cdot 10^6$	0.7926	$11.0 \cdot 10^6$

Table 2
The influence of the applied chemicals on the dehydrogenase activity of the studied strains

Strains tested	Simazine	Atrazine	2.4-D	Control
	The dehydrogenase activity of the strains in the per cent of control			
Nocardia rosea	86.13	93.4	50.0	100.00
Nocardia corallina	164.2	152.7	63.5	100.00
Nocardia erythropolis	114.2	120.5	67.6	100.00
Nocardia opaca	93.5	90.27	86.1	100.00
Nocardia rubropertincta	118.4	105.6	79.5	100.00
Nocardia blackwellii	45.6	69.1	36.3	100.00
Nocardia salmonicolor	56.5	55.9	27.9	100.00

Table 3
The influence of the applied chemicals on the CH-decomposing capacity of the studied strains

Strains tested	Simazine	Atrazine	2.4-D	Control
	CH-decomposition in %			
Nocardia rosea	47.78	44.11	42.26	48.54
Nocardia corallina	49.22	40.95	37.87	46.81
Nocardia erythropolis	44.58	45.77	28.18	35.11
Nocardia opaca	50.74	50.02	35.90	56.52
Nocardia rubropertincta	47.82	38.38	35.90	36.18
Nocardia blackwellii	42.62	43.74	29.91	49.19
Nocardia salmonicolor	47.50	48.20	37.89	50.51

intact residues (Table 3). Appearance of carbonyl and carboxyl groups suggests that this material was strongly oxidated by the strains.

Summarizing the effects of chemicals on the growth, dehydrogenase activity and CH-decomposing capacity of the strains, it can be stated that 2,4-D, unequivocally inhibits growth, dehydrogenase activity and CH-decomposing capacity of the examined strains in the concentration and under the conditions applied. Stimulating effect of simazine and atrazine was detected in the case of *Nocardia corallina, Nocardia erythropolis* and *Nocardia rubropertincta,* but the other four strains were inhibited by these compounds.

Under the influence of the chemicals, the life cycle of the tested strains had changed.

While photographs of 24 hour-old untreated strains show a strong mycelial growth, the photographs of the strains treated with chemicals show total fragmentation of the mycelia (Fig. 1a, b). An interesting change was observed in the case of *Nocardia blackwellii* under the effect of 2,4-D treatments. This strain developed colonies with an aberrant morphology, (Fig. 2a, b).

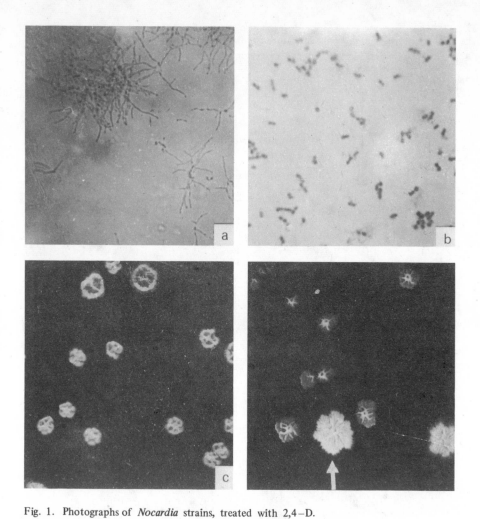

Fig. 1. Photographs of *Nocardia* strains, treated with 2,4–D.
   a Untreated strain of *Nocardia opaca* (1000 x).
   b 2,4-D-treated strain of *Nocardia opaca* (1400 x).
   c Colonies of untreated strain of *Nocardia blackwellii* (2.5 x).
   d Colonies of 2,4–D-treated strain of *Nocardia blackwellii* (2.5 x).

These colonies as it is seen in Figure 1c have a white flower-like crust, and they are similar to *Streptomyces* colonies.

Electron-microscopic investigations of material taken from aberrant colonies showed structures similar to spores of *Actinomyces*. It should be noted, that these structural changes might also be provoked by X-ray irradiation or chemical mutagens (ethylenimine). Whether these mutations of *N. blackwellii* are stable, and, if so, to what extent, remains to be studied in the future.

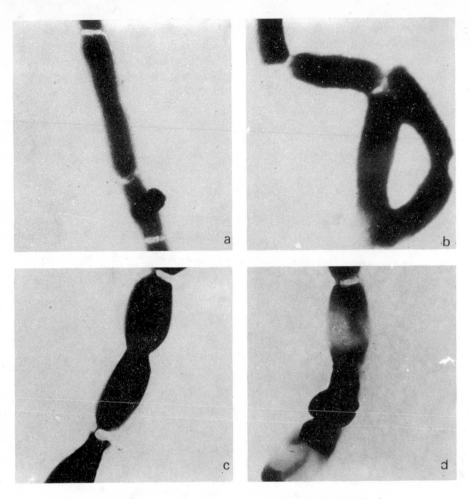

Fig. 2. Electron-microscopic photographs of strain of *Nocardia blackwellii.*
a and b Untreated strain of *Nocardia blackwellii* (16125 x).
c and d The variety of *Nocardia blackwellii,* developed by the influence of a 2-4-D
treatment 30375 x).

SUMMARY

The effect of atrazine, simazine, 2,4-D on strains of *Nocardia erythropolis* CBS
4277, *Nocardia corallina* CBS 14347, *Nocardia rubropertincta* 14352, *Nocardia
opaca* CBS 4276, *Nocardia blackwellii* CBS 27235, *Nocardia salmonicolor* CBS 19657
and *Nocardia rosea* AEMT was studied. 2,4-D decidedly inhibits the growth of the
examined strains in the concentration of 50 ppm.

Simazine and atrazine exerted a stimulative influence on *Nocardia corallina, Nocardia erythropolis* and *Nocardia rubropertincta,* but an inhibitory effect in the case of the other 4 strains. Under the effect of the applied herbicides, the life cycle of the tested strains changed (the mycelium fragmentation occurred earlier than in other cases).

We have stated that, from among the studied strains in the case of *Nocardia blackwellii,* colonies of deviating morphology appeared as influenced by 2,4-D. These colonies have a white, flower-like layer, and they resemble *Actinomycetes* colonies. According to the electronmicroscopic photographs, in contrast to the mycelium fragments of the original strain of *Nocardia blackwellii,* some structures similar to the spores of *Streptomyces* can be seen on the electron-microscopic photographs of this mutant. The study of the problem of how stable the morphological variation of *Nocardia blackwellii* is, and what genetic character it represents, is under investigation.

REFERENCES

Buday F., Kiss Mária and Gergely Z. (1973): MÉM. *Kísérletügyi Közlemények,* LXVIIC Kertészet, 105–119, Budapest.
Burschel, P. (1963): *Forstarchiv, Hannover,* **34,** 221–233.
Fletcher, W. W. (1956): *Nature* London, 177, 1244.
Gamble, S. J. R., Mayhew, C. J. and Chappel, W. E. (1962): *Soil. Sci.* 74, 347–350.
Hale, M. G., Hulcher. F. H. and Chappel, W. E. (1957): *Weeds* 5, 331–341.
Hauke-Pacewiczowa, T. (1971):*Pam. Putawski,* **46,** 5–48.
(Ilyaletdinov, A. N. and Zharokova, R. G.) Илялетдинов, А. Н., Зхарокова, Р. Г. (1963) : *Тр. ин-та микробиол. и вирусол. А. Н. Каз. ССР.* 7, 163–167.
Kiss M. (1966):*Agrártud. Egyetem Közleményei,* 101–113.
(Klyutshnikov, L. J. and Petrova, A. N.) Ключников, Л. Ю., Петрова, А. Н. (1960) : *Микробиол.* 29, 238.
Magee, L. A. and Colmer, A. R. (1960): *Sugar Bull.* **38.** 242–245.
(Mastakov, S. M., Gurinovitsh, E. S., Zimenko, T. G. and Kabaylova, I. V.) Маштаков, Ш. М., Гуринович, Е. С., Зименко, Т. Г., Кабайлова, И. В. (1962) : *Микробиол.* 31, 85–89.
Mickovsky, M. (1955): *Godiven Zb. Zemyod, Sum. Fak. Univ. Skopye.* Zemoyodelstvo Skopye. 6–8, 197–216.
Pántos Gy., Gyurkó P., Takáts T. and Varga L. (1962): *Erdészettud. Közlemények* 2, 5–57.
Pochon, J., Tardieux P. and Charpentier, M. (1960): *Compt. Rend. Acad. Sci.* 250, 1555–1556.
Szegi J. and Gulyás, F. (1971): *Agrokémia és Talajtan* 20, 590–598.
Voderberg, K. (1961):*Nach. bl. dtsch. Pfl. Schutzd.* Berlin t. 15, 21–24.
Worsham, A. D. and Giddnes, J. (1957): *Weeds* Geneva, 5, 316–320.

THE ROLE OF SOIL MICRO-ORGANISMS IN THE TRANSFORMATION OF PLANT NUTRIENTS

THE ROLE OF MICROFLORA IN THE DECOMPOSITION OF PLANT RESIDUES IN THE FISHPOND LITTORAL ZONE

by

Blanka, ÚLEHLOVÁ and Eliška, DOBROVOLNÁ-VAŠULKOVÁ
Botanical Institute of the Czechoslovak Academy of Sciences,
Brno, Czechoslovakia

Odum (1971) describes wetlands as typical detritus based food chain systems. Microflora here play an important role in the release, uptake and cycling of mineral nutrients as well as in the productivity and development of plant stands. During integrated ecosystem studies of a littoral ecosystem at the Nesyt fishpond, southern Moravia, Czechoslovakia, in 1965–1974, which were a part of the IBP (Květ 1973), the microflora (Úlehlová and Vašulková 1975), microbial activities (Dobrovolná-Vašulková in press), and changes in chemical composition of the plant materials in the course of their decomposition were investigated.

The present study is concerned with describing the microbial populations and chemical changes of plant residues of the principal littoral helophytes i.e. *Phragmites communis* Trin. and *Typha angustifolia* L., and comparing the changes in the release and uptake of mineral nutrients of reed residues either scattered by the wind or decomposed while submersed in the water.

MATERIAL AND METHODS

The highly eutrophic "Nesyt", i.e. "the insatiable", covering about 300 ha, is the greatest and the most productive fishpond of the water system near Lednice (lat. 48°48′22″, long. 16°46′22″). The fish crop amounted to 516 kg/ha for a two-year period 1966–1967, 576 kg/ha for 1968–1969, and 767 kg/ha for 1970–1971. Plant residues and soil or mud samples were collected in the littoral vegetation on the southern shoreline at monthly intervals during 1971 and 1972. The samples were analysed for microflora by incubating the diluted water extracts on the following media: meat-peptone agar, peptone agar, cellulose agar, Ashby agar and glucose-yeast extract agar (Aaronson 1970). The chemical analyses of the plant remnants and soil were carried out subsequent to mineralization according to the methods described by Koppová *et al.* (1955). The decomposition of litter in water was studied using the litter mesh bag method (Witkamp and van der Drift 1961). The 25 g samples were placed in mesh bags (mesh size 1 mm) in shallow water of the littoral for 180 days. Then the samples were taken in to the laboratory, rinsed with water, weighed and analysed by standard chemical methods.

RESULTS AND DISCUSSION

Table 1 gives the maximal and minimal counts of micro-organisms present in or on the plant residues in different stages of decomposition, in the water and in the soil from littoral of Nesyt fishpond, as estimated on several agar media. It can be seen that the highest counts were found in the partially decomposed plant residues. They amounted to 10^8 germs per 1 g of dry matter. The lowest counts were found in the pond water, i.e. 10^3 germs per ml. The overall data indicate that the population density of micro-organisms depends on the concentration, quality and heterogeneity of the respective energetic sources, as well as on the total surface area available for the colonization by micro-organisms. The results agree with those of Gosselink and Kirby (1974).

Figures 1–3 show the changes of mineral composition. Figure 1 relates to the plant residues of *Phragmites communis* in terrestrial zone of the littoral, Figure 2 to residues of the same species but in the aquatic zone of the littoral, with water depth ranging from 5 to 25 cm, and Figure 3 to the plant residues in the littoral zone covered by *Typha angustifolia* with a water layer 25–50 cm. The appropriate stages of decomposition of plant residues sampled for analysis are illustrated in the upper part of each graph. Standing dead plants and litter in the initial stage of decomposition, semidecomposed litter, and soil were analysed in the case of the *Phragmites* residues in the terrestrial zone. Standing dead, plant litter and detritus were analysed in the case of *Phragmites* residues in the aquatic zone. With *Typha angustifolia* the samples were restricted to the standing dead plant litter floating on the water surface and detritus (mud) on the pond bottom.

The curves show that generally the organic matter content decreased while the contents of ash and individual mineral constituents increased with advancing stages of decomposition, the increases for calcium (from 0.3 to 3%) and nitrogen (from 0.3 to 1.5%) being the most conspicuous. The differences in the chemical composition between dying and standing dead plants is interesting. Inspite of a relatively short time interval separating these stages a marked decrease of the nitrogen, phosphorus and potassium contents was recorded. As possible causes of such changes the following factors are to be considered:

1) the loss of leaves, which are considerable in nitrogen and somewhat richer in phosphorus than the culms, as documented in Table 2;

2) the translocation of some nutrients from the above ground organs to the roots and turions, accompanied by eventual reverse transport of surplus calcium, and

3) the mechanical leaching of the plant structures.

A comparison of the changes in chemical composition of the *Phragmites communis* residues in the terrestrial and aquatic zones as visualized in Figure 1

Table 1
Minimal and maximal microbial counts in different materials of the Nesyt fishpond

	Concentration factor		PA*	MPA**	Ashby
Standing	10^7	min.	0.8	0.4	0.2
dead air		max.	33.3	35.8	14.0
Litter-	10^8	min.	2.3	1.5	2.8
terrest. soil surface		max.	3,3	1.7	3.8
Litter-	10^8	min.	7.3	3.1	1.9
aquat. bottom		max.	19.5	3.6	4.2
Mud	10^7	min.	7.3	0.01	1.6
		max.	31.1	1.2	7.6
Water	10^3	min.	–	4.8	6.4
		max.	–	9.9	10.6

*peptone agar
**meat-peptone agar

and 2 is worthy of note. A smaller decrease of the organic matter content takes place in plant residues of the aquatic habitat where the anaerobic conditions prevail and the concentrations of mineral substances such as calcium, potassium and phosphorus in plant residues are also less pronounced. On the contrary the nitrogen content of the plant residues increased by 1.7% concurrently with a 6% decrease of the organic matter content in the aquatic zone, contrasted with the 1.2% nitrogen increase in the residues of the terrestrial zone, where the decrease of organic matter contents represented 18%, all compared with the original contents. The relatively high increase in the nitrogen contents of residues in the aquatic zone indicates that an active accumulation of nitrogen accompanies the decomposition. The results agree with similar observations quoted by Odum and de la Cruz (1967) and de la Cruz (1973).

The pattern of chemical changes at the site of *Typha angustifolia* differs somewhat from those at the sites of *Phragmites*. First of all the standing dead plants of *Typha* do not remain as long as do that of *Phragmites*, partly due to different mechanical properties, partly due to the greater impact of waves and the resulting mechanical damage in the *Typha* zone, directly adjoining the open water area of the pond. The broken plant parts mostly drift away, mix with other materials and finally decompose and are deposited in other areas of the pond. The difference between the initial and final organic matter contents is therefore much greater than the comparable decreases at both *Phragmites* sites. It corresponds to 32.4%, the increase in nitrogen content being only 1.1%.

At the beginning of the winter of 1972 a number of *Phragmite* stalks, one or two years old, protruding above the water table, were collected for chemical analyses. The resulting data are presented in Table 3. They show that besides the weight decrease the standing dead lost *in situ* only about 7% of organic matter in

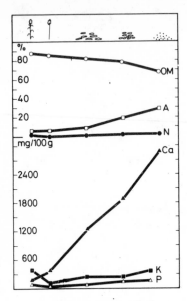

Fig. 1. Changes in chemical composition of plant residues of terrestrial *Phragmites communis Trin.* during decomposition.

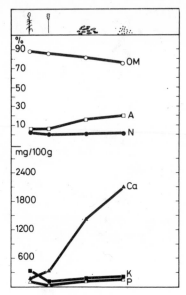

Fig. 2. Changes in chemical composition of plant residues of aquatic *Phragmites communis Trin.* during decomposition

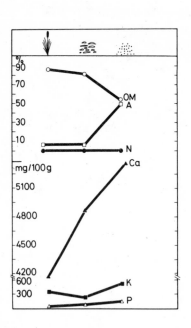

Fig. 3. Changes in chemical composition of plant residues of *Typha angustifolia* L. during decomposition

Table 2
Chemical composition of dead leaves, shoots and roots of *Phragmites communis*

Material	Org. m. %	N%	PO$_4$	K	Na	Ca	Mg
					mg/100 g		
Leaves	80.4	1.13	274	195.5	105.5	1,980	93.4
	70.4–92.2	0.8–1.4	225–320	157–250	65–137	1,250–2,700	75–122
Shoots	90.5	0.47	231	376.5	122.0	700	91.2
	84.5–95.5	0.3–0.5	150–495	117–835	72–200	600–2,000	63–137
Roots	73.6	1.73	655	735.0	242.5	6,400	109.5
	70–77	1.6–1.8	585–725	700–770	220–265	5,200–7,600	100–119

Table 3
Chemical composition of above water standing dead shoots of *Phragmites communis*

Material	Org. m. %	N%	PO$_4$	K	Na	Ca	Mg
					mg/100 g		
Shoots of the current year	90.46	0.47	231	376.5	122	700	74.0
	84.5–96.5	0.35–0.53	150–495	117–835	72–200	600–800	63–94
Shoots of the last year	83.77	0.77	228	140.8	80.8	1,683	84.7
	81–88	0.59–0.88	185–260	110–180	77.5–85.0	1,400–2,000	75–96
Differences	–6.69	+0.30%	–3	–235.7	–21.2	+983	+10
Detritus	67.36	1.76	441	283.0	226.0	6,090	95.2
	61.5–74.8	1.5–1.9	140–605	170–415	70–330	5,200–8,450	48–119

Table 4
Chemical composition of *Phragmites communis* shoots decomposing
in the fishpond littoral during summer and winter

Material	Org. m. %	N%	PO_4	K	Na	Ca	Mg
			mg/100 g				
Control shoots	85.6	0.13	102	68.7	28.7	255	23
Shoots exposed 180 days in summer	I. 80.9	0.34	70	47.5	37.5	400	20
	II. 81.8	0.46	160	42.5	45.0	825	34
Shoots exposed 180 days in winter	I. 57.8	0.49	37.0	45.0	40.0	400	25
	II. 62.2	0.32	42.5	37.5	27.5	400	19

I. exposed on the bottom under 10—15 cm water layer in the plant stand of Phragmites comm.
II. exposed on the bottom under 25 cm water layer in the lagoon.

one year. However, the nitrogen content of the plant material increased in the same period from 0.47% to 0.77%, which is nearly twice as much. It may be supposed from the results that the plant material with a wide C/N ratio is a suitable energetic source for organisms able to bind atmospheric nitrogen, which by their activities narrow down the C/N ratio. Similar conclusions were arrived at by Kaushik and Hynes (1968, 1971) and Mathews and Kowalczewski (1969).

Contrasted with the nitrogen increase, the content of monovalent cations decreased to even less than one third, apparently by leaching, although direct exchange relations are not excluded. It was observed in laboratory experiments by Planter (1970) that potassium was the fastest to be washed out from *Phragmites* plant material. Apparently the same holds true also under field conditions. According to Table 3, the ageing standing dead of *Phragmites* further shows a considerable increase in calcium, and a lesser one in magnesium. Such an increase may result from ionic reactions between the bivalent cations of the pond water and the plant residues, and/or their sessile micro-organisms.

Chemical changes taking place during the decomposition of dead stalks of *Phragmites* enclosed in litter mesh bags and submersed in the pond water either at the *Phragmites* site or in the bare lagoon were studied both in summer and winter. The results of pertinent chemical analyses are presented in Table 4. The data show that the loss of organic matter hardly reached 10% in the summer months while it amounted to about 30% in winter. Similar data for phosphorus contents reveal practically insignificant changes in summer, but a strong deprivation (by 60%) in winter. The submersed *Phragmites* residues, analogously to the standing dead in situ, accumulated nitrogen and calcium to a considerable degree.

The differences in decomposition rates of plant residues between winter and summer exposures may be supposed to result from different oxygen solubilities in water as well as from differences in the type of prevailing microflora.

The authors acknowledge the skilful assistance of M. Findeisová and Mrs. A. Svobodová.

SUMMARY

Chemical composition of plant litter and of plant residues at various stages of decomposition was estimated in three distinct littoral zones of macrophytes during the integrated IBP study of the Nesyt Fishpond in southern Moravia, Czechoslovakia. Simultaneously the microbial populations of all plant materials were studied and the decomposition rates of the autochthonous plant material as well as of cellulose were measured.

REFERENCES

Aaronson Sh. (1970): *Experimental microbial ecology.* – Academic Press, New York and London.

Cruz A. A. de la (1973): *Assoc. Southeastern Biologists Bull.* **20**, 147–156.

Dobrovolná-Vašulková E.: *Decomposition of littoral vegetation in Nesyt and Opatovický fishpond.* (in print).

Gosselink J. G. and Kirby C. J. (1974): *Limnol. and Oceanogr.* 19, 825–832.

Kaushik N. K. and Hynes H. B. N. (1968): *J. Ecol.* **56**, 229–243.

Kaushik N. K. and Hynes H. B. N. (1971): *Arch. Hydrobiol.* 68, 465–515.

Koppová A., Pirkl J. and Kalina J. (1955): *Věd. práce VÚRV.* 119–127.

Květ J. (Ed.) (1973): *Studie ČSAV.* 15.

Mathews C. P. and Kowalczewski A. (1969): *J. Ecol.* 57, 543–552.

Odum E. P. and Cruz A. A. de la (1967): *Estuaries AAAS.* 383–388.

Odum E. (1971): *Fundamentals of ecology.* Philadelphia, W. B. Saunders Com.

Planter M. (1970): *Polskie Archiw Hydrobiol.* 17, 357–362.

Úlehlová B. and Vašulková E. (1975): *Folia Microbiol.* 20, 80–81.

Witkamp M. J. and van der Drift, J. (1961): *Plant and Soil* 15, 295–311.

RESEARCH INTO THE SEASONAL CHANGE
OF ORGANIC C- AND N-MINERALIZATION CAPACITY
IN SOILS OF NON-TEMPERATE CLIMATES

by

R. SCHAEFFER and Angela URBINA
Laboratoire d'Ecologie végétale, Université de Paris XI
Orsay, France
Institute de Investigaciones Agropecuarias,
Santiago de Chile, Chile

In extensive areas of the world, mainly under the tropics, the management of soil microbial resources remains to be developed, for hitherto research about soil microbial activity proceeds chiefly from the temperate climates of the northern hemisphere.

Yet the unhalted demographic pressure in many countries, where soil and humus conservation already has to contend with harsh natural conditions, leads to an increasing demand for food, in total discrepancy with the development of "sustained-yield tropical agroecosystems", as discussed by Janzen (1973).

Thus it appears urgent to foster a better knowledge of the ecology and biochemical activity of the soil population in the vast regions where the abrupt change from traditional extensive cropping practices to mechanized, intensive, short-term exploitation of soil resources has brought about a state of unbalance, a menace of breakdown. The former were integrated into the functioning of natural ecosystems whereas the latter are highly artificial and agressive.

The seasonal evolution of the soil metabolic capacity, and likewise of the biogeochemical cycles, has to be investigated further in order to specify standard patterns allowing for a discriminative use of the land. Hence rather than descriptive or numerical analysis, the study of the metabolic activity of physiological groups of the microbiocenosis, at the integrated level of biochemical balances, appears primeval.

There exists a need for a methodology, simple enough to be carried out with elementary equipment, at lowest cost, as well as in large series to yield significant data, yet complex enough to allow insight into the fundamental processes of soil metabolism, as related to the global environment. Our work along this line in W-Africa (Ivory Coast, virgin savana), South-eastern Asia, Central and South America (cultivated land) was aimed at contributing to maintain the agricultural practices, the nature of the crops and the land use within a tolerable range. One of the procedures developed and applied concerns the organic C- and N-mineralization capacity. Soil respiration, integrating all of the environmental factors, was considered as an index of global activity, and accumulation of mineral-N as an expression of the interrelationship between heterotrophs and autotrophs under aerobic conditions.

MATERIAL AND METHODS

Factorial assays were set up to:

— establish the influence, individually or globally, of the physical and micro-climatic environmental factors, as well as their rôle in microbial activity
— analyze the function, according to their nature, of various organic substrates in soil metabolism.

In situ experiments yield an estimation of the actual activity, related to the sum of the environmental factors, including the accessibility of the organic substrates. By comparing it with the potential capacity, obtained under controlled optimum conditions *in vitro,* means are given to construe the seasonal dynamics and, by extrapolation, foresee the possible and most probable trajectories of further development.

Metal boxes (10 cm ϕ, 10 cm high, 750 ml) are filled with soil (2 mm, pooled from multiple samples, sieved, homogenized, adjusted to a given humidity, eventually supplemented with a substrate, slightly compacted). These boxes are sturdy, reusable (plastic bags are often pierced), no-cost material of adequate volume. Large series may be set up, allowing a precise control of changes in soil metabolic activity. The lid, in which a 6 cm ϕ hole is cut, is fixed on the box already capped with a piece of nylon mesh. Then the box is turned over and buried at the level of the sampling, or at another depth. Most evident advantages of this procedure are:

— sieving eliminates non-soil elements as roots, gravel and fauna, homogenizes, aerates and restores crumb structure, distributes micropopulation and organic substrates. It is equivalent to replications, for a standard, representative response in activity is obtained with each sample.
— capping with nylon mesh avoids entry of earthworms, roots and restricts loss of organic substrate, yet water vapour and gases diffuse freely. It was found better than perforated lids or lids with a soldered stainless steel grid, as used before.
— inverting avoids lixiviation by rain, retards penetration of phreatic water, maintains humidity.

In some cases a set of boxes is buried at a given period of the year, the number of boxes corresponding to an equivalent number of samplings at subsequent periods. In other cases, a new set of boxes is prepared with soil taken at the time when sampling of the previous series takes place: periodically, a composite sample of field soil is taken, sieved, homogenized, analyzed for mineral N, conditioned in boxes for burial. Sub-samples are incubated *in vitro* in Erlenmeyer flasks: 6 weeks for mineral-N (Bremner and Keeney, 1965), 4 weeks for CO_2 evolution ($Ba(OH)_2$ /oxalic acid/ phenolphthalein). CO_2 evolution is also measured *in situ* (Lundegårdh), on undisturbed soil after removal of the epigeous vegetation, or on homogenized soil submitted to the natural changes in temperature.

Nitrate accumulation in the buried box corresponds to potential activity under field conditions; comparison with samples of undisturbed soil yields insight into loss of N (lixiviation by rain, irrigation, groundwater, uptake by plant roots, denitrification). As there is no input of organic C into the box, and little production of easily metabolizable C, the immobilization of mineral N is poised after an initial period of adjustment.

Four treatments are considered:

Natural Soil (NS): in complete contact with the environment. Its actual activity at a given time integrates all the acting factors.

Incubated Natural Soil (INS): brought to optimum conditions of humidity (field capacity), temperature (28 °C) and aeration.

Conditioned Soil (CS): partly removed from contact with the physico-chemical environment and entirely from biotic influences. Humidity constant in box, but sample submitted to the natural thermoperiods.

Incubated Conditioned Soil (ICS): soil of box, incubated under constant optimum conditions.

In order to evaluate the accumulation potential of a soil for nitrates, the results of these 4 treatments are compared; they reflect mostly the influence of the factors which acted upon the soil in the period immediately before the sampling. Thus all the samples taken at a given time may be compared and an arithmetical mean drawn which yields a most probable annual curve of activity under the conditions of a given treatment.

The results from the four treatments described are weighted in the following balance:

— accumulation of mineral-N:

INS–ICS: difference due to presence of plants (root excretions), of recently incorporated organic matter.

CS–NS: global effect of permanent optimum humidity versus hygroperiods, of absence versus presence of plants.

INS–NS: effect of optimum humidity and temperature.

ICS–CS: effect of optimum temperature.

— evolution of CO_2:

INS–ICS: as above.

INS–NS: as above.

Work on soils of the Central Valley in Chile will illustrate our endeavour. The climate of this area is of the mediterranean type: rainfall occurs mainly in winter which is mild, summer is very dry although moderately hot. The practice of irrigation extends the period favourable to biological activity to the whole of the year. Under dry-farming, strong increments in nitrate-production are observed from autumn through spring.

Maipo alluvial soil is a typic haploxerol. Crops are rye/clover from September to December and clover from January to October. Climate is semi-arid (360 mm rain). San Vicente alluvial soil is a deep vertisol under wheat from September to December and left fallow thereafter. Data on these soils are summed up in Table 1:

Table 1
Physico-chemical data on soils of the Central Valley (Chile)

	Clay	Silt	Sand	FC	PWP	CEC meq.	P Olsen ppm	CaCO$_3$	C%	N%$_0$	pH
Maipo:											
La Platina	27	29	44	25	10	15	19.2	5.6	1.3	1.2	7.8
San Vicente:											
La Estacada	43	20	37	24	12	36	9.2	0	2.3	2.4	7.2
Bolsico	38	28	34	35	23	40	4.8	0	3.2	2.6	7.5

Figure 1 compares sites of Maipo soil under either irrigation or dry-farming. The curve representing the results of incubated samples is based on arithmetical means, as discussed. Differences are evident, related to the mode of cultivation, the state of soil as well as the season and the inherent character of the incident year (1969 was very dry). But there is coincidence in the response to similar treatments between the behaviour of the irrigated and the dry-farmed soil. Nitrate accumulation takes a different course when natural soil, as compared with conditioned soil, is submitted to irrigation. It is different also with dry-farmed soil, under both treatments.

Still more information is to be had by comparing the increments in accumulated nitrate, as shown in Fig. 2. The seasonal course of the potential activation, as achieved under *in vitro* incubation, shows that both natural and conditioned soil behave similarly and this is not changed substantially by the water regime. Finally, as regards mineralization of organic C, the amount of CO$_2$ evolved (Fig. 3, mean values) from soil submitted to relatively optimal thermic and hydric conditions, follows a definite trend. When an increase in accumulated organic matter takes place, that is in winter for irrigated soil and in summer for dry-farmed soil, the amount of nitrates found is at its high level. The difference in response between natural and conditioned irrigated soil, large in winter, falls off sharply in spring and then rises slowly, whereas in the case of dry-farmed soil there is a large peak in

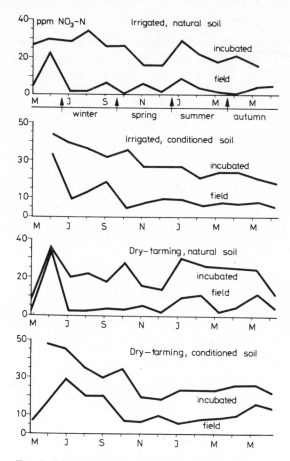

Fig. 1. Maipo alluvial soil (Chile), sampled and incubated at monthly interval.
Accumulation of nitrate during the annual
cycle (71/72)

summer. This periodicity seems to be commanded by changes in the level of
available energetic substrate.

As regards San Vicente vertisol (Fig. 4) sampling has been done at characteristic
phenological stages of the crop (wheat): sowing, tillering, heading, flowering, milky
grain, harvest. The course of the respiratory activity, when compared with the net
production of nitrates, evidences phases of biological immobilization of mineral-N,
mainly so in natural soil (Bolsico). The change in the amount of accumulated
nitrate in the conditioned samples follows in general that measured in natural soil,
at a higher level. Yet the conditioned soil is not in contact with plants and does not
experience any input or output of organic matter. The difference in accumulated

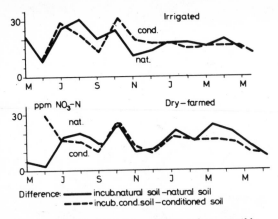

Fig. 2. Alluvial soil (Maipo, Chile) taken monthly. Increments in nitrate, according to treatment

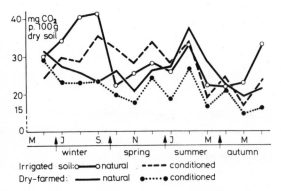

Fig. 3. In vitro (28 °C, field capacity), cumulative (33 days) mineralization of organic C. Maipo alluvial soil (Chile), sampled and incubated at monthly interval (71/72)

nitrate between incubated natural and natural soil on the one hand, and between incubated conditioned and conditioned soil on the other shows that the activability potential of nitrification varies according to the seasons. It is highest during winter.

DISCUSSION

It has been clearly established that the episodical or periodical variations in the nature and intensity of the telluric metabolical processes (f. ex.: nitrification: Harder 1931, Lemmermann and Wichers 1920, Schönbrunn 1922) along the annual

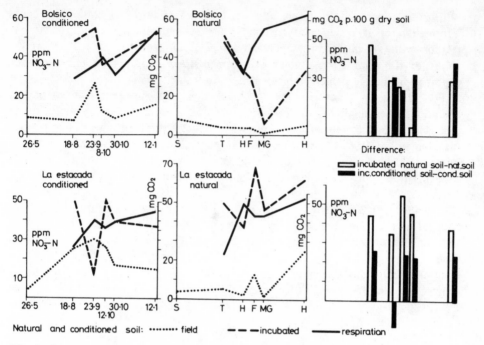

Fig. 4. Seasonal change in nitrate accumulation and mineralization of soil organic C, as related to growth stages of wheat in San Vincente vertisol (Chile, 1969/70)

cycle can be attributed to the seasonal modifications of the micro-environment which rule the microbial population (Burrichter 1958, Engberding 1909, Khudjakov 1958, Samcevich 1955). The modulation of the micro-organisms activity arises from the interaction of the environmental physical, chemical and biological factors among which temperature and water are the most efficient, not only by their limiting thresholds, but also by the rhythm and the amplitude of their fluctuation (Fehér 1937, 1938) which monitor the seasonal periodicity of plant production (Rappe 1963). This gives rise to rhizosphere and litter effects which also regulate the intensity of the soil microbe metabolic functions.

Some authors, following Löhnis (1926) have tried, by preserving the soil from external fluctuations or by testing its metabolic capacity in inoculated synthetic media, to show an endonomous microbial periodicity (Bortels 1958, Johansson 1929, Limbach 1929, Metzen 1936, Thornton and Gray 1930). However, until now no convincing experimental proof supports this hypothesis.

Already Löhnis stated that metabolic assays under constant, monitored conditions should always be conducted together with field trials where the variations of the natural environment are acting globally. Our aim is precisely a factorial analysis enabling the monitoring of the course of microbial activity and thus allowing for a more efficient microbial resources management.

135

The determination of the *in situ* accumulated mineral-N yields all the more information as it is repeated frequently in the annual cycle and brought into relation with the mode of rainfall and temperature, the cultivation practices, the nature of the plant cover. But other treatments, like conditioning and incubation, appear to be indispensable complements.

For the soils submitted to the incubation test, under relatively optimal conditions, the length of this *in vitro* activation is critical. The dynamics of the biological immobilization of the nitrate produced, in function of the seasonal variation in the level of available easily degradable organic matter, complicate the interpretation of the results obtained. One therefore may only rely upon the comparison of curves, of dynamic phenomena corresponding to defined factorial incidences.

It is just that which has been attempted here, with the object of optimizing the N- and C-fertilization programme as a function of the seasonal periodicity of a given soil's mineralizing capacity. Knowledge about this rhythm, in its dependence on the environmental changes, is all the more fundamental as climatic patterns are remote from the temperate model and the rôle of soil humic matter more limiting to ecosystems. Results along this line have been obtained in Argentina (Giambiagi 1969, Giambiagi *et al.* 1970), Chile (Ibañez and Vial 1971, Jünemann 1969), Ivory Coast (Schaefer 1974).

CONCLUSION

The technique applied seems adequate for a factorial exploration into the effect of environmental change on the microbiocenosis functioning. Taking as a test the accumulated mineral-N in natural soil is amply justified because it is equivalent to the amount available to higher plants along the seasonal cycle. The incubated samples of natural soil and conditioned soil yield evidence that not only are the dynamics of mineral-N regulated by the soil water and temperature regime but also by the nature and amount of organic matter, controlling ammonification and inducing variations due to uptake by microbes of part of the mineralized N. In all cases of conditioned soil, there is similarity between the shape of seasonal change in NO_3^--accumulation in conditioned and incubated conditioned soil, as well as the mineralization of soil organic C. In many cases this evidence extends to natural soil.

The potential activation by temperature changes with the characteristic periods of the plant cycle, but also changes the effect of soil water and the influence, positive or negative, of the root excretions and other organic matter input, contributing to episodical changes in the nitrate accumulation potential and soil respiration.

The rhizosphere and litter microbiocenosis are influenced, both in their nature and activity, by the periodicity of plant metabolism and production and, geographically, by the pattern of climatic changes.

Likewise, this modulation also seems to be carried out through the regulatory, poising rôle endorsed by soil humus. Soil humic matter is the result, in its nature, complexity and amount, of historical evolution, the heritage of a succession of influences and changes leaving the imprint of a biochemical code in which the more recent events or the stronger impacts of the past predominate. The metabolic response of soil previously severed from association with higher plants and withdrawn from the natural environmental changes, would follow an intrinsic rhythm and would depend on a residual effect acting as a memory, a projection of the whole past influence of environmental factors into the present.

The pattern of the soil microbes' metabolic activity being maintained during *in vitro* activation or *in situ* conditioning in boxes without neither increments nor losses in substrates, the seasonal regulation appears to be ruled by the dynamic interaction of the microflora with the habitat and by the biochemical pattern of the humified organic matter accumulated in soil. An endonomous rhythm of the soil microflora, if it were to exist, would play but a minor rôle.

REFERENCES

Bortels, H. (1958): *Zbl. Bakt. II,* 6/7., 218.
Bremner J. M. and Keeney D. R. (1965): *Anal. Chim. Acta* **32**, 485–495.
Burrichter, E. (1958): *Ber. deutsch. Bot. Ges.* **71**, 71.
Engberding, D. (1909): *Zbl. Bakt. II.* **23**, 569.
Fehér, D. (1937): *Arch. Mikrobiol.* 8, 249.
Fehér, D. (1938): *Arch. Mikrobiol.* 9, 193.
Giambiagi, N. (1969): *Rev. Ecol. Biol. Sol,* 6 (3), 277.
Giambiagi, N., Ritzi H. and Cerri O. C. (1970): *Rev. Ecol. Biol. Sol.* 7 (3), 351.
Harder A. (1931): *Bot. Archiv.* **31**, 312.
Ibañez, B. S. and Vial L. O. (1971): *Dinámica estacional actual y potencial del N en dos suelos del Valle Central de Chile.* Univ. Católica, Santiago. Thesis Ing. Agrón. 67 p.
Janzen, D. H. (1973): *Science* **182**, 1212.
Johansson, N. (1929): *Sv. botan. Tidskr.* **23**, 241.
Jünemann, O. (1969): *Dinámica de la mineralización e inmovilización potenciales del N y del C en dos suelos aluviales del Valle Central (Chile).* Univ. Católica, Santiago. Thesis.
Karapurkar, Y. M. (1933): *Kühn-Archiv.* **37**, 143.
(Khudjakov, Ja. P.) Худяков, Я. П. (1958) : *Труды ин-та микробиол.* АН СССР **5**, 150.
Lemmermann, O. and Wichers L. (1920): *Zbl. Bakt. II,* **50**, 33.
Limbach, S. (1929): *Zbl. Bakt. II,* **79**, 354.
Löhnis, F. (1926): *Vorlesungen über landwirtschaftliche Bakteriologie.* 2. Auflage. Berlin.
Metzen, O. von (1936): *Zbl. Bakt. II,* **94**, 1.
Rappe, G. (1963): *Oikos,* **14** (1), **44** (2), 224.
(Samcevich, S. S.) Самцевич, С. С. (1955) : *Микробиол.* **24**, 615.
Schaefer, R. (1974): *Analyse d'un écosystème tropical humide.* In: IBP/RCP n° 60, CNRS. Activité métabolique du sol: fonctions microbiennes et bilans biogéochimiques dans la savane de Lamto (Côte-d'Ivoire). Publ. Lab. Zool. ENS, n° spécial Lamto, fasc. **5**, 167.
Schönbrunn, B. (1922): *Zbl. Bakt. II.* **56**, 545.
Thornton, H. G. and Gray P. H. H. (1930): *Proc. Roy. Soc. London,* B **106**, 399.

BIOLOGICAL IMMOBILIZATION OF FERTILIZER NITROGEN IN THE SOIL

by

Zhivka, VOINOVA-RAIKOVA
"Poushkarov" Institute for Soil Science,
Sofia, Bulgaria

Immobilization of fertilizer nitrogen is an important cycle in the biological transformation of nitrogen in the soil. 25–30 per cent of fertilizer nitrogen introduced is considered to be used by micro-organisms, included in the composition of their cells and, for some time, unavailable to plants. The rate and dynamics of biological immobilization of nitrogen are. determined by the amount, composition and dynamics of soil microflora (Voinova-Raikova 1969, Sapozhnikov 1973, Tarvis 1972, 1973).

To control that process requires information on soil conditions and climatic factors. Immobilization of nitrogen is a useful process in autumn and winter as it controls leaching of nitrogen and is harmful during the vegetation period. The mineralization of immobilized nitrogen is an important source of nitrogen available to plants (Dinchev 1964, Kidin and Smirnov 1974, Sapozhnikov 1973, Smirnov and Wójczik-Woitkowiak 1965, Smirnov and Shilova 1972, Tarvis 1973).

MATERIAL AND METHODS

Laboratory, pot and field experiments were carried out to study the rate and dynamics of immobilized fertilizer nitrogen; favourable conditions were created for the dynamics to take place (introduction of fertilizers together with glucose and hay). To accelerate mineralization of immobilized nitrogen under both laboratory and pot experimental conditions biologically active preparations were tested such as heteroauxin, gibberellin, azotogen, as well as waste water of microbiological industry (the plants for fodder yeast and antibiotics) and root residues of legume crops. The aim of the study was to achieve a control of that process as soon as the volume of biological immobilization of nitrogen was established through acceleration of mineralization processes, which resulted in introduction of nitrogen available to plants into the soil during the vegetation period.

RESULTS

In the period between the 14th and 21st day after the introduction of fertilizers, 20–26 per cent of nitrogen fertilizers of the fertilizers introduced (ammonium nitrate and urea) into calcareous chernozem are immobilized; mostly the nitrate nitrogen is immobilized which is a prevailing form in those soils. Till the end of the third month after the introduction of fertilizers, 20 per cent of the nitrogen is immobilized, or in other words, nitrogen is almost not mineralized during the vegetation period. With leached and podzolized chernozems, nitrogen immobilization shows the same rate at the beginning but one month later (after fertilizers are applied) immobilization decreases by 5–10 per cent; in other words, immobilization of nitrogen is a short-term process in those soils (Fig. 1). The dynamics of the microflora in the soils studied shows rapid increase in the number of micro-organisms involved in the use of available nitrogen, while the number of ammonifiers decreases. In calcareous chernozems, there is an increase in the number of actinomycetes, which is most probably attributable to a more difficult mineralization of immobilized nitrogen.

In smolnitzas, the ammonium and nitrate nitrogen introduced with fertilizers are immobilized considerably, up to 20 per cent of the fertilizer nitrogen is immobilized. The dynamics of immobilization fluctuates which means that during vegetation nitrogen is immobilized in a more labile form.

In cinnamonic and grey forest soils, as in chernozems, the biological immobilization of fertilizer nitrogen is more strongly expressed than in soil types of neutral reaction; it decreases gradually and becomes more labile in leached and podzolized soil types. This is related to the composition of the microflora participating in those processes. Comparing the data obtained on the efficiency of fertilizers in the soils of Bulgaria reveals, that in soils characterized by a high and long-term biological immobilization of fertilizer nitrogen (typical calcareous chernozems, typical cinnamonic forest soils, etc.), the efficiency of nitrogen fertilizers is lower; 38–45 per cent of the nitrogen introduced is used by plants. In soils, in which nitrogen immobilization is lower and more labile (leached and podzolized chernozems, grey and cinnamonic forest soils), the efficiency of fertilizers is higher – 45–60 per cent is taken up by plants. In our opinion, the biological immobilization of nitrogen is one of the factors determining efficiency of nitrogen fertilizers.

The laboratory experiments carried out at different soil moisture contents (40, 60 and 80% WHC) show that in chernozems the rate of biological immobilization of nitrogen rises with the increase of soil moisture by about 15%, but the time gets shorter and part of the immobilized nitrogen is mineralized from the 30th to the 45th day after introduction of fertilizer nitrogen. Irrigation of these soils will result in a considerable increase of nitrogen fertilizer efficiency. In the other soil types studied (smolnitza, grey and cinnamonic forest soils) the data obtained from field experiments by Gruev and Atanasov (1974) show similar tendencies but there is a

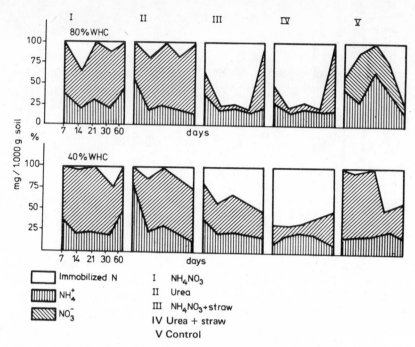

Fig. 1. Immobilization of fertilizer nitrogen on the effect of various treatments

quicker change in the amount and composition of microflora. Increase in the number of micro-organisms taking part in immobilization processes is followed by an increase in the amount of ammonifiers 2—3 weeks after introduction of fertilizers; thereby the mineralization processes are stimulated in the presence of a higher soil moisture — 80% WHC.

A well-expressed relationship is established between immobilization processes and temperature. At 4 °C the processes related to immobilization of nitrogen are dominant, while above 16 °C the mineralization processes prevail. Thus, during the winter months in the presence of organic minerals (root and harvest residues poor in nitrogen), the available nitrogen from either soil or fertilizers is subjected to a biological immobilization in the soil which controls leaching. Lysimeter studies show that up to 1 per cent of fertilizer nitrogen introduced into the soils of the country is washed out (Dinchev 1964, Kidin and Smirnov 1974). Most probably, one of the reasons is the immobilization at lower temperatures, by the microflora involved in the immobilization and the decrease of ammonifying and cellulose-decomposing microflora. Applying fertilizers in autumn accompanied by ploughing in of root and harvest residues or straw, nitrogen is not endangered, by leaching off.

The pot experiments carried out with practices aimed at stimulating the mineral-ization of immobilized nitrogen show that the introduction of root and harvest residues of legume crops (lucerne roots and hay) into the soil markedly increase the amount of ammonifying microflora which leads to the introduction of available

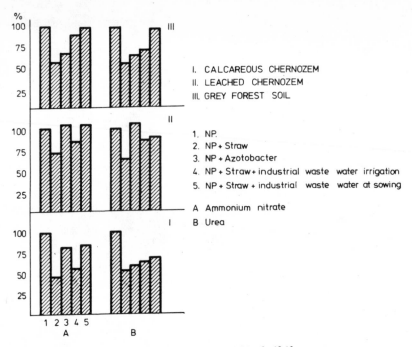

%

I. CALCAREOUS CHERNOZEM
II. LEACHED CHERNOZEM
III. GREY FOREST SOIL

1. NP.
2. NP + Straw
3. NP + Azotobacter
4. NP + Straw + industrial waste water irrigation
5. NP + Straw + industrial waste water at sowing

A Ammonium nitrate
B Urea

Fig. 2. Effect of various treatments on the yield of alfalfa

nitrogen and increase of yields from soils of well-expressed biological immobilization of nitrogen. That could explain the favourable effect of legumes as predecessors. When industrial waste water and *Azotobacter* are used, certain yield increases are also observed (Fig. 2); that is explained by the stimulation of ammonification in the soil. A considerable increase of yield of maize and red clover is observable when waste water is used from yeast and antibiotic plants, the latter being rich in metabolic products (vitamins, enzymes). The yield obtained from the separate cuts of red clover show that on soils characterized by high and long-term immobilization (calcareous chernozem) the yield is small at the beginning, but the third and fourth cuts are equal to the yields obtained from soils of lower biological immobilization of nitrogen. Therefore, the activation of mineralization processes by organic substances, richer in nitrogen, biological stimulators, etc. decreases the rate of biological immobilization of nitrogen in the soil.

CONCLUSIONS

1. A greater immobilization of fertilizer nitrogen was observed in soils of alkaline or neutral reaction than in those of more acid reaction due to a higher sensitivity of microflora taking part in immobilization processes to soil reaction compared to the ammonifying microflora.

2. When soil moisture is increased up to 80% WHC, the rate of biological immobilization of nitrogen increases but for a shorter period, since the intensity of mineralization process increases.

2. At lower temperatures, microbiological processes related to immobilization of nitrogen prevail, while intensity of processes related to mineralization decreases. Immobilization of nitrogen at lower temperatures protects it from leaching off.

4. By controlling biological immobilization of nitrogen, in the soil available nitrogen and the efficiency of nitrogen fertilizers may be increased.

SUMMARY

Laboratory, pot and field model experiments were carried out to study the rate and dynamics of biological immobilization of nitrogen and their determinative factors.

1. In soils having alkaline or neutral reactions, immobilization of fertilizer nitrogen was higher than that of soils with an acidic reaction, due to the higher sensitivity of the microflora taking part in immobilization in comparison to the ammonifying micflora.

2. When soil moisture was raised to 80% WHC, the rate of biological immobilization of nitrogen increased, but for a shorter period, due to the increased intensity of mineralization processes.

3. When the temperature was raised, microbiological processes connected to immobilization of nitrogen prevailed, while some of the processes related to mineralization were diminished. Immobilization of nitrogen at lower temperatures protects it from leaching.

4. The control of biological immobilization of nitrogen in the soil is a considerable reserve for increasing the amount of available nitrogen and the efficiency of nitrogen fertilizers.

REFERENCES

(Dinchev, D. I.) Динчев, Д. И. (1964a): *Агрохимия*, 7, 19—22.
(Dinchev, D. I.) Динчев, Д. И. (1964b): *Почвознание и агрохимия*. 7
(Gruev and Atanasov) Груев и Атанасов (1974): *Запазване и повишаване почвеното плодородие*. сб. Земиздат София.
(Kidin, V. V. and Smirnov, P. M.) Кидин, В. В. и Смирнов, П. М. (1974): *Изв. ТСХА*. 6
(Sapozhnikov, N. A.) Сапожников, Н. А. (1973): *Агрохимия* 2. 3—18.
(Smirnov, P. M. and Wojczik-Woitkowiak, D.) Смирнов, П. М. и Вуйчик-Войтковяк, Д. (1965): *Докл. ТСХА* 109, 25—32.
(Smirnov, P. M. and Shilova, E. I.) Смирнов, П. М. и Шилова, Е. И. (1972): *Изв. ТСХА* 2, 85—91.
(Tarvis, T. V.) Тарвис, Т. В. (1972): *Вопросы численности биомассы и продуктивности почвенных микроорганизмов*, Ленинград.
(Tarvis, T. V.) Тарвис, Т. В. (1973): *Применение стабильного изотопа И^{75}. Исследования по земледелию*. сб. Колос, Москва.
(Voinova-Raikova, J.) Войнова-Райкова, Ж. (1969): *Почвознание и агрохимия* 5

THE EFFECT OF CROP ROTATION ON THE BIOLOGICAL ACTIVITY OF LIGHT-TEXTURED SOIL

by

Zofia KREŻEL
Institute of Agricultural Chemistry,
Soil Science and Microbiology, Agricultural University,
Wroclaw, Poland

Estimation of the biological activity of the soil is based on the examination of the total number of soil micro-organisms or some of their physiological groups. The literature is somewhat contradictory for some indicate a correlation between soil enzymatic activity and the quantity of micro-organisms (Galastian and Avundzhyan 1970), while others (Koepf 1954, Franz 1973) do not find any.

This work aimed at estimating the biological activity of a light-textured soil in different crop rotations by microbiological methods commonly used and by determinations of enzymatic activity of soil.

MATERIAL AND METHODS

The experiments were performed in a light-textured soil (cultivated alluvial soil) from two crop rotations. The soil samples analyzed were taken from:

1) two-field crop rotation (rye-oat), taken in the 8th year of the experiment from two plots which were fertilized differently (Table 2), and

2) four-field crop rotation (potato—oat—lupin—rye), taken in the 13th year of the experiment from the plot with oat cultivated with high dose of inorganic fertilizer. To estimate the biological activity of the soil, chemical, microbiological and enzymatic activity determinations were made.

They were as follows:

1) soil moisture by the gravimetric method,

2) exchangeable acidity of soil,

3) amount of the mineral constituents of the soil by the conventional methods.

The quantity of the main groups of micro-organisms was determined by the plate method of Johnson and co-workers (1960); — the number of the bacteria on the soil extract medium of Allen (1957), — actinomycetes on the Conn's medium (1921), — fungi on the Martin medium with aureomycin (1950). The quantity of micro-organisms from the different physiological groups: — *Azotobacter* — on Ashby's medium from the soil of plots tested and in the soil with addition of: a) $CaCO_3$, b) $MgSO_4$ after the method of Ziemiecka (1929), — ammonifying bacteria on the liquid medium of Pochon and Tardieux (1962).

The intensity of nitrification was estimated as NO_3^- concentration in the samples after 10 days' incubation at 28 °C on the liquid medium of Winogradsky (1953) and colorimetrically of Marczenko (1954). The number of cellulose-decomposing, amylolytic, and bacteria decomposing phospho-mineral compounds was determined as described by Rodina (1968). The activity of soil enzymes was determined by the following methods: saccharase — according to Hofmann and Seegerer (1951), urease — according to Hofmann and Schmidt (1953), asparaginase — according to Hofmann, modified by Balicka and Trzebinski (1956), catalase — according to Kozlov (1962), proteinase according to Hofmann and Niggemann modified by Kreżel and Musiał (1969).

RESULTS

The soil samples taken at the time of oat-harvest showed little differences in moisture. The pH values also differed (6.1—6.6). The samples from two-field crop rotation showed a great deficit of Ca^{2+}- and Mg^{2+}-content (Table 1).

Table 1
Mineral constituent-content of soil (mg/100 g)

No. of plot	Oat in crop rotation and fertilization	Ca^{2+}	Mg^{2+}	K_2O	P_2O_5	Na^+
I. A	2 fields (40—40—60)	0	2	21.8	9.5	17.0
I. B	2 fields (80—80—120)	0	2	21.6	10.0	16.8
II.	4 fields (70—72—110)	16	4.9	25.0	11.2	17.0

The results from the microbiological determinations showed greater biological activity of soil from the plot with oat in four-field crop rotation than that of two-field crop rotation (Table 2).

The quantity of the bacteria, actinomycetes and fungi was largest in the soil from the plot with oat in four-field crop rotation. Similar results were obtained from the determinations of the number of ammonifying, nitrifying, amylolytic and cellulose-decomposing bacteria. It was interesting, that in all the plots tested there was no *Azotobacter,* the best known index of soil fertility. Application of the *Azotobacter*-inoculation of the soil appeared to be successful but only in the soil from four-field crop rotation.

Introduction of $CaCO_3$ or $MgSO_4$ into the soil resulted in the good growth of *Azotobacter* in all the soil samples tested.

In the plot 1B from two-field crop rotation, when the high dose of mineral fertilizer was used, there were higher numbers of bacteria, actinomycetes and amylose- and mineral phosphor-decomposing bacteria. Slight predominance of fungi,

Table 2

Effect of crop rotation and fertilization on quantity of micro-organisms in light-textured soil (g of dry weight)

No. of plot	Oat in crop rotation and fertilization NPK	Total number			% Azotobacter			Amylolytic bacteria	Cellulolytic bacteria	Phosphate-decomposing bacteria
		bacteria	actino-mycetes	fungi	before incuba-tion	after incubation with MgSO$_4$	after incubation without MgSO$_4$			
I. A	2 fields (40—40—60)	$1.8 \cdot 10^6$	3,000	9,000	0	18	0	11,160	1,380	10,000
I. B	2 fields (80—80—120)	$2.7 \cdot 10^6$	4,000	5,000	0	23	0	78,960	1,034	100,000
II.	4 fields (70—72—110)	$5.2 \cdot 10^6$	8,000	13,000	0	64	9	121,800	3,627	100,000

Table 3

Effect of crop rotation and fertilization on enzymatic activity of light-textured soil

No. of plot	Oat in crop rotation and fertilization NPK	Saccharase mg sugar/g soil	Proteinase % gelatine hydrolysed	Asparaginase	Urease	Catalase ml O$_2$/10"	Yield of oat q/ha
				mg NH$_4^+$/100 g soil			
I. A	2 fields (40—40—60)	2.37	61.6	1.29	2.65	3.6	20.1
I. B	2 fields (80—80—120)	2.21	66.0	1.16	2.67	2.6	21.3
II.	4 fields (70—72—110)	2.56	69.1	1.54	2.42	2.0	29.0

ammonifying and cellulolytic bacteria was observed at the plot 1A with a low dose of mineral fertilizer.

The enzymatic activity of the soil tested was found to have a similar pattern (Table 3). The activity of the saccharase, asparaginase, proteinase was somewhat higher in the soil from four-field crop rotation than that from two-field crop rotation soil. The catalase activity decreased when the high dose of the mineral fertilizer was introduced (plot 1B). The same correlation between catalase activity and mineral fertilization was pointed out by Pierwuszina-Grosziewa and Teslinowa (1970). The results of the microbiological and enzymatic activity determinations indicated that the biological activity of the soil from the plots with two-field crop rotation was decreased, particularly in the 1A plot.

However, the amount of the mineral fertilizer was not the main factor influencing the biological activity of the soil, because the greatest activity was found in the plot from four-field crop rotation in spite of the lower doses of the mineral fertilizer used in comparison with those of two-field crop rotation plots. Numerous authors (Pierwuszina-Grosziewa and Siemikina, 1970), found that mineral fertilization of the soil influenced the quantity and activity of micro-organisms to some extent. Our results were in agreement with this observation. The most important factor influencing the soil activity was found to be the Ca^{2+}- and Mg^{2+}-content of the soil (Table 2).

Mg^{2+}-deficit in soil was probably caused by repeating oat cultivation four times in two-field crop rotation.

This observation is in agreement with that described by Timonin (1946) and Jones (1957). The deficit of Mg^{2+} in soil led to the Ca^{2+}-deficit (Albert, 1968) and, in consequence, it decreases the yield of plants (Table 3).

SUMMARY

The biological activity of a light-textured soil from two plots with oat cultivated in two- and four-field crop rotation was examined. The four-field crop rotation (potato — oat — lupin — rye) increased the number of micro-organisms of the main physiological groups and the activity of some soil enzymes. The results could be explained by different amounts of Mg^{2+} and Ca^{2+} in the soil from plots with two- and four-field crop rotation.

The yield of oat was in correlation with the results of the microbiological determinations.

REFERENCES

Albert, A. (1968): *Selective Toxicity*. Methuen, London.
Allen, O. N. (1957): *Experiments in soil bacteriology*. 3rd Revised ed. Burgess Publishing CO. Minneapolis, Minn.

Balicka, N. and Trzebinski, M. (1956): *Acta Microbiol. Pol.* **5**, 377.

Conn, H. J. (1921): *N. Y., Agr. Exp. St. Techn. Bull.* 83.

Franz, G. (1973): *Pedobiologia.* B **13**, H. 6, 423—441.

(Galstian, A. and Avundzhyan, Z. S.) Галастян, А. и Авунджян, З. Ш. (1970): *Почвовед.* 6, 6, 721—723.

Hofmann, E. and Niggemann, J. (1953): *Biochem. Zeitschr.* 324—308.

Hofmann, E. and Schmidt, W. (1953): *Biochem. Zeitschr.* **324**, 125.

Hofmann, E. and Seegerer, A. (1951): *Biochem. Zeitschr.* **322**, 174.

Johnson, F. L. Curl, E. A., Band, J. H. and Fribourg, H. A. (1960): *Methods for studying soil microflora — plant diseases relationships.* Burgess Publ. Comp. Minneapolis, Minn.

Jones, L. H. P. (1957): *Plant and Soil.* **8**, 301—314.

Koepf, H. (1954): *Acker-u. Pflanzenbau.* 98, 289.

(Kozlov, K. A.) Козлов, К. А. (1962) : *Почвовед.* 4, 40.

Kreżel, Z. and Musiał, M. (1969):*Acta Microbiol. Pol.* Ser. V **1(18)**, 3—4, 93—97.

Marczenko, Z. (1954): *Kolorymetryczne metody oznaczania pierwiastków,* Warszawa.

Martin, J. P. (1950): *Soil Sci.* **69**, 215—233.

(Pierwuszina-Groszewa, A. N. and Teslinowa, N. A.) Первушина-Грошева, А. Н., Теслинова, Н. А. (1970) : *Изменение активности некоторых ферментов почвы в зависимости от виесения удобрений.* Сб. Физиология микроорганизмов. АН Узб. ССР Ташкент.

(Pierwuszina-Groszewa, A. N. and Siemikina, N. A.) Первушина-Грошева, А. Н., Семикина, Н. А. (1970) : *Изменение микробиологических процессов в почвенном слое, расположенном в глубину 30 см, в зависимости от обработки почвы и внесения различных форм удобрений.* Сб. Физиология растений, Ан Узб. ССР, Ташкент.

Pochon, J. and Tardieux, P. (1962): *Techniques d'analyse on microbiologie du sol.* Ed. de la Tourelle, Paris.

Rodina, A. (1968): *Mikrobiologiczne metody badania wód.* PWRiL, Warszawa.

Timonin, M. J. (1946): *Soil Sci Soc. Amer. Proc.,* **11**, 284—292.

Winogradsky, S. (1953): *Mikrobiologia gleby. Zagadnienia i metody,* PWRiL, Warszawa, 197—216.

Ziemiecka, J. (1929): *Roczn. Nauk Rol.i Leśnych.*

INHIBITION OF NITRIFICATION AND DENITRIFICATION IN CALCAREOUS CHERNOZEM SOIL

by

O. KOSTOV
"N. Poushkarov" Institute for Soil Science,
Sofia, Bulgaria

A number of studies on the inhibition of nitrification and denitrification processes aimed at increasing the efficiency of fertilizers have appeared in recent years. By reducing or discontinuing the nitrification process for a certain time (when applying ammonium fertilizers) the ammonium compounds undergo physico-chemical fixation and immobilization and gaseous nitrogen losses decrease. The nitrification process should be inhibited at the beginning of plant development, when plants are using mineral nitrogen less intensively. Moreover, the substances inhibiting the nitrification and denitrification processes for 3—4 weeks applied together with nitrogen fertilizers is of great practical importance.

MATERIAL AND METHODS

The influence of 2-nitrophenol, 4-nitrophenol, 2,4-dinitrophenol, 2,5-dinitrophenol, 2-aminopyridine, 2-nitroaniline, 3-nitroaniline, 1-cyanoguanidine, 2-chloraniline and 3-chloraniline on the nitrification activity of calcareous chernozem soil, the total biological activity (determined by production of CO_2) and their influence on the yield of vegetative mass of wheat, has been studied in laboratory and pot experiments. To estimate their influence on the denitrifying activity in a calcareous chernozem soil, gas-chromatographic determinations of the air composition were carried out in the course of 28 days, in flasks isolated from the surrounding atmosphere, containing 50 g soil and 21 mg ammonium nitrate. The nitrifying activity was assessed by the method of Fedorov and CO_2 — titrometrically for 10 days. The influence of the inhibitors on nitrification was studied in a laboratory experiment with the application of 600 mg of ammonium nitrate and 400 mg of carbamide. The inhibitors were dosaged as follows: 1-cyanoguanidine — 5% of the fertilizer applied, 2-chloraniline and 3-chloraniline — 2.5% of the fertilizer applied. The different concentrations of the applied substances were aimed at establishing the optimal doses for inhibiting nitrification and plant development.

RESULTS AND DISCUSSION

Figure 1 shows the effect of the substances used in the course of nitrification. It can be seen that the chemical substances inhibit nitrification in the 14-day course under study. 2-aminopyridine, 1-cyanoguanidine have a stronger inhibiting action, and 2-chloraniline, 3-chloraniline had the strongest inhibiting action.

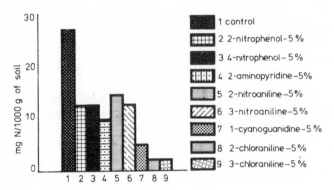

Fig. 1. Inhibition of nitrification by different inhibitors.

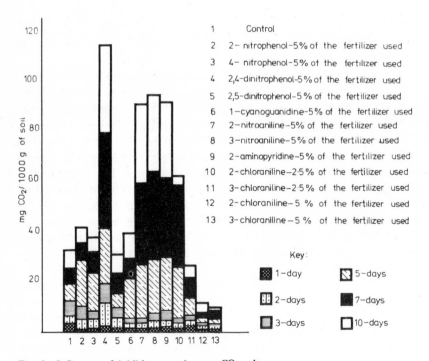

Fig. 2. Influence of inhibitors used upon CO_2-release

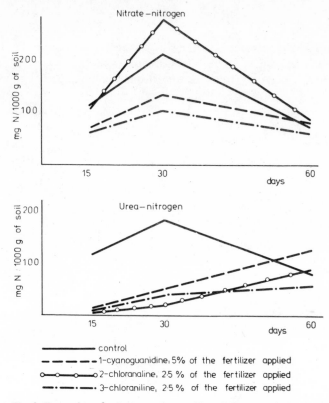

Fig. 3. Dynamics of nitrate- and urea-N as influenced by various inhibitors

The total biological activity of soil microflora was determined by the quantity of CO_2 released (Fig. 2). Most of the inhibitors studied positively influence the CO_2 release. Most CO_2 is released in the variants treated with 2,4-dinitrophenol, 2-nitroaniline, 3-nitroaniline, 2-aminopyridine. Smaller quantities compared to the control were found with the 2,5-dinitrophenol, 2-chloraniline, 3-chloraniline. With the last two inhibitors the soil was treated with lower concentrations — 2.5% of the fertilizer applied. Reducing the inhibitor doses, an increased quantity of CO_2 released was observed. As regards the dynamics of CO_2 release, after the initial depression up to the third day, an increase of CO_2 release follows which is most expressed on the 7th and 10th day of composting.

Therefore, the inhibitors used, possess a strictly selective action — they inhibit only nitrification and do not influence or decrease the total biological activity.

In the laboratory with the most efficient inhibitors — 1-cyanoguanidine — 5%, and 2-chloraniline and 3-chloraniline (each one in doses of 2.5%), the dynamics of nitrification with the application of ammonium nitrate and urea (Fig. 3) was

Table 1
Influence of the inhibitors on the yield of wheat

Treatments		Weight of biomass (mean from 3 pots) in g	In per cent of the control
Control		10.5	100%
2,4-dinitrophenol	— 5.0% of the fertilizer applied	11.0	105%
2,4-dinitrophenol	— 2.5% of the fertilizer applied	12.5	119%
2,5-dinitrophenol	— 5.0% of the fertilizer applied	13.2	126%
2,5-dinitrophenol	— 2.5% of the fertilizer applied	12.2	116%
2-nitroaniline	— 5.0% of the fertilizer applied	12.6	120%
2-nitroaniline	— 2.5% of the fertilizer applied	12.0	114%
2-aminopyridine	— 5.0% of the fertilizer applied	11.0	105%
2-aminopyridine	— 2.5% of the fertilizer applied	12.8	122%
1-cyanoguanidine	— 5.0% of the fertilizer applied	12.1	115%
1-cyanoguanidine	— 2.5% of the fertilizer applied	12.2	116%
2-chloraniline	— 5.0% of the fertilizer applied	15.0	143%
2-chloraniline	— 2.5% of the fertilizer applied	14.4	137%
3-chloraniline	— 5.0% of the fertilizer applied	10.1	96%
3-chloraniline	— 2.5% of the fertilizer applied	11.4	108%

studied. In the variants with ammonium nitrate with each of the three inhibitors, the quantity of nitrate nitrogen up to the fifteenth day was lower compared to the control, and with 1-cyanoguanidine and 3-chloraniline this was true up to the 30th day, after which by the end of the experiment the values of the nitrate nitrogen with these inhibitors approach those of the fertilized control without an inhibitor. With the 2-chloraniline the quantity of nitrate nitrogen is higher, which shows that it inhibits nitrification for a much shorter period of time. The total decrease of the nitrate nitrogen quantity after the 30th day is due to immobilization and denitrification of nitrogen under experimental conditions. The inhibiting effect is more strongly expressed in the variants with carbamide. That phenomenon is most strongly expressed up to the 30th day of composting — 10–20 mg of N with the inhibitors and 120 mg of N as the fertilized control. After the 30th day, inhibition decreases and the quantity of nitrate nitrogen in the variants with the inhibitors gradually increases.

To establish the influence of the efficient inhibitors on denitrification, the quantity of elementary nitrogen in the soil air was determined under anaerobic conditions in a laboratory experiment. It was found that except for the control, no denitrification products were recorded in the variants treated with the inhibitors 1-cyanoguanidine and 2-chloraniline. The quantity of denitrifying bacteria in the variants treated with inhibitors shows that the latter inhibit mainly the denitrifying activity.

In a pot experiment (Table 1), it was found that 2,5-dinitrophenol, 2-nitroaniline, 2-aminopyridine influence the yield positively. The strongest positive effect on the yield is exerted by 2-chloraniline in both of the studied concentrations — 2.5% and 5%.

CONCLUSIONS

1. 1-cyanoguanidine, 2-chloraniline and 3-chloraniline are the strongest inhibitors of nitrification.

2. The inhibiting effect upon nitrification is strongest up to the 30th day.

3. The chemical substances used have a selective effect — they inhibit nitrification and do not influence or increase the total biological activity.

4. 1-cyanoguanidine and 2-chloraniline do not reduce the quantity of denitrifying bacteria but inhibit the denitrifying activity.

5. 2-chloraniline has the strongest positive influence on the yield, while 2,5-dinitrophenol and 2-aminopyridine have a weaker effect.

SUMMARY

The influence of different chemical substances, namely: 2-nitrophenol, 4-nitrophenol, 2,4-dinitrophenol, 2,5-dinitrophenol, 1-cyanoguanidine, 2-nitroaniline, 3-nitroaniline, 2-aminopyridine, 2-chloraniline, 3-chloraniline on nitrification and denitrification in the soil was studied in laboratory and pot experiments.

The substances studied inhibited nitrification to different degrees. The denitrifying activity and the denitrifying bacteria were inhibited most strongly by 1-cyanoguanidine and 2-chloraniline.

The yield of vegetative mass of wheat is positively influenced by the application of 2-nitroaniline, 2-chloraniline, 2-aminopyridine in pot experiments.

SOME PROPERTIES OF DENITRIFYING BACTERIA ISOLATED FROM SEWAGE-IRRIGATED SOIL

by

Éva M. TIMÁR
Research Institute for Soil Science
and Agricultural Chemistry of the Hungarian Academy of Sciences,
Budapest, Hungary

Formation of gaseous compounds from nitrate by dissimilative nitrate-reducing bacteria may be a characteristic step of the soil nitrogen cycle. The permanently changing environmental factors are influencing not only the species composition of denitrifying microflora but cause dynamic changes in qualitative and quantitative characteristics of the process of denitrification. Results of studies on the physiology of denitrifying bacteria isolated from a gravity-type secondary clarifier were published previously (Timár *et al.* 1975). In the present paper the results of investigations on denitrifying bacteria isolated from the sewage of a pig fattening farm are presented.

MATERIAL AND METHODS

Methods of isolation were described in an earlier paper (Timár *et al.* 1975). Two basal media were used to study the utilization of carbon sources; the first is described in the paper of Tsukamura (1960), the second is a medium containing peptone and beef extract according to the formula of Hugh and Leifson (1953). MR-VP, utilization of citrate, liquefaction of gelatine, production of H_2S from peptone, cysteine and sodium thiosulphate, starch hydrolysis, oxidase, catalase, urease, ornithine decarboxylase and arginine dihydrolase were tested according to standard methods described in the "Manual of Microbiological Methods" (1957).

Influence of N-sources (organic, NH_4, NO_3, NO_2) and C-sources, as well as aerobic and anaerobic conditions on the denitrifying properties of the isolates were studied using the following combinations of media:

I. 1. $MgSO_4 \cdot 7H_2O$ 0.5 g, yeast extract 1.0 g, glucose 5.0 g, trace elements (Hoagland) 1.0 ml. These components were dissolved in one litre of 0.15 M phosphate buffer (pH 7.3), then 2.5 g/l $(NH_4)_2SO_4$ was added.

I. 2. As I. 1. but ammonium sulphate was replaced by 0.5 g/l KNO_3.

I. 3. As I. 1. but ammonium sulphate was replaced by 0.3 g/l $NaNO_2$. In the media II. 1., II. 2., II. 3., 5.0 g/l glycerol was dissolved instead of glucose used in the I. series.

Table 1
Utilization of carbon sources by the isolates

Strains	Glucose		Lactose			Glycerol		Xylose
	A*		A	B**		A	B	A
	aerob.	anaerob.	aerob.	aerob.	anaer.	aerob.	aerob.	aerob.
	n a g	n a g	n a g	n a g	n a g	n a g	n a g	n a g
E. cloacae (NCTC 10005)	+ + +	+ + +	+ + +	+ + +	+ + +	+ + −	(+)− −	+ + −
H 1130	+ + +	+ + +	+ − −	+ − −	− − −	+ + −	− − −	+ + +
H 1131	+ + +	+ + +	+ − −	− − −	− − −	+ + −	− − −	+ + +
T 35121	+ + +	+ + +	+ + −	− − −	− − −	+ + −	(+)− −	+ + +
T 35122	+ + +	+ + +	+ + −	− − −	− − −	+ + −	− − −	+ + +
T 401	+ + +	+ + +	+ + −	− − −	− − −	+ + −	− − −	+ + +
H 13222	+ + +	+ + +	+ + −	− − −	+ − −	+ + −	(+)− −	+ + +
H 13221	+ + +	+ + +	+ + −	− − −	+ − −	+ + −	(+)− −	+ + +
H 12	+ + +	+ + +	+(+) ⌐	− − −	− − −	+(+) −	− − −	+ + +
E. aerogen (NCTC 10006)	+ + +	+ + +	+ + +	+ − −	+ + +	+ + −	(+)+ +	+ + +

*A = Tsukamura (1966) medium; **B = Hugh and Leifson (1953) medium; n = growth;

Anaerobic cultures were prepared using the alkaline pyrogallol method. Cultures were incubated at 28 °C. Nitrite — and nitrate after reduction with zinc powder — were detected by Griess-Ilosvay reagent; buffered media were adjusted to pH 3—4 with concentrated acetic acid prior to addition of the reagent. In the case of nitrite, negative culture developed in nitrate containing media the absence of nitrate was checked with the diphenyl-amine sulphuric acid method.

RESULTS AND DISCUSSION

All the eight denitrifying isolates were Gram-negative, oxidase negative, motile rods which utilized citrate as sole source of carbon, formed hydrogen sulphide from peptone, cysteine and from sodium thiosulphate, did not hydrolyse starch and gelatine. Methyl red tests were negative, while VP, catalase, urease, ornithine decarboxylase and arginine dihydrolase tests were uniformly positive. On the basis of these properties, according to the latest edition of the Bergey's Manual (1975), the isolates belong to the II. group of *Enterobacteriaceae*. There are only two species in this group; distinctive characteristics are the presence or absence of arginine dihydrolase and fermentation of glycerol. Comparison of our isolates to named cultures of *Enterobacter cloacae* (NCTC 10005) and *E. aerogenes* (NCTC 10006) showed that the eight isolates and *E. cloacae* are arginine dihydrolase

Arabinose	Sorbitol		Mannitol	Dulcitol	Maltose	Raffinose	Salicin	Inositol
A aerob.	A aerob.	B aerob.	A aerob.	A aerob.	A aerob.	A aerob.	B aerob.	B aerob.
n a g	n a g	n a g	n a g	n a g	n a g	n a g	n a g	n a g
+ + +	+ + +	+ + +	+ + +	− − −	+ + +	+ + +	+ + +	+ − −
+ + +	+ + +	+ + +	+ + +	− − −	+ + +	+ + −	+ + (+)	− − −
+ + +	+ − −	+ + +	+ + +	− − −	+ + +	+ + +	+ + +	− − −
+ + −	+ + +	+ + +	+ + +	− − −	+ + +	+ + +	+ + +	− − −
+ + −	+ + −	− − −	+ + +	− − −	+ + +	+ + −	+ + +	− − −
+ + −	+ + +	+ + +	+ + +	+ + +	+ + +	+ + +	+ + +	− − −
+ + +	+ + +	+ + +	+ + +	+ + +	+ + +	+ + +	+ + (+)	+ + (+)
+ + +	+ + +	+ + +	+ + +	+ + +	+ + +	+ − +	+ + +	− − −
+ + +	+ + +	+ + +	+ + +	+ + +	+ + +	+ + −	+ + +	− − −
+ + +	+ + +	+ + +	+ + +	+ − −	+ + +	+ + +	+ + −	+ + −

a = acid production; g = production of gas; (+) = weakly positive

positive and do not ferment glycerol under aerobic conditions in the presence of organic nitrogen source, in Hugh-Leifson medium. In spite of minor differences observable in the utilization of carbon sources (Table 1), the eight isolates can be identified as closely related strains of *Enterobacter cloacae*. According to the concept of Hormaeche and Edwards (1958) the differences in the ability of utilizing certain C sources are not excluding reasons in the identification of the isolated strains belonging to this group.

Denitrifying properties of the eight isolates were identical, therefore, only data of one representative strain (H 1131) are compared (in Table 2) to data obtained with named cultures of *E. aerogenes* and *E. cloacae*. As Table 2 shows, nitrate is reduced to nitrite in all media tested. Nitrite is accumulated in the media, however, strains forced to live for several generations under anaerobic conditions with nitrate as terminal electron acceptor reduce nitrite further, to gaseous products. (See A and B lines of Table 2.) *E. cloacae* and the representative strain are not able to reduce nitrite and survive in a medium containing glycerol as sole carbon source; on the other hand, yeast extract permits growth without appreciable reduction of nitrite. *E. aerogenes,* which species is able to ferment glycerol, is not inhibited by nitrite under similar conditions.

Denitrifying *Pseudomonas* species showing oxidative metabolism, utilize nitrate in dissimilative pathways under anaerobic conditions. In the case of *Enterobacter* species equally able to ferment organic compounds and utilize nitrate as terminal electron acceptor, it is not so easy to decide whether nitrate is used either in

Table 2

Denitrifying properties of a typical isolate compared with those of two named *Enterobacter* strains

Nitrogen source	I. 1	I. 2		I. 3		II. 1	II. 2		II. 3	
	$(NH_4)_2SO_4$	KNO_3		$NaNO_2$		$(NH_4)_2SO_4$	KNO_3		$NaNO_2$	
	g	g	NO_2^1	g	NO_2^2	g	g	NO_2^1	g	NO_2^2
Strains:										
E. cloacae A*	+	+	+	+	+	−	+	+	−	+
(NCTC 10005) B**	+	+	−	+	+	−	+	−	(+)	+
H 1131 A	+	+	+	+	+	−	+	+	−	+
H 1131 B	+	+	−	+	+	−	+	−	(+)	+
E. aerogenes A	+	+	+	+	+	+	+	−	+	−
E. aerogenes B	+	+	−	+	−	+	+	−	+	−

A* = first anaerobic subculture
B** = cultured under anaerobic conditions for several generations
NO_2^1 = produced from NO_3 as only N source
NO_2^2 = presence of NO_2 as only N source
g = growth
(+) = weakly positive

assimilative or in dissimilative pathways. *E. cloacae* and our isolates unable to ferment glycerol, grew well on this compound with nitrate under anaerobic conditions, while replacement of nitrate with ammonium sulphate did not permit any growth. Therefore it can be supposed that nitrate was used by the isolates as terminal electron acceptor, too. Further investigation on the question is in progress.

SUMMARY

Denitrifying bacteria were isolated from waste water of a pig fattening farm and from soil irrigated with this waste. The majority of the isolates showed fermentative metabolism and could be identified as *Enterobacter cloacae,* in spite of minor variances in the utilization of carbon sources. The glycerol non-fermenting isolates and a named strain of *E. cloacae* (NCTC 10005) grew on glycerol under anaerobic conditions, in the presence of nitrate.

REFERENCES

Bergey's Manual of Determinative Bacteriology (1975): Buchanan, R. E. and Gibbons, N. E. (Eds) Williams and Wilkins Co., Baltimore.
Hugh, R. and Leifson, E. (1953): *J. Bacteriol.* **66**, 24−26.
Hormaeche, E. and Edwards, P. R. (1958): *Int. Bull. Nomencl. Taxon.* **10**, 71−74.
Manual of Microbiological Methods (1957): Soc. Amer. Bact., Com. Bact. Technic, Mc-Graw-Hill Book Co., New York.
Timár, M. É., Pátkai, T. and Baranyi, K. (1975): *Agrokémia és Talajtan,* **24**, 85−98.
Tsukamura, M. (1960): *J. Gen. Microbiol.* **45**, 253−273.

EXAMINATION OF EFFICIENCY OF RHIZOSPHERE MICRO-ORGANISMS LIVING IN THE ROOT ZONE OF POPLAR *POPULUS* PLANTS

by

Tatyana PÁNTOS-DERIMOVA
University of Forestry and Timber Industry
Sopron, Hungary

Biological circulation of nutrients was studied on a $16,000 \, m^2$ humic sandy soil area, on the experimental field of poplar *Populus "I-214"* plantation. The area of each parcel treated with various fertilizers and organic matter was $400 \, m^2$. The experiment was set up in double divided — split-split-plot — arrangement in four replicates.

In the present study the efficiency of the rhizosphere of poplar was investigated.

In the biological circulation of nutrients, and especially in the nutrition of plants, micro-organisms living in the rhizosphere are extremely important. Earlier works on herbaceous plants, and on woody plants have proved that the number of micro-organisms in the rhizosphere is much greater than in the soil not containing living roots. It is also well-known, that micro-organisms inhabiting the rhizosphere differ from soil microflora as far as distribution of species is concerned.

The effects of plants on the micro-organisms living in their rhizosphere is mediated by energetic enzymatic, processes and auxinic materials of the root secretions while the favourable effect of micro-organisms is due to their contribution to the nutrient supply of the plants.

To study these phenomena, samples for microbiological examination were taken from the root surface of trees of control plots and from those fertilized with NPK or from root-free soil, respectively.

The efficiency of the rhizosphere was expressed as a quotient of the number of micro-organisms per 1 g of dry root divided by the number of micro-organisms per 1 g dry soil. The root and soil samples were taken from various distances and depths from the root collar. The numbers of micro-organisms belonging to the main physiological groups were determined according to Pochon with slight modification.

Differences between the plants treated in two different ways were evaluated not only on the basis of the growth of the aerial parts, but development of roots was also taken into consideration. The lateral roots developed in the non-fertilized plot were rather elongated, while roots serving nutrient uptake as a primary function were developed to a much less extent. On the other hand, lateral roots developed in plots fertilized with NPK were shorter, but were covered abundantly by hairy

Table 1

Total number of micro-organisms living in the rhizosphere of poplar and in the soil
(Counts/1 gram dry root or soil)

| Plot | Treatment | Site of sampling | | Rhizosphere | Soil | Efficiency of the rhizosphere |
| | | Distance (cm) | Depth (cm) | | | |
		from the root collar				
1	Control	5–40	5–10	115.740.740	13.510.135	8.561
		150–160	5–10	89.531.680	3.724.197	24.041
		+	10–20	110.521.662	2.657.595	41.587
		+	85	27.216.174	540.657	50.339
25	NPK	5–40	5–10	139.888.090	13.629.692	10.263
		70	20–25	59.935.454	5.259.283	11.396
		+	55–75	70.005.385	2.728.662	25.656
		+	90	39.050.766	1.397.399	27.945

+directly from the root surface.

rootlets. At the tips of the so-called nutritive roots (lying 150–160 cm away from the main axis of the plant, in 5–10 cm depth), the efficiency of the rhizosphere reflected by the total number of micro-organisms was almost three times greater than at 5–40 cm from the main axis (Table 1). The efficiency of the rhizosphere increases with the depth of sampling. This also proves that even in deeper layers, the conditions are much more favourable for micro-organisms in the proximity of roots, in soil not containing living roots.

Similar results were obtained on the plot treated with NPK, but efficiency of the rhizosphere was significantly lower here than on the control plot. This may be explained by the good nutrient supply of the soil.

According to the data of Table 2, the efficiency of the rhizosphere reflected by aerobe nitrogen-fixing micro-organisms was also the highest – 161 – on the control plot along roots lying 5–10 cm deep. The efficiency of the rhizosphere on the plot treated with NPK is hardly observable, (maximum 5). The efficiency of the rhizosphere reflected by the anaerobe N-fixing micro-organisms was also low.

The data obtained on the number of cellulose-decomposing micro-organisms are very interesting. As the data of Table 3 show, the efficiency of the rhizosphere reflected by both the aerobe and anaerobe cellulose-decomposing micro-organisms was less than 1 at each sampling. This is in accordance with our earlier results pointing out that the majority of micro-organisms living in the root zone is unable to utilize cellulose as the sole source of carbon.

The effect of plants on the nitrifying bacteria appeared only on the plot treated with mineral fertilizers. However, according to the data of Table 4, the efficiency of the rhizosphere was very low in this case too (max 3).

Table 2

Number of nitrogen-fixing micro-organisms living in the rhizosphere of poplar and in the root-free soil
(Counts/1 gram dry root or soil)

Plot	Treatment	Site of sampling		Aerobic			Anaerobic		
		Distance (cm)	Depth (cm)	Rhizosphere	Soil	Efficiency of the rhizosphere	Rhizosphere	Soil	Efficiency of the rhizosphere
1	Control	5–40	5–10	370.370	25.998	14.246	1.157	146	7.925
		150–160	5–10	241.046	1.490	161.776	172	37	4.649
		+	10–20	33.367	8.504	4.159	9	37	0.243
		+	85	38.880	3.785	10.272	15	541	0.028
25	NPK	5–40	5–10	519.584	178.234	2.915	1.399	1.363	1.026
		70	20–25	230.521	136.741	1.686	599	736	0.814
		+	55–75	91.546	18.555	4.934	431	382	1.128
		+	90	751	13.974	0.054	105	1.827	0.057

+ directly from the root surface.

Table 3

Number of cellulose-decomposing micro-organisms living in the rhizosphere of poplar and in the root-free soil
(Counts/1 gram dry root or soil)

Plot	Treatment	Site of sampling		Aerobic			Anaerobic		
		Distance (cm)	Depth (cm)	Rhizosphere	Soil	Efficiency of the rhizosphere	Rhizosphere	Soil	Efficiency of the rhizosphere
1	Control	5–40	5–10	55+	25.998	0.002	116	4.580	0.025
		150–160	5–10	895	2.660	0.336	826	1.809	0.457
		+	10–20	354	18.603	0.019	619	1.860	0.333
		+	85	194	1.892	0.103	132	151	0.874
25	NPK	5–40	5–10	999	18.348	0.054	999	5.242	0.191
		70	20–25	807	8.415	0.096	507	3.156	0.161
		+	55–75	375	14.189	0.026	92	3.820	0.024
		+	90	240	2.687	0.089	51	215	0.237

+ directly from the root surface.

Table 4
Changing of proteolytic and nitrification activity of micro-organisms living in the rhizosphere of poplar and in the root-free soil
(Counts/1 gram dry root or soil)

Site of sampling				Indexes of						Nitrifying activity		
Plot	Treatment	Distance (cm)	Depth (cm)	Proteolytic activity after								
				3 days			15 days					
		from the root collar		Rhizo-sphere	Soil	Efficiency of the rhizo-sphere	Rhizo-sphere	Soil	Efficiency of the rhizo-sphere	Rhizo-sphere	Soil	Efficiency of the rhizo-sphere
1	Control	5–40	5–10	27.78	7.28	3.816	69.44	15.60	4.451	4.63	3.38	1.370
		150–160	5–10	34.44	5.32	6.474	103.31	14.90	6.934	5.17	7.26	1.214
		+	10–20	35.37	5.32	6.648	61.89	12.76	4.850	3.32	4.25	0.781
		+	85	54.43	7.57	7.190	132.19	12.98	10.184	0	0	0
25	NPK	5–10	5–10	19.98	7.34	2.722	63.95	16.78	3.811	6.99	2.36	2.962
		70	20–25	32.27	4.21	7.665	78.38	15.78	4.967	4.61	2.10	2.195
		+	55–75	32.31	2.18	14.821	86.16	13.10	6.577	6.73	2.18	3.087
		+	90	27.4	2.15	12.577	45.06	16.12	2.795	3.00	1.07	2.804

+ directly from the root surface.

The efficiency of the rhizosphere calculated on the basis of proteolytic activity, appeared in the samples. It was also pointed out earlier that some part of the micro-organisms living in the rhizosphere is able to utilize proteins as a source of both N and C (carbon) (Table 4).

SUMMARY

The rhizospheric effect of the poplar was examined by the author. Samples were taken from the root surface of trees of the control and those treated with NPK as well as from different distances and depth of root-free soil. The quantitative determination of micro-organisms representing the main physiological groups was carried out according to the Pochon method with some modifications.

The rhizospheric effect was determined with the absolute ratio of microbe number related to 1 g dry root as well as 1 g absolute dry soil.

On the basis of the root examination, it could be established that there are great differences between the plants from the two treatments, not only the growth of the upper parts, but the development too. The lateral roots were extended longitudinally in the non-fertilized plot. However, the root hairs serving nutrient uptake could be found in relatively small amounts. In the plot treated with NPK the lateral roots were shorter but villous root hairs formed in great amounts.

The rhizospheric effect was determined for the number of the "total" microorganisms and the nitrogen-fixing and cellulose-decomposing microbes as well the change of proteolytic and nitrifying activities.

RHIZOSPHERIC MICROFLORA AS A SOURCE OF SOME GROWTH SUBSTANCES

by

Aneta TALEVA
"N. Poushkarov" Institute for Soil Science,
Sofia, Bulgaria

A number of authors have proved that many micro-organisms synthesize and discharge compounds in the rhizospheric zone which stimulate seeds, sprouting and growth of plants (Berezova and Rempe 1951; Vozniakovskaya and Rybakova 1964; Vozniakovskaya and Nurzhanov 1961; Kreslin 1965; Krassilnikov 1966). Moreover, a stimulating effect of microbial metabolites on plant growth and yield has also been demonstrated. The research on the interrelationship between micro-organisms and plants and on increasing the yields of agricultural plants by the introduction of useful micro-organisms or their metabolic products is of considerable importance for agricultural practice.

MATERIAL AND METHODS

To study the rhizospheric microflora, experiments were carried out with wheat "Bezostaja" variety using three soil varieties — carbonate chernozem, leached chernozem and grey forest soil with two doses of nitrogen and phosphorus in the following combinations: N_1, N_1P_1, N_1P_2, N_2, N_2P_1, N_2P_2. The nitrogen was introduced as NH_4NO_3, where N_1 is 700 mg/3 kg of soil, and phosphorus as KH_2PO_4, where P_1 is 400 mg/3 kg of soil. $N_2 = 1400$ mg NH_4NO_3, $P_2 = 800$ mg KH_2PO_4. Specific micro-organisms were isolated from the wheat roots and from the soil surrounding them, the plants being grown under continuous cropping and after various preceding crops on leached chernozem in field conditions.

The microbiological analyses were carried out according to the method of Berezova and Rempe (1951). Meat-peptone agar, starch-ammonia agar and wort agar were used for isolating the specific types of wheat rhizosphere.

Fertilizer application increases the quantity of rhizospheric micro-organisms and mainly the quantity of the non-sporogenous ammonifiers and bacteria which use mineral nitrogen (Table 1). Mineral application intensifies the processes related to nitrogen mineralization and increases the rhizospheric effect.

This positively affects plant nutrition and increases foliage yields by 50 to 100%. There is an increase in the quantity of the bacteria (mainly of the *Pseudomonas* type) and a release of growth substances — vitamin B_{12}, heteroauxine, etc. The activity of urease and the catalytic activities also increase. The urease activity correlates with the quantity of the ammonifying bacteria — and reaches its peak in variants treated with $N_2 P_2$.

Essential differences in the biochemical activities of the soil from the rhizospheric zone of wheat (grown under the conditions of the soils mentioned) were not observed. Obviously, a plant accounts for the specificity of the rhizospheric microflora, as it had been noted by Berezova and Rempe (1951).

The research on some biochemical activities of pure culture of the *Pseudomonas* type and its varieties isolated from the root zone of wheat from different variants of the experiment (Table 2) demonstrate that wheat seeds develop better after inoculation, forming much more foliage and a well-developed root system. The seeds treated with bacteria, (with rhizospheric micro-organisms), a combination with 3–4 strains, develop the richest foliage which increases by 16% compared to the untreated crops and the weight increasing by 145%.

270 strains belonging to the *Pseudomonas* type were isolated from the rhizospheric and root zone of wheat grown under field conditions and in pot experiments. Their stimulating or depressing effect had been determined by the biotest method according to the difference between sprout and root weights.

The influence of the concentrations of microbial metabolites on the stimulating processes of sprouting is demonstrated in Figure 1. The wheat seeds of "Bezostaya" variety were inoculated with diluted suspensions of bacteria. *Pseudomonas fluorescens* stimulated the production of foliage and root in a dilution of bacteria 1 : 1000. The concentrated solution and the suspension diluted 10 times depressed the development of foliage and roots. The culture solution of spore-forming bacteria *(Bacillus megatherium)* depressed root formation in all concentrations but stimulated the production of foliage, which intensified with the higher degree of dilution. Diluted only 10–100 times culture filtrates of almost all types of micro-organisms studied, exhibited a depressing effect on seed germination, only 50% of the seeds had germinated.

Consequently, the stimulating or inhibiting effect of the products of the rhizospheric microflora greatly depended on the concentration of the microbial metabolites, which should be taken into consideration in research work. On the basis of data in the studies presented above, the following conclusions can be drawn:

Table 1

Effect of fertilizer application on yields and biological activity in the rhizospheric zone of wheat in carbonate chernozem, leached chernozem and grey forest soil

Variant	Calcareous chernozem				Leached chernozem				Grey forest soil			
	Quantity ammonif. bact. in millions	Rhizosph. effect	Yields in g	Vit. B_{12} µg/100 g	Quantity ammonif. bact. in millions	Rhizosph. effect	Yields in g	Vit. B_{12} µg/100 g	MPA*	Rhizosph. effect	Yields in g	Vit. B_{12} µg/100 g
Control	6.4	3.5	9	12	6.1	6.6	5	4	4.3	2.9	4.2	2
N_1	5.3	6.3	8	6	9	3.12	5	2.5	6.4	4.7	5	4
$N_1 P_1$	11.2	18.8	69	27	56	60.1	110	40	7.3	16.5	54	22
$N_1 P_2$	25.9	21.4	75	33	65	13.8	113	26.6	7.2	37.8	63	26
N_2	2.5	7.4	8	10	6	8.8	4.5	5	1.8	5.3	4	–
$N_2 P_1$	17.8	24.5	73	31	29	30	80	28.2	7.2	16.4	68	48
$N_2 P_2$	21.6	23.8	76	59	81	44.5	91	30	10.7	11.4	76.5	53

*MPA = meat-peptone agar.

169

Table 2
Influence of root microflora on height and growth of wheat

Variant	Fermentation activity		Dry substance in % compared to the control	Weight of roots in % compared to the control
	Urease in μ g/ml	Catalase cm^3 O_2 for 2'		
Control	12	0	100	100
Seeds inoculated with *Pseudomonas fluorescens*	31	1.9	118	126
Seeds inoculated with a combination of *Pseudomonas fluorescens*	56	3	161	145
Seeds treated with a solution of vitamin B_{12}	10	0.8	121	148

1. The quantity of ammonifying bacteria and the bacteria utilizing mineral nitrogen, actinomycetes and fungi in the rhizospheric and root zone of wheat, increases considerably under application of nitrogen and phosphorus fertilizers.
2. 87% of the 270 strains isolated from the rhizospheric and root zone of wheat had a stimulating effect, 62% of them activate seed germination and increase the foliage and 25% stimulate root formation.
3. The quantity of micro-organisms is higher in the rhizospheric zone of wheat than that in the soil. The rhizospheric microflora releases heteroauxin, vitamin B_{12}, urease and catalase which correlate positively with the quantity of the rhizospheric and root microflora and wheat yields.

SUMMARY

The changes in the rhizospheric microflora of wheat under application of nitrogen and phosphorus in three types of soil (carbonate chernozem, leached chernozem and grey forest soil) were studied. It was found that fertilizer application increases the quantity of rhizospheric micro-organisms, especially the quantity of asporogenous ammonifiers and bacteria capable of utilizing mineral nitrogen. The quantity of micro-organisms in the rhizospheric zone of wheat is higher than in the soil. The rhizospheric zone is rich in heteroauxin, vitamin B_{12}, urease and catalase; these are in a positive correlation with the quantity of rhizospheric and root microflora and wheat yields. 87% of the 270 strains of bacteria isolated from the rhizospheric zone of wheat show a stimulating effect. 62% of them activate seed germination and the emergence of foliage, and 25% stimulate root formation. The activating or inhibiting effect of wheat germination depends on the concentration of the metabolic products of rhizospheric micro-organisms.

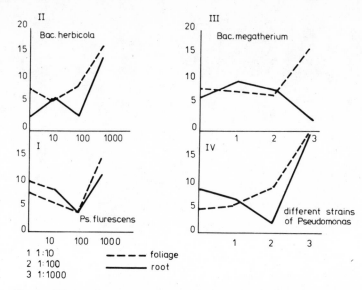

Fig. 1. Effect of the concentration of microbial metabolites on the stimulating process of sprouting

REFERENCES

(Berezova, E. F. and Rempe, E. H.) Березова, Е. Ф. и Ремпе, Е. Х. (1951) : *Труды научно-исследовательского и-та с-х микробиологии.* Вып. XII. стр. 39, 56.

(Kreslin, D. J.) Креслинь, Д. Я. (1965) : *Методы микробиологического стимурирования роста и развития растении.* Изд-во Зинатие, Riga.

(Krassilnikov, N. A.) Красильников, Н. А. (1966) : *Методы изучения почвенных микроорганизмов и их метаболитов.* Изд-во Московского университета, стр. 186.

(Vozniakovskaya, J. M. and Rybakova, Z. P.) Возняковская, Ю. М. и Рубакова, З. П. (1964): Сб. *Вопросы семеноводства, семеповедения и контрольно семенного дела,* Moscow.

(Vozniakovskaya, J. M. and Nurzhanov, I. S.) Возняковская, Ю. М. и Нуржанов И. С. (1961) : *Тезисы докладов Всесоюзной конференции по сельскохозяственной микробиологии.* Leningrad.

ISOLATION OF *AGROBACTERIUM TUMEFACIENS* FROM THE SOIL OF VINEYARDS WITH SELECTIVE METHODS

by

Rózsa NAGY and E. MANNINGER
Research Institute for Viticulture and Enology,
Budapest, Hungary

Research Institute for Soil Science
and Agricultural Chemistry of the Hungarian Academy of Sciences,
Budapest, Hungary

The pathogenic *Agrobacterium tumefaciens*, causes heavy losses mainly in the agricultural monocultures. In the Hungarian grape plantations considerable damage was observed especially on the table-grape cultivars in the past decade. In 1968 this was recorded in 15 sites both with hard and sandy soil (Lehoczky and Reinhart 1968). The disease has been spreading since then (Fig. 1).

Tumours on the root of the grape as well as on certain parts of it above soil level are the symptoms of the disease. The formation of the pathogenic tumour-tissue results in the deprival of nutritive materials, in the necrosis of the rind-tissue (Fig. 2), and in serious cases, in the necrosis of the infected vine-stocks.

Since 1971 we have been dealing with the problem in a research-team at the Research Institute for Viticulture and Enology. Since the pathogen can infect the plant from the soil, too, in 1973 we started to isolate the *Agrobacterium tumefaciens* from the soil. From among the soil-bacteriological investigations carried out on samples originating from various sites of the country, that taken from the Afuz Ali plantation of Lakitelek, a Research Station of our Institute will be discussed.

To isolate *Agrobacterium tumefaciens* from the soil is not an easy task, due to its slow growth, on most of the culture-media it is backward to other soil-bacteria and microscopic fungi, and is suppressed by other micro-organisms. Moreover, the separation is very difficult because the colony is similar to that of many soil-bacteria. Its colony on broth-agar media is small, white, circular, smooth, glistening, translucid and entire (Bergey 1957).

The size and shape of individual cells correspond to many other soil-bacteria; their widths are $0.7–0.8\,\mu$, their lengths amount to $2.5–3.0\,\mu$, they move individually by 1–4 flagella, are Gram-negative and are encapsulated. As a consequence of these difficulties selective culture-media are necessary to isolate *Agrobacterium*. The literature usually suggests a wide spectrum of antibiotics for the sake of selective cultivation (Schroth *et al.* 1965). The purchase of certain antibiotics encounters serious difficulties. That is why the method of Clark (1969) was chosen. The authors considered the 30 milliequivalent Mn^{2+} suitable for the isolation of *Agrobacterium tumefaciens*.

173

Fig. 1. Scant grape-plantation due to the damage caused by *Agrobacterium tumefaciens*

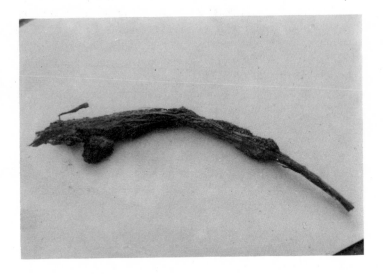

Fig. 2. Arm damaged by tumour

Fig. 3. Plants treated with physiological solution

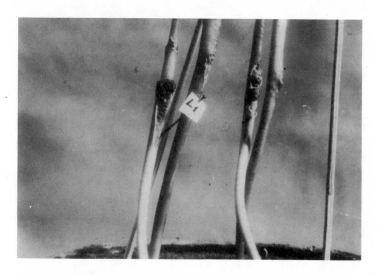

Fig. 4. Plants inoculated with a checked strain

Table 1

Morphological characters and biochemical test of bacteria

	Strains							
	I/a	I/b	I/c	I/2	III/1	III/2	III/3	III/4
Size [μ]	0.7 2.8	0.7 2.1	10.7 1.7	1.0 2.5	1.0 2.5	1.0 1.7	1.1 2.8	0.8 2.8
Gram's staining	−	−	−	−	−	−	−	−
Motility	+	+	+	+	+	+	+	+
Growth on Na-selenite medium	−	−	−	+	−	−	+	+
Congo red absorption	−	−	−	−	−	−	−	±
Nitrate reduction	+	+	+	+	+	+	+	+
3-ketolactose test	−	−	+	−	−	−	+	+
Acid production from:								
glucose	−	−	−	+	+	+	−	+
fructose	+	+	+	+	+	+	+	+
arabinose	+	−	+	+	±	+	−	+
galactose	+	−	+	+	−	−	−	+
mannitol	+	−	+	+	−	+	−	+
salicin	+	−	−	+	+	+	−	+

The employed culture-media consisted of the following components: Agar-agar: 1.2 g, Lactose 0.5 g, KNO_3: 0.1 g, $MgSO_4 \cdot 7H_2O$: 0.01 g, $NaHPO_4$ (anhyd): 0.018 g, Dist. water: 100 ml, FeDTA [0.25 w/v]: 1.0 ml, $MnSO_4 \cdot 4H_2O$ [33.5% w/v]: 1.0 ml, Final pH: 6.8.

The soil-samples were taken from the upper 30 cm layer of soil, 5 cm away from tumorous roots

A soil-solution prepared with sterilized physiological solution was added to the selective culture medium in various dilutions, and kept at 28 °C for three days. 52×10^4 colonies to 1 g soil were counted. Representatives of each morphologically different colony type were isolated obtaining in this way 8 different bacteria strains.

Fig. 5. Formation of tumour by strain of *Agrobacterium tumefaciens* isolated from the soil

The following were carried out with these strains: the size of the cells, the Gram-stain, the individual movements of the bacteria, the growth on Na-selenite culture medium, the congo-red absorption, the nitrate-reduction, the 3-ketolactose reaction (Bernaerts and De Ley, 1963) and the fermentation of 6 carbohydrates which are characteristics of identification were investigated. One of our strains, marked III/4 gave specific rections in the course of the investigations (Table 1).

Besides the above-mentioned investigations we have inoculated plants with our strains to verify their tumourigenic characteristics. Inoculation was made by injecting the suspension of 24-hour old bacteria cultures under the epidermis. Two-leaf-old *Helianthus* seedlings were the test-plants. Evaluation was carried out two weeks after inoculation.

Two kinds of control were used in the series of investigations: a plant-variant injected with sterilized physiological solution (Fig 3), and a bacterium strain with checked tumourigenic characteristics isolated from a tumour-tissue (Fig. 4).

The inoculations on test-plants verified the result of our microbiological and biochemical findings. Out of our 8 bacterial strains, the one marked III/4 formed tumour on the *Helianthus*-plants (Fig. 5).

The strain L/1 was provided from the strain-collection of J. Lehoczky from the Department of Grapevine Protection of the Research Institute for Viticulture and Enology and we would like to express our thanks for his help in this way as well.

Our investigations proved that the *Agrobacterium tumefaciens,* isolated from the soil by our methods, is indeed a pathogenic bacterial strain.

SUMMARY

The authors have isolated *Agrobacterium tumefaciens* from infected sandy soil with a selective method. The selectivity was guaranteed by using a medium containing 30 m equivalent/1 Mn^{2+}. To state the identity of the bacterium culture the independent movement and their size were studied, moreover it was examined whether they were Gram-negative or Gram-positive and whether they broke down the six compounds which were characteristic in respect of the determination or not. The bacteria were studied to ascertain if they grew on a medium containing Na-selenite and they absorb the congo red or not. Finally some tests were carried out with plants to study the tumour formation.

REFERENCES

Bergey (1957): *Manual of Determinative Bacteriology.* Baltimore.
Bernaerts, M. J. and De Ley, J. (1963): *Nature,* **197,** 406–407.
Clark, A. G. (1969): *J. appl. Bact.* **32,** 348–351.
Lehoczky, J. and Reinhart, G. (1968): *A szőlő védelme.* Mezőgazdasági Kiadó, Budapest.
Schroth, M. N., Thompson J. P. and Hildebrand D. C. (1965): *Phytopath.* **55,** 645–647.

INTERACTION BETWEEN NODULE BACTERIA
AND LEGUMINOUS PLANTS

PRODUCTION OF *RHIZOBIUM* PREPARATIONS IN HUNGARY

by

T. SOÓS
Phylaxia Veterinary Biologicals and Feedstuffs Co.
Budapest, Hungary

It is well-known that the expenses of livestock farming and animal breeding to a large extent are due to the costs of fodder which, however, can be decreased essentially when the fodders consist of home-grown crops of the farms. Thus, increasing the production of *Papilionaceae* fodder plants is essential as they abound relatively in proteins and in other fodder-components of vital importance. By exploitation of the available sowing area instead of increasing them, this can be achieved. The lack of *Rhizobium* bacteria of high activity in the soil is often the cause of the poor yield of *Papilionaceae* production. *Rhizobium* bacteria of higher virulence (infectivity) and of effectivity (nitrogen-fixing capacity) than of those of natural occurrence in the soil can be achieved by applying seed inoculated with *Rhizobium* bacteria.

Rhizobium strains of optimum capacity (nodulating and nitrogen-fixing) have to be used for Rhizonit-Forte inoculum production. Thus isolation of *Rhizobium* bacteria of *Papilionaceae* roots originating from various areas of the country is carried out every year to obtain more effective strains than the disposable ones.

For this reason in the last two years, strains have been isolated and inoculum has been produced from the *Papilionaceae* of great importance as follows: alfalfa *(Medicago sativa)*, meadow clover *(Trifolium pratense)*, field pea *(Pisum sativum)*, villous vetch *(Vicia villosa)*, kidney bean *(Phaseolus vulgaris)*, soybean *(Glycine max)*, birdsfoot trefoil *(Lotus corniculatus)*, common sainfoin *(Onobrychis viciaefilia)*. The productivity of strains has been tested in plant experiments; the strains of maximal productivity have been propagated by fermentation and the obtained ferment-liquid mixed to turf-vehicule in "NAUTA" mixer resulted in the Rhizonit-Forte inoculum.

MATERIAL AND METHODS

Tubers of blossoming *Papilionaceae* have been collected from various areas of the country. The nodules were sterilized in a solution of 0.25 g sublimate dissolved in 100 ml of 75% alcohol then washed thoroughly six times. The smaller nodules were

Table 1
Comparative examination of *Rhizobium meliloti, Rh. trifolii, Rh. leguminosarum, Rh. phaseoli* and *Rh. sp.* strains

Test plant (cultivation period)	S t r a i n s	Crop g/10 plants	Rate %	Nodule per 10 plants	N%
Medicago sativa (42 days)	Untreated	0.73	100.0	0	1.44
	Lucerne 73/1	1.65	226.0	21	3.71
	Lucerne 73/3	1.97	269.8	33	3.95
	Lucerne 73/6	2.25	308.2	35	3.82
	Lucerne 73/8	2.13	291.6	29	3.71
	Standard strains:				
	Rh. meliloti 441	2.12	290.4	32	3.95
	Alfalfa 7/1	2.28	312.3	43	3.71
Trifolium pratense (42 days)	Untreated	1.10	100.0	0	1.85
	Meadow clover 73/1	4.67	424.5	61	3.63
	Meadow clover 73/2	3.68	334.5	55	3.60
	Meadow clover 73/3	4.00	363.6	38	3.71
	Meadow clover 73/4	3.28	298.1	38	3.83
	Standard strains:				
	Rh. trifolii 311/a	3.12	283.6	46	3.59
	Meadow clover 72/5	3.07	279.0	25	3.71
Pisum sativum (45 days)	Untreated	17.15	100.0	0	2.37
	Field pea 73/1	32.01	186.64	210	3.12
	Field pea 73/2	30.10	175.51	185	2.97
	Field pea 73/3	36.50	212.82	135	3.17
Vicia sativa (45 days)	Untreated	30.90	100.0	0	1.93
	Villous vetch 73/1	61.80	200.0	120	3.41
Phaseolus vulgaris (49 days)	Untreated	30.65	100.0	0	2.43
	Kidney bean T/4	72.00	234.9	204	3.78
	Kidney bean 3	58.50	190.8	206.3	3.56
Onobrychis viciaefolia (49 days)	Untreated	6.00	100.0	0	2.28
	Common sainfoin 73/1	6.14	102.3	0	2.34
	Common sainfoin 73/2	5.77	96.2	0	2.49
	Common sainfoin 73/3	6.01	100.2	0	2.37
Lotus corniculatus (49 days)	Untreated	0.18	100.0	0	1.41
	Birdsfoot trefoil 72/3	0.22	122.2	84	2.52
	Birdsfoot trefoil 72/4	0.29	241.6	41	3.08

crushed with a glass-staff and the larger ones were lanced and the obtained liquid was smeared onto bean- and Czapek-agar. The petri-dishes were incubated at 28 °C for 24 to 72 hours and the pure culture of the obtained colonies streaked with the surface-streaking method. The productivity of the strains proved to be *Rhizobium* on the basis of morphological examination of the colonies (Kerpely *et al.* 1959) as

Table 2
Comparative examination of *Rhizobium japonicum* strains

Test plant (cultivation period)	Strains	Crop g/20 plants	Rate %	Nodule	N%	
					stem	root
Soya max (49 days)	Untreated	44.10	100.0	0	1.15	1.39
	Soya 73/1	41.75	94.7	108	2.39	2.65
	Soya 73/2	46.05	104.4	135	2.40	2.77
	Soya 73/4	46.00	104.3	33	2.50	2.77
	Soya 73/5	41.87	94.9	35	2.45	2.87
	Soya 73/6	44.42	100.7	0	2.56	2.78
	Soya 73/7	50.23	113.9	121	2.60	3.46
	Soya 73/8	46.90	106.3	24	2.65	3.38
	Soya 73/9	47.03	106.6	58	2.67	2.91
	Soya 73/10	51.40	116.5	0	2.73	2.99
	Soya G2	52.45	118.9	0	2.76	2.97
	Soya G3	46.75	106.0	160	3.12	4.08
	Soya G6	37.80	85.7	116	2.86	3.87
	Standards:					
	Rh. jap. 646	52.10	100.8	198	3.14	3.90
	Rh. jap. 631	44.48	127.0	143	3.27	4.10

well as of the number of nodules produced on their roots: the examination has been carried out in Roux-tubes in sterile culture-pots under semi-sterile conditions. The total nitrogen was determined by the Kjeldahl method. The results are presented in Tables 1 and 2.

The strains of the largest productivity were propagated by fermentation (Soós 1960). The strains were fermented separately, and mixed well with peat.

The peat was dried, ground sieved and autoclaved and trace elements were added to it.

20 to 25% of the ferment liquid was added to the peat and was mixed in NAUTA mixer for 20 minutes. The inoculum was stored in 2 kg packs at 2 °C till delivery.

The inoculum was tested for

a) bacterial count,

b) sterility and

c) productivity by the National Institute for Agricultural Quality Testing.

In recent years loss of productivity of powerful strains has been frequently observed in the course of inoculum production. The strains, their ferment-liquids and the inoculum of every batch was tested again to detect whether the loss of productivity ensues in the course of fermentation or during the mixing process. With these control procedures, the stage of inoculum production in which the fault may occur can be detected and the production of an effective inoculum can be assured (Table 3).

Table 3
Control test of lucerne-melilot Rhizonit-forte product

Treatments	Dry weight of total plant g/12 plants	Rate %	N%
Untreated	0.14	100.0	2.23
Batch No 1	0.59	421.4	3.71
Batch No 2	0.29	207.1	2.77
Batch No 3	0.42	300.0	3.70
Batch No 4	0.25	178.5	3.76
Batch No 5	0.30	214.3	3.13
Batch No 6	0.22	157.1	2.64
Batch No 7	0.22	157.1	2.64
Batch No 8	0.33	235.7	3.12
Alfalfa 7/1 from agar	0.30	214.2	2.53
Lucerne 441 from agar	0.28	200.0	3.16
Meliloti 5/7 from agar	0.35	250.0	3.06
Lucerne K from agar	0.27	192.8	3.31
Alfalfa 7/1 from fermentor	0.39	278.5	2.30
Lucerne 441 from fermentor	0.32	228.5	3.07
Meliloti 5/7 + Lucerne K from fermentor	0.28	200.0	3.03

According to our investigation the inoculum can be used for six months from the time of production.

In 1975, Rhizonit-Forte inoculum was prepared for inoculation of seed as follows: alfalfa for 20,000 ha, meadow clover for 10,000 ha, field pea-villous vetch for 25,000 ha, kidney bean for 500 ha, birdfoot trefoil for 1,000 ha and soybean for 15,000 ha. In addition inoculum for lupin and common sainfoin has been prepared for experimental purposes (Fig. 1).

Further problems will be evoked in this field too by the continuous progress of the chemicalization viz., such *Rhizobium* strains should be selected which can tolerate and develop symbiosis when nitrogen-fertilizers are applied. The inoculation of seed should be carried out in the factory.

SUMMARY

Rhizobium strains of powerful nodule-forming and of high nitrogen-fixing activity are needed for *Rhizonit-Forte* inoculum production. Thus, isolation of *Rhizobium* bacteria from *Papilionaceae* roots originating from various parts of the country is carried out every year to obtain more effective strains.

New *Rhizobium* strains were isolated from nodules of flowering *Papilionaceae*. The strains of the highest productivity were propagated by fermentation. Four strains were selected from every plant.

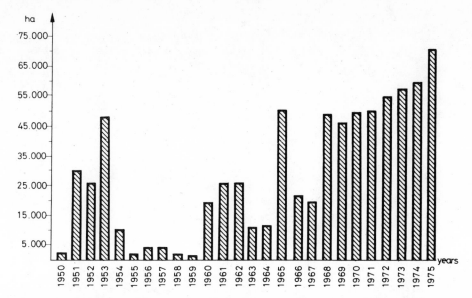

Fig. 1. Development of Baktonit, Rhizonit and Rhizonit—Forte from 1950 to 1975

The ferment-liquid was added to peat. The complete inoculum contains 500 million *Rhizobium* bacteria. Every batch of the complete inoculum was tested by the National Institute for Agricultural Quality Testing.

The continuous progress of chemicalization poses further problems in this field too; Rhizobium strains able to develop symbiosis in the soil containing nitrogen-fertilizers should be selected and the problem of inoculation of the seed in the factory should by solved.

REFERENCES

Kerpely, A., Manninger, E. and Zámori É. (1959): *Orsz. Mezőgazd. Minőségvizsgáló Intézet Évk.* (Yearbook of National Institute for Agricultural Quality Testing). [4] 263—275.
Soós, T. (1960): *M.Sc. Thesis,* University of Agricultural Sciences, Gödöllő.

EFFECTIVENESS OF SYMBIOTIC NITROGEN FIXATION DETERMINED BY THE ACETYLENE METHOD AND BY COMPARING WITH A NON-LEGUMINOUS CROP

by

A. I. CHOUNDEROVA, S. M. ALISHOVA and I. K. ZUBKO
All Union Research Institute of Agricultural Microbiology,
Leningrad, USSR

The acetylene method widely used for studying asymbiotic nitrogen fixation is being applied recently also to symbiotic nitrogen fixation (Francis and Alexander 1972, Hardy *et al.* 1968, Hardy and Jackson 1967). This method in comparative studies on the activity of different strains of nodule bacteria in plant symbiosis has been used with good results. This sensitive method can, moreover, be applied to determine symbiotic fixation rates of nitrogen.

The effectiveness of symbiotic nitrogen fixation by leguminous plants can be assessed by comparing non-leguminous crops as well as with the inoculation method (Trepachev *et al.* 1967) as we attempted too.

MATERIAL AND METHODS

Pot trials were carried out using pea variety. Ramonskii 77, and an oat variety, Handner. The pots contained 1.2 kg of sand with the initial nitrogen content 98 per pot on Prianishnikov substrate without addition of nitrogen.

Seeds were disinfected with 15% hydrogen peroxide for 15 min. 15 oat seeds and 10 pea seeds were planted in each pot; seedlings were thinned, 3 pea plants and 12 oat plants were left in each pot. Pea seeds were inoculated with a 3-day-old culture of *Rhizobium leguminosarum.* In half of the test pots, peas were not inoculated; in this case root nodules were formed by spontaneous infection.

There were also some pots without any plants for assessing the rates of the potential asymbiotic nitrogen fixation in a substrate. 60% total moisture capacity was kept in sand, watering was made by weight; 18 replications were carried out.

The rates of symbiotic and asymbiotic fixation of molecular nitrogen were determined by the modified method of Balandreau and Domergues (1971). Below we shall call this method as "the bell method". At the 4th, 8th, 15th, 20th, 25th and 30th days after emergence, i.e. at 4–4–7–5–5–5-day-intervals between assays, the pots with and without plants were covered hermetically with glass bells of 2800 ml volume. Then acetylene was injected with a syringe into the bells up to slightly overpressure, the bells always remained sealed hermetically. The pots were incubated in a small glass-house in the morning for 3 hours. If an active nitrogenase complex is present within the system, acetylene is reduced to ethylene. After the exposition, gas samples were taken and ethylene was determined using the gas-chromatograph ZVET-164.

The results were calculated using the following formula:

$$\frac{(C_2 - C_1) \cdot N \cdot V}{3 \cdot t} \text{ mg of nitrogen per pot per hour, where}$$

C_2 — total ethylene in nM per 1 ml of gas phase;
C_1 — basic ethylene in nM per 1 ml of gas phase;
N — gram-molecular weight of nitrogen;
V — the gas phase volume (ml) of a glass bell;
t — the time of the reduction of acetylene to ethylene (hours)
3 — ethylene to ammonia ratio showing electron losses at their reduction (3 : 1).

The assays were conducted in 7 replications.

At the same time, weights of green mass, dry matter and total nitrogen (above-ground organs + roots + remnants of germinating seeds) were determined. Nitrogen fixation rates were evaluated in nodules by the acetylene method.

RESULTS

The examination of root systems of pea plants have shown that all the non-inoculated plants produced many nodules due to spontaneous infection. During the whole growing season, these nodules displayed lower nitrogen fixation rates than those produced by a commercial strain 250a (Table 1).

Figure 1 presents data on the nitrogen fixation rates in the pots under glass bells. The data have shown that, both in the pots without plants and with oat plants, a significant nitrogen fixation resulted from the activity of free-living micro-organisms; in the latter case the rates were somewhat higher than in pots without plants.

Determinations of nitrogen fixation rates have evidently shown that the spontaneous infection induces rather an active symbiotic nitrogen fixation. After 8 days of emergence, the nitrogen fixation rates in these pots were much higher than in the pots with oat plants. Later on, the rate of the process increased, the highest was recorded within 20 days after emergence. The same was true for the pea plants inoculated with the strain 250a, beginning from the 4th—8th days after emergence and up to the end of the growing period, but absolute nitrogen fixation rates are much higher; the highest ones were recorded 5 days earlier.

The data on nitrogen fixation rates in pots obtained with the acetylene method and those on nitrogen accumulation in pea and oat plant obtained with the Kjeldahl method were applied to determine symbiotic nitrogen fixation rates in pea plants.

188

Table 1

Nitrogen fixation rates of pea nodules
(nM C_2H_4 per 1 g nodule, fresh weight)

Test variants	Days after emergence				
	8	15	20	25	30
Control	0.16	26.4	616.0	827.0	1064.8
Strain 250a	2.64	48.4	659.5	1196.8	1320.0

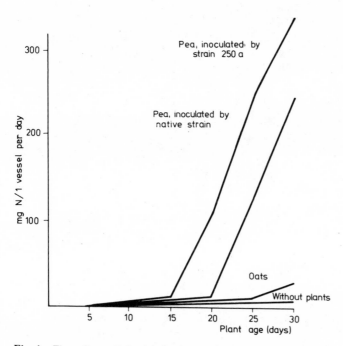

Fig. 1. The change of nitrogen-fixation activity in substrate with plants and without plants

The accumulation of biologically combined nitrogen was assessed by comparing with a non-leguminous crop, total nitrogen amounts were compared directly in pea and oat yields. It should be noted that oat plants accumulated nitrogen from sand, seeds and the substrate as a result of asymbiotic nitrogen fixation. The data obtained are presented in Table 2.

The calculated data were used to evaluate average rates of symbiotic and asymbiotic nitrogen fixation per hour for a definite growing period as well as to

Table 2
Accumulation of total and symbiotically fixed nitrogen in plants

Plant age (days)	Test variants	Dry weight of plants with roots (g per pot)	Nitrogen amounts in dry matter (%)	Nitrogen accumulation in yield (mg per pot)	Extra nitrogen from nitrogen fixation (mg per pot)
8	Pea, str. 250a	0.50	3.6	18.0	10.2
	Oat	0.52	1.51	7.8	–
15	Pea, str. 250a	0.80	2.54	20.3	10.0
	Oat	0.86	1.20	10.3	–
20	Pea, str. 250a	0.83	2.60	21.6	9.3
	Oat	1.05	1.17	12.3	–
25	Pea, str. 250a	0.92	2.54	23.4	13.3
	Oat	1.06	0.95	10.1	–
30	Pea, str. 250a	1.25	3.60	45.0 ± 2.2	36.3
	Oat	1.03	0.84	8.7 ± 0.5	–

determine the total effectiveness of this process during 4 – 7 days. The extra amounts of nitrogen resulting from symbiotic fixation in pea plants were obtained as a difference between the nitrogen amounts accumulated in pea and oat pots. The data obtained are shown in Table 3.

Comparison with a non-leguminous crop has shown that, at the end of the experiment, 36.3 mg of nitrogen has accumulated in pea yield per pot as a result of symbiosis with an active strain of nodule bacteria (Table 3). With the acetylene method it could be established that during the growing period, pea plants utilized 43.9 mg of nitrogen per pot from air. The data presented in Tables 2 and 3 and obtained with the two methods seem to agree to some extent, since nitrogen accumulation rates are in the same order of magnitude.

The acetylene method has, however, provided the absolute amounts of accumulated symbiotically combined nitrogen which are about 1.2 times higher than those really accumulated by pea plants during the growing period.

This is due, first of all, to unavoidable losses of biologically fixed and mineral nitrogen from a substrate as a result of ammonification, nitrification and denitrification. We assume, however, that 43.9 mg of nitrogen per pot is, to some extent, an approximate value since nitrogen accumulation within 24 hours was calculated with the acetylene method on the basis of the data resulting from a 3-hour exposition during daylight hours. Therefore, we did not consider deliberately any possible effects of the fluctuations in temperature and light intensity during the day. The investigations conducted at the Rothamsted Experimental Station have shown that these factors are very important for symbiotic nitrogen fixation rates in leguminous plants (1974).

Table 3
Nitrogen accumulation rates in pea plants determined by the acetylene method

Plant age (days)	Intervals between test (days)	Test variants	Nitrogen accumulation in the growing period (mg/pot)	Extra nitrogen from symbiotic fixation (mg per pot)	
				in the growing period	total from emergence up to the end of the growing period
4	4	Pea, str. 250a Oat	0.026 ± 0.002 0.026 ± 0.002	0	0
8	4	Pea, str. 250a Oat	0.253 ± 0.01 0.087 ± 0.004	0.166	0.166
15	7	Pea, str. 250a Oat	1.000 ± 0.05 0.262 ± 0.013	0.738	0.904
20	5	Pea, str. 250a Oat	5.072 ± 0.25 0.356 ± 0.02	4.716	5.620
25	5	Pea, str. 250a Oat	15.928 ± 0.8 0.650 ± 0.03	15.278	10.898
30	5	Pea, str. 250a Oat	24.604 ± 1.2 1.603 ± 0.07	23.001	43.899

SUMMARY

The acetylene and the Kjeldahl methods were applied to determine symbiotic nitrogen fixation rates in pea plants. Average rates of symbiotic and asymbiotic nitrogen fixation per hour for a definite growing period as well as total effectiveness of the process were determined. The data on extra amounts of nitrogen resulting from symbiotic fixation in pea plants were obtained as a difference between the amount of nitrogen accumulated in pea and in a non-leguminous plant (oat).

REFERENCES

Balandreau, J. and Domergues, J. (1971): *Comp. Rend. Acad. Sci. Paris,* **275**, (21), 2020.
Francis, A. J. and Alexander, M. (1972): *Canad. J. Microbiol.* **18**,
Hardy, R. W. F. and Jackson, E. K. (1967): *Feder. Proc.* **24**, 725.
Hardy, R. W. F., Holstein, R. C. Jackson, E. K. and Burns, E. C. (1968): *Plant. Physiol.* **43**, 1185.
Report of Rothamsted Exp. Stat. for 1973. (1974): Part 1. Harpende London.
(Trepachev, E. P. Atrashkova, N. A. and Khabarova, A. I.) Трепачев, Е. П., Атрашкова, Н. А. и Кабарова, А. И. (1967): *Агрохимия,* 8, 10–17.

EFFECT OF SODIUM AND CALCIUM CHLORIDES ON THE NODULATION AND SYMBIOTIC N-FIXATION OF SOME LEGUMINOUS PLANTS INOCULATED BY *RHIZOBIA*

by

S. H. SALEM and S. A. EL-BAHRAWI
Zagazig University, Faculty of Agriculture,
Egypt
Tanta University, Faculty of Agriculture,
Egypt

The effect of salinity on either free or symbiotic N-fixation by soil micro-organisms has been studied by some investigators. Iswaran and Sen (1958) found that nitrogen fixation by *Azotobacter* was inhibited by increasing sodium chloride concentration. Others found that increasing the salt in the soil up to 0.5% promoted the growth of *Azotobacter* and *Clostridium pasteurianum.*

The effect of sodium chloride on the nodulation and symbiotic N-fixation of leguminous plants has also been investigated. Bernsteine and Ogato (1966) reported that nodulation of soybean and lucerne was greatly affected by high concentration of sodium chloride in the soil. Kamel *et al.* (1971) stated that reclamation of saline soil increased significantly the numbers of nodule bacteria, dry weight and total nitrogen in broad bean plants. Subba *et al.* (1972) showed that most *Rhizobium meliloti* strains did not tolerate high concentration of sodium chloride.

Few data have been published in our country about the effect of different salt concentrations on the nodulation of leguminous plants. Since saline soils cover a large area of our country, an experiment was conducted to study the effect of sodium and calcium chloride, the dominant salts in saline soils, on the nodulation capacity and symbiotic N-fixation of some economically important leguminous plants, such as broad and cowpea plants.

MATERIAL AND METHODS

Pot experiments were carried out to study the effect of different concentrations of sodium and calcium chlorides on the nodulation and symbiotic nitrogen fixation of the inoculated broad bean *(Vicia faba)* and cowpea *(Vigna sinensis)* plants.

In the course of the relationship between rhizobia and leguminous plants, the mentioned plants are considered as representatives of different cross-inoculation groups. They were chosen since their respective rhizobia represent both the fast- and the slow-growing organisms.

13 Szegi

Sandy soil was used in this experiment. The sand was previously treated with hydrochloric acid three times. The sand was washed with distilled water after each acid treatment. This had been done in order to remove all the cations probably present on the particles of the sand. The sand was then dried and weighed (3 kg for every pot). The pots were 20 cm in diameter.

The experiment was divided into two sets. The first set was used for sodium chloride treatments, while the second was used for $CaCl_2$ treatments.

Inoculation of leguminous seeds with Rhizobium

The broad bean seeds were inoculated with efficient strains of *Rhizobium leguminosarum* before sowing. The seeds were soaked for 1 hour in a 3 day-old rhizobial liquid culture media. Cowpea seeds were also treated with *Rhizobium* in this way using its corresponding strain of *Rhizobium sp.*

Growing and irrigation

Each pot was sown with 8 inoculated seeds for the broad bean and 10 seeds for cowpea. Tap water was used for irrigation till germination. The plants were, then, watered with Hoagland solution. After 15 days, the plants were thinned to leave 5 plants per pot. Four sets of the nutrient solution were prepared to contain the different concentrations of sodium chloride, control (basal medium), 2,000, 5,000 and 10,000 ppm. The same concentrations were also prepared for $CaCl_2$ treatments. The mentioned solutions were added after 15 days to their respective pots on 3 consecutive days, in order to avoid shocking the young seedlings. Normal Hoagland solution was used, for irrigation every 5 days, so that the whole concentration of the sodium and calcium chlorides, of the different treatments should not be affected.

After 50 days from planting, the plants were gently washed out from the sand. The nodules on every plant root system were counted and the efficient nodules were sorted according to their colour, size and location on the roots. Dry weight of the whole plants was also determined. Total nitrogen was measured by using Nessler reagent; the data obtained were evaluated and taken as a criterion of symbiotic nitrogen fixation.

RESULTS AND DISCUSSION

Broad bean plants

The effect of different concentrations of sodium and calcium chlorides on the nodulation capacity and symbiotic N-fixation of broad bean plants was studied in this work as shown in Table 1. The density of total nodulation on the broad bean roots was not highly affected due to the presence of different levels of NaCl. However, the number of efficient nodules was only affected when the concentration

Table 1

Effect of sodium and calcium chlorides on nodulation, growth and symbiotic N-fixation of broad bean plants inoculated with *Rh. leguminosarum*

Salt concentrations in ppm	Counts of nodules/plant			Total nodules/plant	Dry wt. in g/plant	N%	Total nitrogen in mg/plant	Total nitrogen in percent of control
	Big	Med.	Small					
Control (basal medium)	40	20	—	60	3.28	4.26	139.728	100.00
NaCl 2,000	45	11	—	56	3.04	4.50	136.800	97.26
NaCl 5,000	42	18	—	60	1.37	4.31	59.047	42.26
NaCl 10,000	5	30	10	45	0.88	4.03	26.752	18.91
CaCl₂ 2,000	5	50	—	55	2.73	4.58	125.034	89.49
CaCl₂ 5,000	—	55	5	60	1.23	4.11	50.553	36.19
CaCl₂ 10,000	—	20	12	32	1.10	3.66	40.260	28.82

Table 2

Effect of sodium and calcium chlorides on nodulation, growth and symbiotic N-fixation of cowpea plants inoculated with *Rhizobium sp*

Salt concentrations in ppm	Counts of nodules/plant			Total nodules/plant	Dry wt. in g/plant	N%	Total nitrogen in mg/plant	Total nitrogen in percent of control
	Big	Med.	Small					
Control (basal medium)	20	28	—	48	1.01	5.68	57.368	100.00
NaCl 2,000	30	15	—	45	0.91	4.78	43.498	75.82
NaCl 5,000	18	24	—	42	0.71	4.62	32.802	57.17
NaCl 10,000	10	21	13	44	0.64	3.29	21.056	36.70
CaCl₂ 2,000	21	30	—	51	0.33	4.72	15.576	27.15
CaCl₂ 5,000	12	35	2	49	0.29	4.34	12.586	21.94
CaCl₂ 10,000	—	38	10	48	0.12	3.74	4.488	7.82

of NaCl in the solution was 10,000 ppm. Application of calcium chloride in all concentrations greatly affected the density of efficient nodules on the plant. The presence of 5,000 and 10,000 ppm NaCl in the soil prevented the formation of efficient nodules on the root system. Generally, the number of total nodules was slightly affected with the addition of $CaCl_2$ except in the case of the last concentration (10,000 ppm), where it gave a relatively low value. The results agreed in part with those obtained by Bernsteine and Ogata (1966). They reported that nodulation of soybean and lucerne was greatly affected by high concentrations of sodium chloride. Moreover, Kamel *et al.* (1971) stated that leaching the salts from the soil resulted in highly significant increase in the number of nodule bacteria in broad bean plants.

The dry matter of the plants was gradually decreased as the concentration of NaCl was increased. The decrease in the dry weights was clearly shown in the last concentration when 10,000 ppm was used. The dry weights of the plants were 3.28, 3.04, 1.37 and 0.88 g/plant for the treatments of the control (basal medium), 2,000, 5,000 and 10,000 ppm NaCl respectively. In the case of $CaCl_2$ treatments, the same general trend was also obtained but the decreases in the dry weights were clearly shown, when 2,000 and 5,000 ppm $CaCl_2$ were added, in comparison to those of NaCl treatments. The dry weight of the plants treated with 10,000 ppm $CaCl_2$ was slightly higher than that treated with the same level of NaCl. It seems that $CaCl_2$ affected the nodulation and growth of the plant more than sodium chloride did.

The nitrogen percentages of the plants were almost not affected as the concentrations of NaCl or $CaCl_2$ were increased. However, the actual amounts of total nitrogen (uptake of N by the plants) were highly affected by the application of either NaCl or $CaCl_2$, especially in case of high concentrations.

Sodium chloride applications gave gradually decreasing amounts of total nitrogen as its concentration was increased. However, in the first concentration where 2,000 ppm NaCl was used, the decrease in the nitrogen content was not so great, while in other concentrations, the decrease was very clear compared to that of the control treatment. The amounts of total nitrogen uptake were 139.728, 136.800, 59.047 and 26.752 mg N/plant for those treated with 0, 2,000, 5,000 and 10,000 ppm NaCl respectively. The effect was also clear as indicated in the nitrogen percent compared to the control.

Application of $CaCl_2$ resulted in nearly the same general trend as the NaCl treatments. The actual amounts of total nitrogen were 139.728, 125.034, 50.553 and 40.26 mg N/plant for the pots treated with 2,600, 5,000 and 10,000 ppm $CaCl_2$ respectively.

From the microbiological point of view, it seemed generally, that the efficiency of *Rh. leguminosarum* was proportionally affected as the concentration of the salt was increased. As the concentrations of both NaCl and $CaCl_2$ were increased, the symbiotic nitrogen fixation by *Rhizobium* strains was greatly decreased, especially in the last concentration when 10,000 ppm was added as shown in Table 1.

The presence of high concentrations of the salt may affect the absorption balance by the plant for other nutrients that may play a great role in the enzyme activity of symbiotic N-assimilation. However, the growth of the plants may also be affected by high osmotic pressure resulting from the high concentration of sodium and calcium chlorides in the soil. Nieman and Bernsteine (1959), Kamel *et al.* (1971) and Maria (1974) also came to the same general conclusion. Eventually the carbohydrates required to reach the *Rhizobium* in the nodule may not be sufficient for high symbiotic N-fixation capacity (Fred and Wilson (1934), Wilson and Fred (1939), Allen and Allen (1950), and Alexander (1961)).

The inhibitory effect of high salt concentration could more directly affect the plant than the *Rhizobium* living inside its roots. *Rhizobium* seemed to be indirectly affected by the salts since the inhibitory action observed in this work was efficient only on nodules and was not recorded for total nodulation.

Cowpea plants

Data in Table 2 showed that the nodulation on the root system of cowpea plants follows the same general trend, with regard to the number of total nodules, as was observed in case of nodulation of broad bean plants. Efficient nodules were increased in numbers when 2,000 ppm NaCl was used, while 5,000 and 10,000 ppm NaCl gave lower values in comparison to that of the control. The numbers of efficient nodules were 20, 30, 18 and 10 nodules/plant for the control (basal medium), 2,000, 5,000 and 10,000 ppm NaCl respectively. It is clear from the data that sensitivity of *Rhizobium sp.* (cowpea) to salinity was quite different from that of *Rh. leguminosarum* (broad bean). Salinity affected the formation of efficient nodules for cowpea to a greater or lesser extent than that for broad bean (Tables 1, 2). Since *Rhizobium* of cowpeas is considered a slow-growing *Rhizobium*, and *Rh. leguminosarum* as fast-grower, it might be concluded that slow-growing rhizobia are slightly affected by high concentrations of salinity than fast-growing organisms. Some investigators, such as Allen and Allen (1950), and Lie (1969) considered that fast-growing rhizobia are more sensitive to different factors than the slow-growing types.

Data also showed that application of $CaCl_2$ gave relatively lower values of efficient nodules than that observed in the case of NaCl, when 2,000 and 5,000 ppm $CaCl_2$ were used. No efficient nodules were recorded when 10,000 ppm $CaCl_2$ was applied.

The dry matter of cowpea plants was decreased as the concentration of the salt was increased. This was especially clear in the case of $CaCl_2$ treatments.

The changes in the nitrogen percentage in cowpea plants were affected by the salt application. The actual amounts of total nitrogen were also greatly affected due to application of different salts in comparison to that of the control. The values decreased as the concentration of either NaCl or $CaCl_2$ were increased. The values of total nitrogen were 57.368, 43.498, 32.802 and 21.056 mg N/plant for the control, 2,000, 5,000 and 10,000 ppm NaCl respectively. The respective values for CaCl$_2$ treatments were 57.368, 15.576, 12.586 and 4.488 mg N/plant.

In this work, it seemed that symbiotic nitrogen fixation in cowpea plants was not affected by high concentrations of NaCl to the same degree as broad bean plants (Tables 1 and 2). This is also another proof that *Rh. leguminosarum,* behaved differently than *Rhizobium sp* (cowpea) regarding the sensitivity to salinity. This may be attributed, as it has been mentioned before, rather to the tolerance of the slow-growing rhizobia to salinity in the soil than the fast-growing rhizobia.

From the above discussion, it can be concluded that high concentrations of sodium and calcium chlorides have no observable effect on total nodulation of both broad bean and cowpea plants. However, the mentioned salts greatly affected the formation of efficient nodules on both plants. Dry weights and total nitrogen uptake by the plants were also affected by the high concentrations of both salts. Consequently, the symbiotic N-fixation was also inhibited as the concentration of the salt in the soil was increased.

Therefore, in saline soil, it is highly recommended to reduce the salt concentration by leaching, before cultivation of the inoculated leguminous plant, to an extent that does not affect the absorption of different elements by the plant to give vigorous plant growth and efficient nodulation. Such elements might also be important for the enzyme activity of symbiotic N-fixation by *Rhizobium* associated with the plant.

SUMMARY

In pot experiments, using sandy soil, different concentrations of sodium and calcium chlorides were used to study the effect of salinity on the nodulation capacity and symbiotic N-fixation of some leguminous plants.

High concentrations of sodium and calcium chlorides have no observable effect on total nodulation on the roots of both broad bean and cowpea plants. The mentioned salts greatly affected the density of efficient nodules, dry weights and symbiotic N-fixation. It seemed that high levels of CaCl$_2$ affected the nodulation and the growth of the plants more than did sodium chloride.

The concentration of 10,000 ppm of either NaCl and CaCl$_2$ showed the greatest inhibitory effect on the nodulation and symbiotic N-fixation of the plants.

The inhibitory effect occurred directly on the plant rather than on the *Rhizobium* since it was only observed for efficient nodules and not for total nodulation.

Generally, fast-growing rhizobia as represented by *Rh. leguminosarum* were more sensitive to high concentrations of sodium chloride than the slow-growing rhizobia as represented by *Rhizobium sp.* (cowpea).

REFERENCES

Alexander, M. (1961): *Introduction to soil microbiology* John Wiley & Sons, Inc. New York & London.

Allen, E. K. and Allen, O. N. (1950): *Bact. Rev.,* **14,** 273–330.

Bernsteine, L. and Ogato, G. (1966): *Agron. J.* **58,** 201–203.

Fred, E. B. and Wilson, P. W. (1934): *Proc. Natl. Acad. Sci. U. S.,* **20,** 403–409.

Iswaran, V. and Sen, A. (1958): *Soil and Fertilizer,* **22,** 117.

Kamel, M., Hamissa, M. R., Ibrahim, A. N. and Khadr, M. S. (1971): *Agric. Res. Min. of Agric. Cairo,* **6,** 126–134.

Lie, T. A. (1969): *Plant and soil,* **31,** 391–406.

Maria, A. M. (1974): *M. Sc. thesis,* Fac. of Agr. Univ. of Tanta, Egypt.

Nieman, R. H., and Bernsteine, L. (1959): *Amer. J. Bot.* **46,** 667–670.

Subba, R. N. S. Lakshmi-Kumari, M., Singh, C. S. and Magu, S. P. (1972): *Indian J. of Agric. Sci. New Delhi* **42,** 384–386.

Wilson, P. W., and Fred, E. B. (1939): *J. Am. Soc. Agron.* **31,** 497–502.

RELEASE OF VITAMIN B_{12} FROM *RH. LEGUMINOSARUM*

by

Denka CHANOVA
"N. Poushkarov" Institute for Soil Science,
Sofia, Bulgaria

According to data quoted by different authors nodule bacteria (Bagdasarian 1965, Burton and Locchead 1952, Garkavenko 1959, 1963) synthesize and release vitamin B_{12} having a positive effect on sprouting, growth and development both of legume and non-leguminous crops (Zaremba and Malinskaya 1963).

Vitamin B_{12} plays an important role in the fixation of molecular nitrogen by legume crops (Kliewer and Evans 1962, 1963). The strains of nodule bacteria active on beans, lucerne and lupin according to some authors (Shemakhanova and Bunyko 1969, Semakhanova and Sidorenko 1971) differ from the weakly active ones as regards vitamin B_{12} contents in the nodules.

MATERIAL AND METHODS

The following were studied: determination of the amount of vitamin B_{12} produced by *Rh leguminosarum;* effect of mineral nutrition of peas on the amount of vitamin B_{12} released; effect of age of bacterial culture on the vitamin produced and the possibilities of using the amount of vitamin B_{12} released from nodule bacteria as an index of efficiency of strains.

Investigations were made with 18 strains isolated from peas having different mineral nutrition under the conditions of a pot experiment with leached chernozem and cinnamonic pseudopodzolic soil. The conditions of the experiment were described in another work (Chanova 1973). N-fixing activity of strains was determined on a sand crop (Fedorov 1952). The amount of vitamin B_{12} was determined by *Escherichia coli* test 113/3 (Nachev and Gesheva 1964), a modification of the method of Kutzeva (1961).

The data obtained on production of vitamin B_{12} from the strains of *Rh. leguminosarum* isolated from leached chernozem show that all the strains tested produce vitamin B_{12} (Fig. 1). The amount of the vitamin produced varies from 3.8 to 35 nanogamma/ml. The statistical evaluation of the data (from 12 replications) shows that they are fully reliable (> 3). The highest amount of vitamin B_{12} (35 nanogamma/ml) was produced by strain No. 37, characterized by the highest N-fixing activity (210 mg/pot N), and the lowest (3.8 and 4.0 nanogamma/ml), by

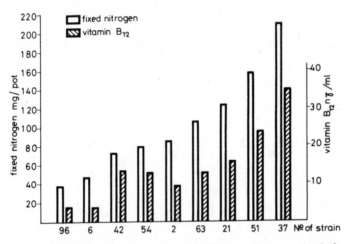

Fig. 1. Production of vitamin B_{12} by *Rh. leguminosarum* leached chernozem

strains Nos 6 and 96, characterized by the lowest N-fixing activity (48 and 38 mg/pot N). With the rest of the strains the relationship established is rather similar. Therefore, there is a tendency towards a positive relationship between the N-fixing activity and vitamin B_{12} production by the strains of *Rh. leguminosarum.* This is in agreement with the studies by Garkavenko (1963).

The data obtained show that the amount of the vitamin produced by the strains studied does not depend on mineral nutrition of peas with nitrogen, phosphorus and potassium at different rates and ratios (Table 1 and Fig. 1).

Studies were also made with strains isolated from cinnamonic pseudopodzolic soil. The data quoted (Fig. 2) show that all the strains of *Rh. leguminosarum* tested produce vitamin B_{12}. The amount of the latter varies from 2.8 to 21 nanogamma/ml and does not depend on mineral nutrition of peas (Table 1 and Fig. 2). The highest amount of B_{12} (21 nanogamma/ml) is produced by the strains Nos 176 and 149, characterized by the highest N-fixing activity (143 and 133 mg N per pot),

Table 1
Origin of strains of *Rh. leguminosarum*

Leached chernozem		Cinnamonic pseudopodzolic soil	
No. of strain	Isolated from the variant	No. of strain	Isolated from the variant
96	$N_3 P_2 K$	113	control
6	N_1	137	$N_1 P_1$
42	$N_1 P_2$	155	$N_2 P_3$
54	$N_1 P_3$	161	$P_2 K$
2	control	157	$P_1 K$
63	$N_3 P_3$	175	$N_1 P_2 K$
21	P_2	181	$N_2 P_3 K$
51	$N_3 P_2$	149	$N_1 P_3$
37	$N_2 P_1$	176	$N_1 P_3 K$

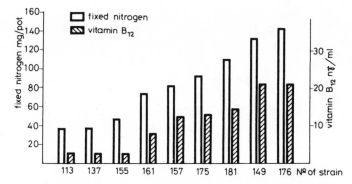

Fig. 2. Production of vitamin B_{12} by *Rh. leguminosarum* cinnamonic pseudopodzolic soil

and the lowest (2.8 nanogamma/ml) in the case of the strains Nos 113, 137 and 155 with the lowest N-fixing activity (37 and 47 mg/pot N). A similar relationship is observed with the rest of the strains, too. A tendency towards a positive relationship could be observed between the N-fixing activity and the capacity of the bacteria to produce vitamin B_{12}. Differences were observed in the amounts of the vitamin produced; they were higher in strains isolated from leached chernozem compared to those isolated from cinnamonic pseudopodzolic soil.

The production of vitamin B_{12} by *Rh. leguminosarum* is related to the age of culture according to Garkavenko (1963) and Bagdasarian (1965). To clarify the effect of age of bacterial culture on the production of vitamin B_{12}, studies were made with strain No. 37 isolated from leached chernozem and with strain No. 176 isolated from cinnamonic pseudopodzolic soil. Investigations were carried out on every

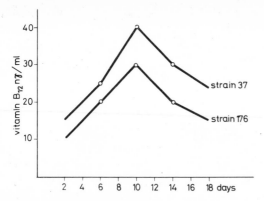

Fig. 3. Dynamics of release of vitamin B_{12} from *Rh. leguminosarum*

second day starting from the day of inoculation of the bacterial culture upto the 18th day.

The results obtained (Fig. 3) show that the production of vitamin B_{12} is initiated on the second day and reaches its maximum on the 10th day; then its amount gradually decreases. Therefore, a conclusion might be drawn that the production of vitamin B_{12} by *Rh. leguminosarum* depends on the age of the culture. The decrease of the production after the tenth day could be explained by a partial fixing or destruction in the cells. The difference appears to be proportional to the rate of production of a certain amount of vitamin B_{12} that is considerably greater with the strain isolated from leached chernozem, No. 37.

Investigations of that kind should be taken into consideration when selecting strains for production of Nitragin.

CONCLUSIONS

1. All the strains of *Rh. leguminosarum* studied (isolated from leached chernozem and cinnamonic pseudopodzolic soil) produce vitamin B_{12}.

2. The amount of the vitamin produced depends on activity, age and origin of the strain. The strains characterized by a higher N-fixing activity produce more or less greater amounts of vitamin B_{12} compared to the weakly active ones. The release of the vitamin begins on the second day and reaches its maximum on the tenth day. The strains isolated from leached chernozem show a production of higher amounts of vitamin B_{12} compared to those isolated from cinnamonic pseudopodzolic soil.

3. The amount of the vitamin B_{12} produced from all the strains studied does not depend on the mineral nutrition of peas.

204

SUMMARY

Studies were made on 18 strains isolated from peas having different mineral nutrition under the conditions of a pot experiment with leached chernozem and cinnamonic pseudopodzolic soil. All the strains of *Rh. leguminosarum* isolated from leached chernozem and cinnamonic pseudopodzolic soil produced vitamin B_{12}. The amount of the vitamin depends on the activity, age and origin of the strain. The strains characterized by a higher N-fixing activity produce greater amounts of vitamin B_{12}, than the weakly active ones. The release of the vitamin begins on the second day and reaches its maximum on the tenth day. The strains isolated from leached chernozem show a greater production of vitamin B_{12} than those isolated from cinnamonic pseudopodzolic soil. The amount of the vitamin B_{12} produced from all the strains studied does not depend on the mineral nutrition of peas.

REFERENCES

(Bagdasarian, E. T.) Багдасарян, Е. Т. (1965) : *Микробиол.* **34**, 502—505.

Burton, M. O. and Locchead, A. G. (1951) : Canad. J. Bot. *29*, 382.

(Shemakhanova, N. M. and Sidorenko, O. D.) Шемаханова, Н. М. и Сидоренко, О. Д. (1971) : *Новое в изучении биологической фиксации азота.* Наука, Москва

(Chanova, D. K.) Чанова, Д. К. (1973) : *Почвознание и агрохимия* № **6**, 117—123.

(Fedorov, M. V.) Федоров, М. В. (1952) : *Биологическая фиксация азота атмосферы.* Сельхозгиз, Москва.

(Garkavenko, A. I.) Гаркавенко, А. И. (1959) : *Изв. Молд. фил.* АН СССР, № 1

(Garkavenko, A. I.) Гаркавенко, А. И. (1963) : *Микроорганизмы в сельском хозястве* сб. МГУ, Москва.

Kliewer, M. and Evans, H. (1962): *Nature* **194**, 4823, 108—109.

Kliewer, M. and Evans, H. (1973): *Plant Physiol.* **38**.

(Kutzeva, L. S.) Куцева, Л. С. (1961) : Сб. 5, АН СССР, 133.

(Nachev, L. and Gesheva, P.) Начев, Л. и Гешева, Р. (1964) : *Микробиол.* **33**, 739—734.

(Semakhanova, N. M. and Bunyko) Шемаханова, Н. М. и Бунько (1969) : *Изв. АН СССЗ сер. Биол.* 413, № 3.

(Zaremba, B. P. and Malinskaya, S. M.) Заремба, В. П., Малинская, С., М. (1963) : *Микроорганизмы в сельском хозяйстве,* МГУ, Москва.

THE USE OF CO-ELECTROPHORESIS IN THE IDENTIFICATION OF *RHIZOBIA*

by

Krisztina KÖVES-PÉCHY and K. SZENDE
Research Institute for Soil Science and Agricultural Chemistry
of the Hungarian Academy of Sciences,
Budapest, Hungary

In routine work with *Rhizobia* it often becomes necessary to identify a new strain at the species level which is not very easy however. The taxonomic keys which are given in handbooks are ambiguous, the inoculation of the host plants are laborious and uncertain.

As an additional result in our taxonomic work with *Rhizobia* the co-electrophoresis of the mixed proteins of an authentic strain and from the unidentified one, proved to be useful for the identification of the different strains. In the present paper the profitable use of this method will be demonstrated.

MATERIAL AND METHODS

Bacteria. The strains of *Rhizobia,* used in these experiments were *R. lupini, R. phaseoli, R. leguminosarum* and *R. meliloti.* All of them originated from the CCM collection, Prague, Ruzyne, Czechoslovakia.

Culture conditions. The bacteria were grown overnight on a horizontal shaker in a mannitol-yeast extract medium at 28 °C. The composition of the.medium was the same as was given by Vincent (1970) with the modification that the yeast water was replaced by 1 gram per liter Difco yeast extract.

Preparation of the cell-free extracts. The cultures were centrifuged and treated by a lysis buffer, lysozyme and Tween 80, according to Echols and Green (1971) with a slight modification and centrifuged again in the cold. The supernatant was used as cell-free extract in the polyacrylamide gel electrophoresis. The protein concentration of the sample was determined by Biuret method.

The conditions of the polyacrylamide gel electrophoresis. The electrophoresis was carried out on a vertical Shandon electrophoresis apparatus with a Wokam constant voltage stabilizer. The buffer system was the same as in Ornstein (1964) and Davis (1964): Tris-glycine-system, pH 8,9. The gels were prepared by the method of Davis (1964). The concentration of the spacer gel was 2.5 per cent and for the resolving gel this was 7.0.

Approximately 100 microgrammes of soluble protein (in 0.5—0.7 ml) was layered on the top of the gel. In the case of the co-electrophoresis two samples were mixed in equal quantities (i.e. 50—50 microgrammes per gel). Beside the co-electrophoresis gels there were two reference gels also for the control of each component of the mixed proteins.

The electrophoresis was performed at 5 °C with the anode in the lower electrode chamber and at 4.0 mA per gel for 3 hours. The run was stopped when the bromphenol blue marker arrived to the same position on the gels.

Staining and evaluation of the gels. After removing the gels from the glass tubes they were fixed overnight in 20 per cent sulpho-salicylic acid, then stained with 0.25 per cent (w/v) Coomassie Brillant Blue R 250 for soluble proteins in methanol-acetic acid–water (5 : 1 : 5) for two hours and destained in 7 per cent (v/v) acetic acid at room temperature. The gels were scanned with a Joyce Loebl "Chromoscan" densitometer at yellowish-green filter and the obtained densitometer scans were compared and/or the R_f values calculated.

In the case of malate-dehydrogenase (Mdh) (E. C. N. 1.1.1. 37) the gels were stained for 90 minutes according to Brewer (1970) in Tris-DL-malic acid buffer with the phenazin methosulphate-NB tetrazolium-DPN method, at pH 7.0 and fixed in 50 per cent ethanol. They were stained and scanned as previously.

RESULTS

The co-electrophoresis was studied with strains of rhizobia belonging to the same or different species. On the obtained protein patterns there are some reference bands which are comparable on the different densitometer tracings in single runs and in the co-electrophoresis. These peaks were numbered and examined for their presence or absence on the tracings.

Figure 1 demonstrates this in two different ways. The *C* and *E* curves are densitometer tracings of two *R. phaseoli* strains. *E* is *R. phaseoli* (Cat. N⁰ 233, from Argentina) and *C R. phaseoli* (Cat. N⁰ 347 from USSR). The profiles are nearly the same in single and in the co-electrophoresis (Curve *D*).

The situation is different if we compare the *R. phaseoli* (Cat. N⁰ 233.) to *R. lupini* (Cat. N⁰ 75). In that case, the profiles are fairly distinguishable and therefore the co-electrophoresis pattern (Curve *B*) is more complex. Some peaks are present on *R. lupini* (Curve *A*), as 11, 16, 32, 36, etc. but not on *R. leguminosarum,* or only their dimensions are small. The patterns are very complex however, and therefore the peaks sometimes are hardly identifiable and it remains undecided whether some bands are analogues with faster or slower migration values or different.

These difficulties can be eliminated if we use only one or two proteins in the comparisons. In our experiments (Köves-Péchy and Szende 1974, Péchyné-Köves and Szende 1974) the migration values of malate dehydrogenases gave small

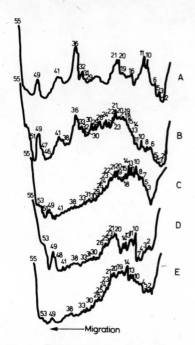

Fig. 1. Electrophoretic and coelectrophoretic patterns of soluble proteins in *Rhizobia*

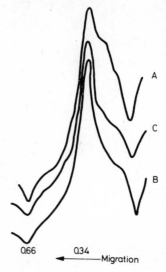

Fig. 2. Electrophoretic and coelectrophoretic patterns of malate dehydrogenases in different strains of *R. leguminosaurum*

variations within species level and these were higher — in most cases significantly — between species level.

On Figure 2 *A* and *B* curves are the densitometer tracings of the malate dehydrogenases of two *R. leguminosarum* (*A* = Cat. N⁰ 227, Romania, and *B* = Cat. N⁰ 389, GDR, respectively). with a peak at 0.34 R_f value. In the co-electrophoresis (Curve *C*) there are no demonstrable differences between the two strains in Mdh migration velocity. At 0.66 R_f value there is a band with a low optical density. This band corresponds to the fast running tetrazolium-oxidase (Baptist *et al.* 1969), a non-specified enzyme. The R_f values are just the same in the different strains as in the case of Mdh.

In Figure 3 the situation changes however. The above mentioned *R. leguminosarum* (Cat. N⁰ 389) gives a slower moving peak at R_f 0.34 (Curve *B*) and the *R. meliloti* (Cat. N⁰ 263, Argentina) (has a faster moving Mdh with a 0.38 R_f value) (Curve A).

In the co-electrophoresis (Curve *C*) two peaks appear, one of them corresponds to the *R. leguminosarum* Mdh, the other to the *meliloti*'s one. The R_f of tetrazolium oxidases are the same in each sample. It is necessary therefore to select the adequate proteins for such comparisons.

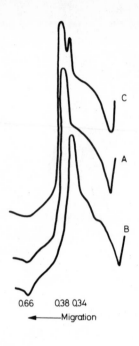

0.66   0.38 0.34

←——Migration

Fig. 3. Electrophoretic and coelectrophoretic patterns of malate dehydrogenases in *R. leguminosarum* and *R. meliloti*

DISCUSSION

In practice the identification — by common consent — of a bacterium as a *Rhizobium* is based on the concept that *Rhizobium* is a particular bacterium which is able to form nodules on legume roots and which produces a symbiotic N_2 fixing association with it, (Dixon 1969). The distinction at species level is not so easy however. The morphological characteristics and "biochemical traits" are not decisive (DeLey and Rassel 1965). Serology — based on internal proteins — sometimes gives erroneous results (Vincent and Humphrey 1970). The proof of invasiveness and nodulation on different tester plants is laborious, and in many cases results in cross-reactions (Rev. by Dixon *loc. cit.*)

A relatively easy approach to the solution resulted from our taxonomic work with *Rhizobia* by disc electrophoresis on polyacrylamide gels (Köves-Péchy and Szende 1974, Péchyné-Köves and Szende 1974). To avoid any false results, originating from the microheterogeneity of gels during the run, we checked mixed combinations of proteins in the electrophoresis and found that the electrophoretic profiles of proteins in such a co-electrophoresis was the same or nearly the same if we used proteins from different strains of one species and the differences increased in combinations of proteins originating from different *Rhizobium* species.

210

The comparison of soluble proteins is sometimes cumbersome, the profiles are complex and the tracing of the presence or absence of the characteristic peaks is difficult. The use of specific proteins — in our case the Mdh — is more successful however. The method is a simple one, does not require costly equipment and compared to the inoculation experiments is not time-consuming, it requires only 1—2 days.

SUMMARY

The distinction between *Rhizobia* at species level is methodically laborious and also time-consuming.

A relatively easy approach to the solution resulted from our taxonomic work with *Rhizobia* by disc electrophoresis on polyacrylamide gels. We checked mixed combinations of proteins and found that the electrophoretic profile of proteins in such co-electrophoresis was the same or nearly the same if we used proteins from different strains of one species, and the differences increased in combinations of proteins originating from different *Rhizobium* spp. Therefore in using proteins from an authentic strain in a mixture with proteins of the questionable strain in co-electrophoresis, we can easily decide the taxonomic position of the latter.

REFERENCES

Baptist, J. N. *et al.* (1969): *J. Bacteriol.* **99**, 180—188.

Brewer, G. J. (1970): *Introduction to isozyme techniques.* Academic Press. N. Y.

Davis, B. J. (1964): *Disc electrophoresis. II.* Ann. N. Y. Acad. Sci. **121**, 404—427.

DeLey, J. and Rassel, A. (1965): *J. gen. Microbiol.* **41**, 85—91.

Dixon, R. O. D. (1969): *Ann. Rev. Microbiol.* **23**, 137—158.

Echols, H. and Green, L. (1971): *Proc. Nat. Acad. Sci. U. S.* **68**, 2190—2194.

Köves-Péchy, K. and Szende, K. (1974a): *Abstr. of Papers of the XIth Conference on the Taxonomy of Bacteria.* 11—12.

Ornstein, L. (1964): *Disc electroforesis.* I. Ann. N. Y. Acad. Sci. 121, 321—349.

Péchy-Köves K. and Szende K. (1974b): *MTA Agrártud. Közl.* **33**, 65—76.

Vincent, J. M. (1970): *A manual for the practical study of root nodule bacteria.* Blackwell. Oxford, England.

Vincent, J. M. and Humphry, B. (1970): *J. gen. Microbiol.* **63**, 379—382.

EXPERIMENTAL STUDIES ON THE EFFICIENCY OF THE INOCULATION OF VARIOUS SOYBEAN VARIETIES

by

T. SOÓS and K. KÓNYA
Phylaxia Veterinary Biologicals and Feedstuffs Co.,
Budapest, Hungary
University of Agricultural Sciences,
Gödöllő, Hungary

Soybean on account of its high protein content is assuming ever greater importance in Hungary. By extending soybean cultivation the protein programme can most successfully be accomplished.

Studies have been carried out in various parts of the country to estimate how the foreign species can acclimatize compared with the Hungarian ones. (Kurnik 1972).

An important pratice in the cultivation technology of soybean is to mix the seed before sowing its specific nitrogen-fixing bacteria. In this way, nitrogen-fixing bacteria develop on the roots of the plant in the course of the growth of soybean and the bacteria supply the plant with organic-bound nitrogen as a result of symbiosis.

Our aim was to determine in small plot experiments, the effect of *Rhizonit I.* and *II.* preparations on two soybean species. *Rhizonit I.* was produced from *Rhizobium japonicum* isolated by the authors and *Rhizonit II.* from strains from the USSR and Bulgaria.

MATERIALS AND METHODS

The experiment was carried out in a brown forest soil of the Gödöllő University of Agricultural Sciences. In this field soybean had not been previously cultivated. In autumn, the field was fertilized homogeneously with 260 kg/ha mixed active agent which contained 200 kg/ha ammonium nitrate, 400 kg/ha superphosphate and 200 kg/ha potassium chloride of 60% providing an average fertilizer level. The fertilizer was added to the soil at a depth of 25 to 30 cm by ploughing.

The G/3 and G/6 *Rhizobium japonicum* strains were isolated from tubers of soyplants cultivated in sandy soil. The seeds of these plants were treated with *"Rhizoleg"* soy-inoculum and their pure culture was obtained by surface-streaking method. The strains proved to be *Rhizobium* on the basis of morphological properties of the colonies and the nitrogen-fixing capacity. The latter was detected by an increase of dry weight of inoculated plants grown in sterile silica sand. Total nitrogen was determined by the Kjeldahl method.

Table 1

Results of field experiments. Phenological and crop data of soya varieties treated with Rhizonit I. and II.

Variety	Treatments	Height of stock cm	Average number of root nodules legumes per plants		%	1000 seeds weight g	Crop	
							100 kg/ha	%
"Iregi Sz. 1."	Control	62	–	10.7	100	172	8.67	100
	Rhizonit I.	76	10.8	13.6	127	161	12.30	141
	Rhizonit II.	66	8.5	11.5	107	165	10.12	116
"AMSOY"	Control	73	–	10.5	100	152	12.12	100
	Rhizonit I.	82	8.9	22.7	216	152	16.12	132
	Rhizonit II.	83	5.4	14.8	140	160	14.37	118
	$P_5\%$						3.60	

The 646 and 631 *Rhizobium japonicum* strains were obtained from the Leningrad Institute of Agricultural Microbiology and the D-2 strain from Bulgaria the "N. POUSHKAROV" Research Institute of Soil Science. The inoculum was prepared according to Soós's method (Soós 1960).

The *Rhizobium* strains, the fermented liquid, as well as the effectiveness of *Rhizonit I.* prepared from strains G/3 and G/6, also properties of *Rhizonit II.* prepared from strains 646, 631 and D-2 were tested before use.

Two soybean cultivars were tested in the experiment, notably the Hungarian "Iregi Sz. 1." and the American "Amsoy". The seeds were provided by courtesy of the Plant Producing Enterprise.

The experiment was carried out in random block arrangement. 6 treatments with four repetitions in plots of 40 m^2. The seeds were sown on the 24th and 25th April 1974. The space between the rows was 40 cm and 20 to 22 seeds were applied to every metre.

The control plots were sown first, then, the "Iregi Sz. 1." cultivars treated with *Rhizonit I.* followed by the "Amsoy" cultivar. The Seeds treated with *Rhizonit II.* were then sown.

RESULTS AND DISCUSSION

In Table 2 the height of the plants can be seen as well as the amount of legumes developed, the weight of 1000 seeds and the quantity of seed-crop. The yields have been evaluated by mathematical-statistical methods.

The growth of the plants treated with *Rhizonit I.* and *II.* was more remarkable than that of the control. The formation of nodules was enhanced by *Rhizonit I.* and *Rhizonit II.* in both cultivars; no nodules were found on control plants. This result

Table 2
The effect of different inocula produced in agar cultures or fermentor

| Treatment | Stem and leaf green g/20 plants | Rate % | Nodule | | N% | |
			per 20 plants	weight	stem	root
Untreated control	71.65	100.00	–	–	0.71	1.05
G/3 strain from agar	85.60	119.46	212	5.70	2.66	5.47
G/6 strain from agar	91.20	127.28	262	7.22	3.13	4.70
646 strain from agar	93.60	130.63	282	7.03	2.14	4.63
631 strain from agar	83.30	116.25	261	5.01	2.32	4.18
D-2 strain from agar	91.15	127.21	238	6.47	2.46	5.14
G/3 from fermentor	76.00	106.07	125	5.69	2.23	5.22
G/6 from fermentor	82.10	114.58	128	6.81	2.26	5.64
646 from fermentor	95.95	133.91	103	7.55	2.26	5.19
631 from fermentor	81.00	113.04	120	6.34	2.50	5.84
Rhizonit I.	89.85	125.40	169	6.57	2.95	5.62
Rhizonit II.	66.80	93.23	163	6.20	2.61	5.18

contradicts the results obtained by Hamatová-Hlavacková (1965), who found the formation of nodules as a variety- and strain-specific phenomenon. In our experiments, however, this was not observable; the origin of *Rhizobium* strains plays no role in the formation of nodules.

As the statistical analysis of data showed, inoculation of seeds with *Rhizonit I.* resulted in an increase of the yield in both test plant varieties, however, this increase was significant only in the case of the "Amsoy" variety. *Rhizonit II.* had not increased significantly the yields, in spite of the fact that it caused formation of nodules on the roots of both variety tested. Similar results are reported by Skrdleta and Pelikan (1973).

SUMMARY

In the course of fulfilling the requirements of the soy-program, efforts have been made in order to acclimatize foreign soybean species instead of the cultivation of Hungarian ones. Thus, field experiments have been carried out involving *Rhizobium* inocula both with Hungarian and foreign seeds.

According to the experiments, the plants treated with *Rhizonit I.* and *II.* have grown on more vigorously than the control ones.

The nodule production was increased in both soybean species on the effect of *Rhizonit I.* and *II.* treatment.

As the statistical analysis of data showed, inoculation of seeds with *Rhizonit I.* resulted in an increase of the yield in both test plant varieties, however, this increase was significant only in the case of the "Amsoy" variety. *Rhizonit II.* had not increased the yields significantly in spite of the fact that it caused formation of nodules on the roots of both varieties tested. Similar results are reported by Skrdleta and Pelikan (1973).

REFERENCES

Hamatová-Hlavacková, E. (1965): *Ved. Práce* (9), 193–209.
Kurnik, E. (1972): *Amerikai szójafajták termesztési kísérletei, 1972.* Takarmánytermesztési Kutató Intézet, Iregszemcse.
Skrdleta, V. and Pelikán, J. (1973): *Zbl. Bakt. II.* 745–752.
Soós, T. (1960): *M. Sc. Thesis,* Gödöllő, University of Agricultural Sciences.

THE ROLE OF SOIL ORGANISMS IN THE
DECOMPOSITION OF PLANT RESIDUES

EFFECT OF VARIOUS TEMPERATURES ON MINERALIZATION OF ORGANIC SUBSTANCES IN SOIL

by

B. NOVÁK and J. KUBÁT
Research Institutes of Plant Production,
Prague, Czechoslovakia

This paper presents data of part of the model experiment after the substrate was added to the soil incubated at different temperatures.

MATERIAL AND METHODS

The aggregates (2—4 mm) from the arable layer of the clay-loamy slightly leached chernozem soil were incubated in respiration vessels. The Warburg apparatus and micromanometric technique were used for the short term experiments — up to 16 hours (Kleinzeller et at. 1954). The oxygen uptake was measured. Using one litre cylindrical flasks and the interferometric technique in prolonged experiments — up to 4 days (Novák 1973), the evolved CO_2 was determined.

The soil was moistened to 20% w/w. The control and the amended soil was used. The amendments consisted of glucose (0.5%) or glucose (0.5% i.e. 0.2% C) plus $(NH_4)_2SO_4$ (0.02% N).

RESULTS AND DISCUSSION

Figure 1 demonstrates the temperature effect on the non-amended soil in the short-term experiments. The rate of the oxygen uptake increased in the first phase of incubation. This phase could be compared to the lag-phase of the growth curve of micro-organism cultures. It lasts for about 8 hours at 20 °C and 25 °C incubation and for 6 hours at the 30 °C incubation.

The deflexion of the 20 °C curve was significantly greater than that of the 30 °C curve, resulting in the final respiration rates being even closer to the average respiration rates than the initial values. If we symbolize the respiration values of non-amended soil as B (= basal), the following equations might be suggested:

— for the initial rate:
$$B_{20} : B_{25} : B_{30} = 1 : 1.5 : 2.5$$

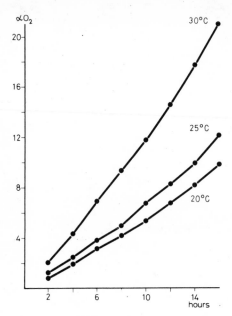

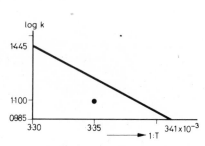

Fig. 1. Cumultative respiration curves (O_2 – uptake) of non-amended soil samples (μl O_2 per 1 g soil)

Fig. 2. Graphical expression of the temperature dependence obtained from Fig. 1 computed according to Arrhenius' equation

– for the final rate:
$$B_{20} : B_{25} : B_{30} = 1 : 1.37 : 2.10$$
– for the mean rate:
$$B_{20} : B_{25} : B_{30} = 1 : 1.25 : 2.16$$
Comparing the obtained data to the Arrhenius' equation
$$\log k = a - b/T$$
a slight deviation was found (Fig. 2). The temperature effect of the temperature interval 20–25 °C is smaller than that of the 25–30 °C interval. Considering the complexity of the effect the agreement of findings with the theory is fairly good. The results correspond to the empirical formula estimating the effect of temperature on the chemical reactions:

$$\frac{T + 10}{T} \doteq 2.$$

The addition of glucose (G) to the soil samples increased the soil respiration by approximately 5 times (Fig. 3). The relationship between the respiration intensity of

220

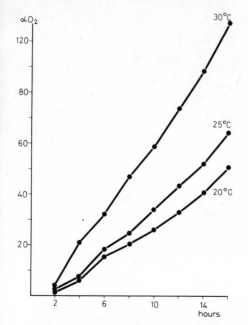

Fig. 3. Cumulative respiration curves (O_2 – uptake) of the glucose amended soil (μl O_2 per 1 g soil)

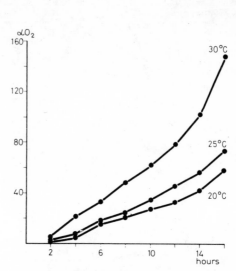

Fig. 4. Cumulative respiration curves (O_2 – uptake) of the glucose plus inorganic nitrogen amended soil (μl O_2 per 1 g soil)

individual temperature variants remained almost the same as in the non-amended soil being on the average:

$$G_{20} : G_{25} : G_{30} = 1 : 1.26 : 2.16$$

With these findings the added glucose used by soil microflora can be concluded in the same way as the soil organic matter. Without an incorporation of nitrogen and other biogenous elements, glucose is **preferably** used as the energy resource. Consequently, the soil organic matter was similarly used to cover the energy needs of soil microflora. The other processes resulting in formation of new bioplasm may be only minute.

Figure 4 presents the respiration curves after the addition of glucose plus inorganic nitrogen into the soil. Whereas the respiration rates of all the temperature variants did not differ much from that of the glucose amendment, the significant increase of respiration intensity occurred in the progressive phase of incubation. The respective rates were as follows:

– for the initial phase:

$$NG_{20} : NG_{25} : NG_{30} = 1 : 1.16 : 2.47$$

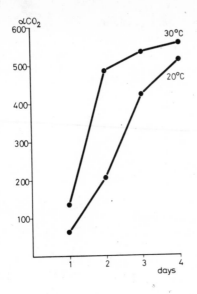

Fig. 5. Cumulative respiration curves (CO_2 — evolution) of the glucose plus inorganic nitrogen amended soil (mg CO_2 per 100 g soil)

— for the average:
$$NG_{20} : NG_{25} : NG_{30} = 1 : 1.27 : 2.56$$
— for the final phase:
$$NG_{20} : NG_{25} : NG_{30} = 1 : 2.78 : 7.77$$

These ratios indicated that glucose was utilized preferably for the energy needs in the initial phase only. The inorganic nitrogen enables the formation of new proteins in the following phase. The increased temperature shortened the "lag-phase" of protein synthesis and accelerated the synthesis itself. It may be presumed that new enzymes were formed among the new proteins raising the further intensity of metabolism.

If we prolonged the incubation the effect of the substrate exhaustion appeared (Fig 5). 8.4% of the added substrate was mineralized on the first day at 20 °C and twice as much (18.4%) at 30 °C. The respective values for the second day were 19.9% and 48.0%, for the third day 28.5% and 7.0%, and for the fourth day 13.0% and 2.3%. During the entire experiment 69.8% of the substrate was mineralized at 20 °C and 75.7% at 30 °C.

It is evident that the sum of mineralized substrate does not characterize the temperature effect on the metabolic processes of soil microflora. After the mineralization of about two-thirds of the substrate the respiration intensity decreased regardless of the temperature. This is in agreement with the findings of several authors (Apfelthaler and Novák 1969, Domsch 1963, Drobník 1962, Novák 1973) indicating that 60–70% of glucose is rapidly mineralized and the rest stabilized. The rise of the temperature caused almost the same mineralization increase on the second day as on the first one. This temperature effect was less pronounced than in the short-term experiments. The main reason was evidently the longer time intervals between the individual measurements. To the end of the second day of the incubation, the mineralization extent at 30 °C achieved such a degree (66.4%) that the stabilization effect was very probable. This level was reached a day later at the 20 °C incubation.

SUMMARY

The high temperature increased the mineralization of the soil organic matter and of glucose added in the same proportions. If nitrogen was added to glucose the synthetic processes in the soil probably occurred and the temperature effect was strengthened. In the prolonged experiments the temperature effect was predominated by the process of substrate stabilization.

REFERENCES

Apfelthaler, R. and Novák, B. (1969): *Rostl. výroba* **15,** 157–162.
Domsch, K. H. (1963): *Die Messung von Abbau im Boden.* In: Soil Organisms. Proceedings of the Colloquium on Soil Fauna, Soil Microflora and their Relationships. Volsterbeek – Wageningen, the Netherlands pp. 10–16.
Drobník, J. (1962): *Fol. Microbiol.* **7,** 126–131.
Kleinzeller, A., Málek, J. and Vrba, R. (1954): *Manometrické metody a jejich použití v biologii a biochemii.* SNTL, Praha.
(Novák, B.) Новак Б. (1972): *Испльзование органических удобрений, изготовленных из городских отбросов.* Сб. Органические удобрения, Колос, Москва.
Novák, B. (1973): *Zbl. Bakt. II.* **128,** 316–335.

THE EFFECT OF NUTRITIVE CONDITIONS
ON THE DECOMPOSITION OF CORN-STALK

by

B. TÓTH
Agricultural University, Department of Chemistry,
Keszthely, Hungary

In our modern corn production systems, corn-stalks are left in the stubble-fields in a chopped state. In autumn, however, with an adequate supplement of chemical fertilizers they are ploughed in to the upper 20 cm thick layer of the field.

In such a way 90 cwt/ha corn-stalks get into the field every year, composed mainly of cellulose, hemicellulose, and lignin. The microbiological decomposition of this large quantity of plant residues, using a reasonable dosage of chemical fertilization, which is economically feasible is our main concern.

MATERIAL AND METHODS

The carbon dioxide-producing capacity of the experimental soil was measured under laboratory conditions, using various doses of chemical fertilizers, with and without corn-stalks. As an experimental soil we had brown forest soil in the vicinity of Keszthely, having the following properties:

pH_{KCl}	6.51
pH_{H_2O}	6.92
total organic matter	2.47%
total N-content	0.37%
K-content 24.4 mg K_2O/100 g soil	
P-content 13.8 mg P_2O_5/100 g soil	

CO_2-production was measured according to the method described by Szegi (1962). To 200 g air-dried soil 4 g of ground air-dried corn-stalk were added in each pot, then the water content of soils was stabilized at 60% WHC.

The following treatments were used:

1) 200 g soil;
2) 200 g soil + 4 g (2%) corn-stalk;
3) 200 g soil + PK (=20 mg P_2O_5 + 20 mg K_2O/pot);

4) 200 g soil + PK + 4 g corn-stalk;
5) 200 g soil + PK + N_1 (= 20 mg N/pot);
6) 200 g soil + PK + N_1 + 4 g corn-stalk;
7) 200 g soil + PK + N_2 (= 100 mg N/pot);
8) 200 g soil + PK + N_2 + 4 g corn-stalk;
9) 200 g soil + PK + N_3 (= 500 mg N/pot);
10) 200 g soil + PK + N_3 + 4 g corn-stalk;
11) 200 g soil + PK + N_3 (= 1000 mg N/pot);
12) 200 g soil + PK + N_4 + 4 g corn-stalk.

Nitrogen supplement was added in the form of ammonium sulphate. The experiment lasted for 20 weeks, the quantity of CO_2 released from soil was measured every second week, at 28 °C temperature.

RESULTS AND DISCUSSION

The results of the experiment are shown in Figures 1–6. It is evident from the figures that the presence of corn-stalks causes a considerable increase in the quantity of CO_2 released from the soil. Figure 1 shows the results of the 1st and 2nd treatments.

Figure 2 indicates that K and P supplements do not significantly influence the CO_2-producing capacity of the soil, even a certain decrease can be observed in the soil without corn-stalks. This might be due to the high K-concentration.

The quantity of carbon dioxide released by the microbiological decomposition of corn-stalk is highly increased by adding a relatively low N-supplement as it is demonstrated in Figure 3. This value does not increase if further 100 ml N/pot are added (Fig. 4), contrary to our expectations. The reason for this is not known

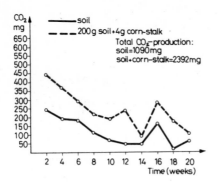

Fig. 1. Evolution of CO_2 from soil enriched by corn-stalk

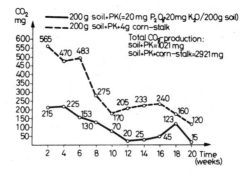

Fig. 2. Evolution of CO_2 from soil enriched by PK fertilizers and corn-stalk

226

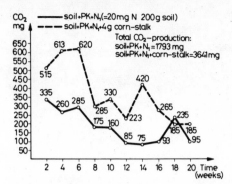

Fig. 3. Evolution of CO_2 from soil enriched by N_1 + PK fertilizers and corn stalk

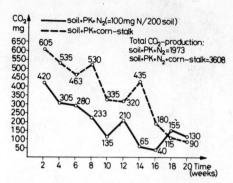

Fig. 4. Evolution of CO_2 from soil enriched by N_2 + PK fertilizers and corn stalk

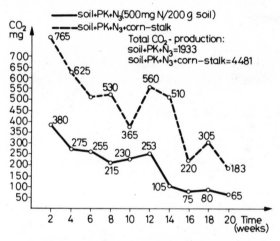

Fig. 5. Evolution of CO_2 from soil enriched by N_3 + Pk fertilizers and corn-stalk

(Figs 3–4). It is very interesting if we compare the data of Figure 5 with those of Figure 6.

Both treatments resulted in a much higher CO_2-production, than we had observed formerly, but comparing them with each other, the increase of the total quantity of carbon dioxide is not in a linear correlation with the amount of N-fertilizer applied.

In each treatment, the larger amount of the total quantity of released CO_2 is produced during the first 6–8 weeks of decomposition.

It can also be observed that during decomposition of corn-stalk, CO_2-production shows a relative maximum.

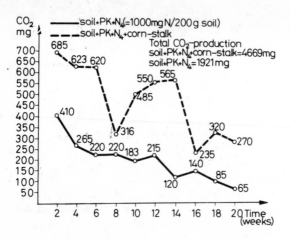

Fig. 6. Evolution of CO_2 from soil enriched by
N_4 PK fertilizers and corn-stalk.

Presumably this is caused by the autolysis of the cells of micro-organisms performing the initial decomposition. Then the ammonification of N-containing cellular material takes place, resulting in a new N-source for the organisms decomposing the materials of corn-stalk. Our presumption will be examined further in the future.

SUMMARY

The CO_2-producing capacity of a brown forest soil was analysed in a laboratory during decomposition of corn-stalk supplemented with various doses of N-fertilizers. The increased N-doses raised the quantity of CO_2 produced, but use of doses above 500 mg N/200 g soil are not justified by quicker decomposition of corn-stalks.

REFERENCE

Szegi, J. (1962): *Agrokémia és Talajtan* 11, 105–111.

DATA ON THE EFFECT OF INCREASING MINERAL FERTILIZER DOSES AND COMBINATIONS ON CELLULOLYTIC ACTIVITY OF SOIL

by

H. GAMAL EL-DIN, I. KÁDÁR and F. GULYÁS
Research Institute for Soil Science and Agricultural Chemistry of
the Hungarian Academy of Sciences
Budapest, Hungary

Fertilizers are used extensively in modern agriculture. While there are numerous works dealing with problems related to the application of high NPK doses, data on their effects on biological processes in soil are scarce. Since soil fertility is dependent to a large extent on the activities of micro-organisms, it is essential for the effects of high doses and combinations of NPK fertilizers on biological processes in soil to be investigated.

The present paper reports data on the effect of high NPK doses on cellulolytic activity of soil, shows the relationships between cellulose decomposition and available P in soil, and the statistical relation between cellulolytic activity of soil and its productivity.

MATERIAL AND METHODS

The experiment was carried out on a calcareous chernozem soil lying under continental climate. Mean annual temperature is 11 °C, mean annual rainfall is 590 mm. The chemical characteristics of the soil are as follows: pH in H_2O 7.6 in KCl 7.1; Humus 3%, $CaCO_3$ 5%, tot. N 189 mg%, $AL-P_2O_5$ 6 mg%, and $AL-K_2O$ 13 mg%. The doses and sources of applied nutrients were as follows:

Nutrient	Fertilizer	Doses kg/ha			
		1	2	3	4
N	Ammonium nitrate	0	100	200	300
P_2O_5	Superphosphate	0	500	1000	1500
K_2O	Potassium chloride	0	500	1000	1500

Phosphorus and potassium together with the half doses of nitrogen were applied in the autumn of 1973, before ploughing. The remaining amount of N was added in the spring of 1974. The test plant in the year of our study (1973/74) was winter-wheat (Kavkaz) and the previous crop was lucerne.

The cellulolytic activity of the soil was determined by the cellulose test (Unger 1960), in which 5 g of dried cotton wool was packed in polyethylene gauze-bags and buried at about 15 cm below the soil surface. At the end of the experiment period, the bags were removed and the amounts of decomposed cellulose estimated. Four bags were used for every soil plot, i.e. eight replicates for every treatment. The bags were buried on the first of April and removed on the first of July (1974).

RESULTS

The results of cellulose decomposition with different treatments (mean of 8 replications) are presented in Figure 1. The decomposed cellulose is expressed as a percentage of the starting weight. The data show that application of N-fertilizer had no considerable effect on cellulolytic activity of the soil. Regarding the effect of P-fertilizer, the applied doses caused a considerable increase in the activity. Potassium fertilizers had little positive effect on the cellulolytic activity at 500 kg/ha. With higher K doses, the activity decreased in comparison to the control. Among the applied NPK combinations, the lowest one showed a significant increase in cellulolytic activity in contrast with the highest combination.

Figure 2 indicates the relationship between cellulolytic activity and available P_2O_5 in soil with average N and K_o doses. The results show that there is a highly positive correlation between variables under investigation.

When the relation between cellulolytic activity and soil productivity was studied statistically, the correlation coefficient (r) was equal to 0.7369 and significant at 1% confidence level.

DISCUSSION

One of the important aspects of modern fertilization research is investigation of the effects of marked fertilizer application on crop production and physico-chemical characteristics of the soil. The following discussion is concerned with the effects of high NPK doses on cellulolytic activity of the soil.

Concerning the N fertilizer; its negligible effect was not surprising. This was partly because of the previous history of the experimental area, during which considerable amounts of biologically fixed N were added, and partly because of the absence of the other nutrients, particularly phosphorus.

The beneficial effect of applied P doses was also proved by the highly significant correlation between amounts of available P_2O_5 in the soil and its cellulolytic activity. According to the literature, increasing doses of mineral P can increase the cellulolytic activity of the soil at a low original P content (Rankov and Dimitrov 1971).

230

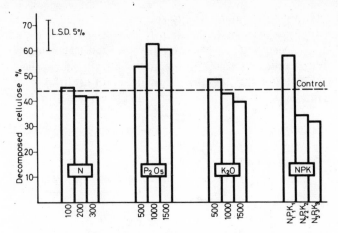

Fig. 1. The effect of high NPK fertilizer doses on soil cellulolytic activity

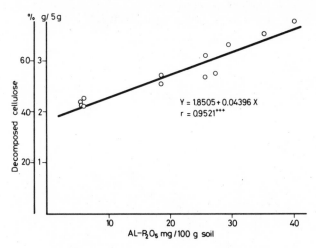

Fig. 2. Relationship between cellulose decomposition and
available P_2O_5 in soil

Studies have shown that by increasing potassium fertilization, the cellulolytic
activity of the soil was increased (Uebel 1970). Therefore, the slight increase in
cellulose decomposition rate in soil plots which received 500 kg K_2O/ha may be due
to the presence of sufficient amounts of K in the experimental soil. Evidence from
a number of experiments has shown that relatively large quantities of K can be
returned to the soil in the unharvested portion of many crop plants. Moreover, K

added in lucerne residues did not differ in availability and was equal to K added in KCl (Grimes and Hanway 1967). The other explanation for the effects of K is the presence of high chloride-ion concentration, which may have masked the beneficial effect of the lowest K fertilizer dose and caused the depressive effect at the highest one. However, the literature indicates that the cause of inhibition of nitrification in the presence of high amounts of KCl was primarily the chloride-ion concentration (Hahn *et al.* 1942).

From the obtained results, the correlation between soil productivity (yield of test plant) and its cellulolytic activity was proved statistically. A certain correlation was also reported by other investigators (Todorova 1972), suggesting that the cellulolytic activity of a soil can reflect correctly the changes in the soil following fertilization.

SUMMARY

In field experiments on a calcareous chernozem soil, the effect of high N, P and K fertilizer doses on the cellulolytic activity of the soil were studied. The applied N doses did not show a considerable effect, while P doses significantly increased the cellulolytic activity of the soil. Corcerning K-fertilizer, the lowest dose showed a slight increase and the highest one a slight decrease. The yield of the test plant (winter-wheat) correlated significantly with the cellulolytic activity of the soil.

REFERENCES

Grimes, D. W. and Hanway, J. J. (1967): *Soil Sci. Soc. Amer. Proc.* 31, 705–706.
Hahn, B. E., Olson, F. R. and Roberts, J. L. (1942): *Soil Sci.* 54, 113–121.
Rankov, V. and Dimitrov, G. (1971): *Effect of phosphorous fertilizer on the cellulose decomposing activity of soil.* In: Symposium on the effect of introduction of chemicals in agriculture on microbiological processes in the soil. Sofia, Bulgaria.
Todorova, B. (1972): *Symp. Biol. Hung.* 11, 139–142.
Uebel, E. (1970): *Pedobiologia.* 10, 149–160.
Unger, H. (1960): *Z. Pflanzenernähr. Düng. Bodenkde.* 91, 44–52.

THE RESIDUAL EFFECT OF MINERAL FERTILIZERS ON CELLULOLYTIC ACTIVITY OF SOIL

by

H. GAMAL-EL-DIN
Research Institute for Soil Science and Agricultural Chemistry of
the Hungarian Academy of Sciences,
Budapest, Hungary

With increased usage of NPK fertilizers, accumulation of unused fertilizers and their effects on subsequent crops is becoming an important consideration in fertilizer programmes. Many data have shown that significant amounts of NPK nutrients accumulate in a wide range of soils and affect yields of a variety of crops.

Data concerning the residual effect of mineral fertilizers on the biological activity of soil are rare. Therefore, the aim of the present work is to find out to what extent the NPK fertilizer residues effect the cellulolytic activity of the soil.

MATERIAL AND METHODS

The experiment was carried out on a calcareous chernozem soil under continental climate. The depth of the humic layer is about 50–80 cm, pH in H_2O 7.6; in KCl 7.1; humus 3%; $CaCO_3$ 5%; $AL-P_2O_5$ 6 mg% and $AL-K_2O$ 13 mg%. The experiment was started by the Fertilization Department of our Institute in 1963/64 as a long-term fertilization field experiment. In 1973/74, thirty-two treatments out of this experiment were selected for the present study. These treatments were given four doses each year (1963/64–1973/74) of nitrogen: 0, 39, 78 and 117 kg N/ha and two doses of PK: (44 kg P_2O_5 + 48 kg K_2O) /ha and (73 kg P_2O_5 + 80 kg K_2O) /ha. In the 1973/74 period, the four doses of nitrogen were applied: 80, 160, 240 and 320 kg N/ha with one PK dose: (120 kg P_2O_5 + 180 kg K_2O) /ha. The applied fertilizers were ammonium nitrate, superphosphate and potassium chloride. The test plant in the year of study was maize (MV 602 hybrid).

The cellulolytic activity of the soil was determined by the cellulose test (Unger, 1960). Pieces of dried cotton wool (5 g) were packed in polyethylene gauze-bags and buried at about 15 cm below the soil surface. At the end of the experiment, the bags were removed and the amount of decomposed cellulose was estimated. For each treatment, 8 bags were used and the period of experiment was 20 weeks.

According to the analyses of variance — not given here —, the main effects of the studied factors, as well as the interactions between them were found to be significant. Figure 1 summarizes the results. Decomposed cellulose is expressed as a percentage of the initial weight, and the average of decomposed cellulose in the control plots was 19% as indicated by the broken line. Differences between decomposed cellulose in control $(N_0 P_0 K_0)$ its means in all investigated treatments were statistically significant.

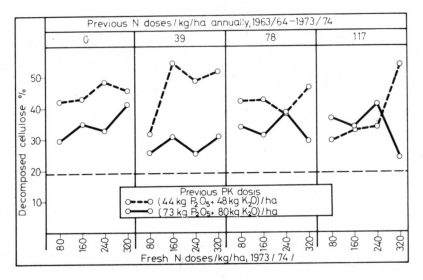

Fig. 1. Cellulose decomposition at different treatments

Effect of previous N doses:

The cellulolytic activity varied slightly with different previous N doses. However, the starved treatment (N_0) showed the highest activity after receiving fresh N dressings. In the fresh N dressings, the cellulolytic activity rose on increasing the N doses (Table 1).

Effect of previous PK doses:

In the two previous PK doses, the higher one showed the highest cellulolytic activity (Table 2). It is interesting to note that the cellulolytic activity increased clearly with increasing fresh N doses at the higher previous PK dose; while the differences at the lower dose were almost negligible.

Table 1
Effect of different previous and fresh nitrogen doses on cellulolytic activity of soil

(A) Fresh N doses (kg/ha) (1973/74)	(B) Previous N doses (kg/ha) annually (1963/64−1973/74)				Mean
	0	39	78	117	
1	2	3	4	5	6
80	35.87	28.62	38.12	33.00	33.90
160	40.25	42.62	37.00	33.25	38.28
240	40.75	32.50	38.37	37.25	37.22
320	43.50	41.25	38.00	38.87	40.40
Mean	40.09	36.25	37.87	35.59	37.45

$LSD_5\%$: A = 2.23
B = 2.23
AB = 4.45

Table 2
Effect of different previous PK doses with different fresh N doses on cellulolytic activity of soil

(C) Previous PK doses per ha annually (1963/64−1973/74)	(A) Fresh N doses (kg/ha) 1973−74				Mean
	80	160	240	320	
1	2	3	4	5	6
44 kg P_2O_5 + + 48 kg K_2O	31.38	33.31	34.44	31.37	32.62
73 kg P_2O_5 + + 80 kg K_2O	36.44	43.25	40.00	49.44	42.28
Mean	33.90	38.28	37.22	40.40	37.45

$LSD_5\%$: A = 2.23
C = 1.57
AC = 3.15

Fig. 2. The residual effect of mineral fertilizers on cellulolytic activity of soil

DISCUSSION

Data in the literature have indicated that application of mineral fertilizers exerts a beneficial effect on the cellulolytic activity of soil (Pokorná-Kozová 1974, Todorova 1972). The results presented in this study concern the residual effects of NPK fertilizers on this activity.

The apparent absence of the marked effect of previous N dressings is not surprising, since the N fertilizer not taken up by the crops may be lost in different ways (leaching, ammonia volatilization, ammonium fixation, biological immobilization, denitrification). However, inorganic nitrogen fertilizers are usually considered to have no residual effect, at least none of practical importance (Jansson 1963). It is evident from our results that the previous PK dressings had a considerable effect on cellulolytic activity of the soil, although fresh PK fertilizers were applied. The residual effect of PK depends on the amount of fresh N fertilizer used. The same results were achieved in experiments with crop plants (Balla 1974). Since the effect of P and K are considered in our experiment together, it is not clear whether the observed beneficial effect is due to P or to K or to PK. However, results from experiments carried out on chernozem soil in Hungary showed that K fertilizer had no marked residual effect and P can be considered as responsible for the extra yields of Sudan grass with fresh N fertilizer (Balla 1974).

SUMMARY

In the field experiment carried out on a calcareous chernozem soil, the residual effect of mineral fertilizers on cellulolytic activity of soil was studied. The results showed that previous PK fertilizers had a considerable positive effect on cellulolytic activity. The residual effect of previous PK dressings depended on the amount of fresh N fertilizer applied. In contrast, previous N dressings had an insignificant residual value. On the other hand, the starved treatments (N_0) showed higher cellulolytic activity than enriched ones when fresh N was given.

REFERENCES

Balla, H. (1974): *Agrokémia és Talajtan.* **23**, 86–92.
Jansson, S. L. (1963): *Soil Science.* **95**, 31–37.
Pokorná-Kozová, I. (1974): *Rostlinná výroba.* **20**, 875–882.
Todorova, B. (1972): *Symp. Biol. Hung.* **11**, 139–142.
Unger, H. (1960): *Z. Pflanzenernähr., Düng., Bodenkde.* **91**, 44–52.

CHANGES IN MICROCENOSIS AND MINERALIZATION RATE OF WHEAT STRAW DUE TO AERATION AND BENTONITE

by

K. KUBISTA
Agricultural University, Faculty of Agronomy,
Department of Microbiology,
Prague-Suchdol, Czechoslovakia

Wheat straw is very frequently used nowadays as a substrate in the cultivation of cucumbers in glass-houses (Vlček 1973). By adding bentonite, we tried to increase the sorption capacity of straw (Lhotský 1970). A substantial effect of bentonite on straw-decomposing organisms needs to be assumed as well (Káš, et al. 1969, Nováková 1972, Kubista 1972, Kobus 1970, Zviagintsev 1963) Bentonite has various effects on micro-organisms, not only altering in the number of micro-organisms and their cenosis, but changing their metabolism. According to some researchers, sorbents decrease oxidation-reduction potential and thus improve the conditions for anaerobic bacteria (Tschistiakow 1932, Hattori and Furusaka 1959, Íerusalimsky 1934). The present paper deals with the results of experiments on the effects of bentonite and of aeration on micro-organisms and on the mineralization rate of decomposing wheat straw.

MATERIAL AND METHODS

The experiments were carried out in four variants and seven repetitions using plastic cylindric vessels. Each vessel (105 mm in ϕ and 500 mm in length) was filled with 190 g of pressed straw. The height of the straw layer was 300 mm. Straw was enriched with nutrients in the form of commercial fertilizers (1.8 g N, 0.13 g P, 0.48 g K). The C/N ratio was thus adjusted to 23 : 1. Then 19 g of natural ground bentonite (originating from Braňany in Czechoslovakia) were added to half of the vessels. 500 ml of soil suspension were poured on straw and the vessels were hermetically sealed with a lid provided with two inserted tubes through which CO_2-free air was allowed to pass in and out. In the case of the aerated variants, air was introduced at the bottom of the vessels, under the straw layer. Mineralization rate was determined according to the amount of liberated carbon dioxide. The number of micro-organisms was determined by the plate method (bacteria on Thornton's agar, actinomycetes on agar with starch, micromycetes on agar according to Martin) on the 8th, 15th, 22nd, 65th, 90th and 120th days of incubation.

Variants: 1. straw + nutrients
Variants: 2. straw + nutrients + 10% of bentonite
Variants: 3. straw,+ nutrients + aeration
Variants: 4. straw + nutrients + aeration + 10% of bentonite
Incubation at constant temperature of 30 °C.

RESULTS AND DISCUSSION

The number of micro-organisms in the decomposing straw was high and varied from $6 \cdot 10^8$ to $35 \cdot 10^{12}$ in 1 g of dry straw (Fig. 1). Aeration increased this number by 8% on the average, the increase in the number of micromycetes being the largest, although their proportion in the microbial population was the lowest. Bentonite, on the other hand, decreased the number of micro-organisms both in aerated and non-aerated variants. The average decrease due to bentonite during the whole incubation period was 22%. Bentonite affected not only the number of micro-organisms but also the composition of the microflora. The dominant group in this population was that of the bacteria. Bentonite increased their proportion in the microbial population by 3.5% on the average during the whole incubation period both in aerated and non-aerated variant (Fig. 2). A similar effect of bentonite was also observed during the decomposition of other organic materials in the soil as well as in composts (Kubista 1975).

The changes in the composition of the microbial population may, most probably, be due to the decrease of redox-potential of the environment under the influence of sorbents (Hattori and Furusaka 1959). The increased proportion of bacteria in the microflora was probably caused by facultative incidence of anaerobic bacteria. This supposition is based on the fact that at the end of the experiment the number of anaerobic bacteria in the variant with bentonite was twice larger than in the variant without bentonite.

Bentonite affected not only the number of micro-organisms and the composition of their population but also their metabolism. In the course of the first 48 hours, bentonite increased the rate of mineralization, but in the period of maximum mineralization its rate was lower (Fig. 3). Therefore it can be seen that lesser mineralization is the result not only of added bentonite but also of limited aeration. This indicates that bentonite slowed down the transfer of oxygen in the environment. Lesser mineralization due to bentonite occurred both in the aerated and in the non-aerated variant and lasted for 40 days.

Aeration increased the rate of mineralization which resulted in faster decomposition of easily available substances of straw. After the initial period lasting about 44 days mineralization rate in the aerated variant without bentonite was the lowest. As limited aeration and added bentonite lowered the rate of mineralization during the first 44 days, after this period mineralization in these variants continued at a faster rate than in aerated variants and those without bentonite (Fig. 4). This change

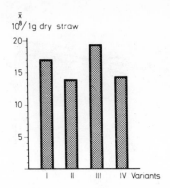

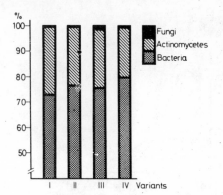

Fig. 1. Micro-organism counts (x̄ indicates average counts of Bacteria + Actinomycetes + Fungi) in 1 g o.d.m. x 10⁸.
Variants: I. non-aerated without bentonite, II. non-aerated with 10% bentonite, III. aerated without bentonite, IV. aerated with 10% bentonite

Fig. 2. Composition of microbe coenoses

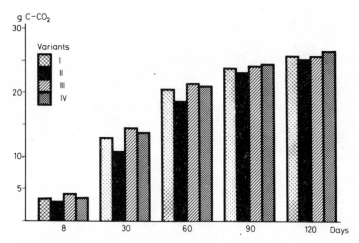

Fig. 3. Amount of oxidized carbon

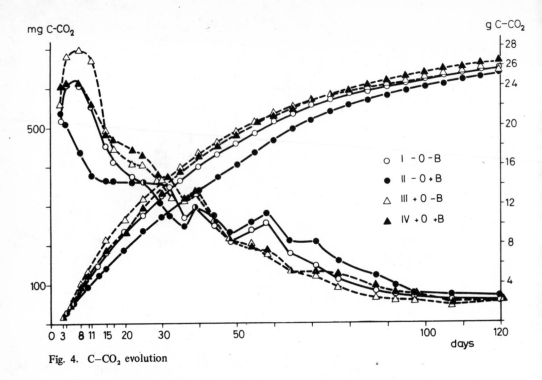

mg C-CO₂ — g C-CO₂

Legend:
○ I − 0 − B
● II − 0 + B
△ III + 0 − B
▲ IV + 0 + B

Fig. 4. C–CO₂ evolution

ın mineralization rate gradually resulted in equalizing the total mineralization level. Only in the variant with aeration and bentonite, due to increased mineralization rate in the second half of the incubation period, an increase in total amount of mineralized carbon occurred. After 120 days 45.5% of total carbon of straw were mineralized.

In conclusion it can be said that the results of the present study are in agreement with those of some other authors, i.e. that added bentonite increases the rate of mineralization during the first 48 hours, later, however, it slows it down (Nováková *et al.* 1974a) and, on the whole, limits it. During the decomposition of organic substances bentonite lowers the number of micro-organisms in the environment (Nováková *et al.* 1974b). Most probably bentonite lowered the redox-potential in the environment. This is indicated by an increased proportion of bacteria in the microbial population and a twice larger number of anaerobic bacteria in the straw enriched with bentonite.

SUMMARY

Adding 10% of bentonite the number of micro-organisms during the decomposition of wheat straw under model conditions decreased. Bentonite resulted in a higher proportion of bacteria in the microflora as well as in the number of

242

anaerobic bacteria. It also affected the rate of mineralization of straw. By aerating straw the number of micro-organisms and mineralization rate was increased. Aeration did not affect the suppressing effect of bentonite.

REFERENCES

Hattori, T. and Furusaka, C. (1959): *Biochem. Biophysica Acta.* **31**, 581–582.

(Jerusalimsky, N. D.) Йерусалимский, Н. Д. (1934) : *Микробиол.,* **3**, 44–74.

Káš, V., Nováková, J., Filip, Z., Kubista, K. and Šíša, R. (1969): *Biologické listy.* **34**, 12–21.

Kobus, J. (1970): *Pamietnik Pulawski – Prace IUNG.* **39**, 189–238.

Kubista, K. (1972): *Symp. Biol. Hung.,* **11**, 229–235.

Kubista, K. (1975): *Materiály vědecké konference VŠZ v Praze* (in press).

Lhotský, J. (1970): *Theory of bentonite behaviour in soil.* ČAZ Praha.

Nováková, J. (1972): *Symp. Biol. Hung.* **11**, 159–165.

Nováková, J., Novák, B. and Štifter, M. (1974a): *Zbl. Bakt.* II. **128**, 339–350.

Nováková, J., Novák, B. and Trčka, P. (1974b): *Zbl. Bakt.* II. **128**, 339–350.

(Tschistiakow F. M.) Чистяков Ф. М. (1932): *Микробиол.* I, 19–29.

Vlček, F. (1973): *Zahradnické aktuality* 32, VÚZ Olomouc.

(Zviagintsev, D. G.): Звягинцев, Д. Г. (1963): *Взаимодействие микроорганизмов с твердыми поверхностями.* МГУ, Москва.

DEGRADATION OF SPECIFICALLY LABELLED PHENOLS AND LIGNIN MODELS BY SOFT-ROT FUNGI

by

J. TROJANOWSKI and K. HAIDER
M. Curie Sklodowska University Institute of Biochemistry and Microbiology,
Lublin, Poland
Institute of Soil Biochemistry,
Braunschweig, G.F.R.

A group of *Ascomycetes* and various *Fungi imperfecti,* growing on wood and producing typical caverns in the cell wall of wood was termed by Savory (Savory 1954a, b) as soft-rot fungi. These fungi cause considerable weight losses to wood materials. Several authors referred to the occurrence of soft-rot fungi in soils. Electronmicroscopic pictures of typical caverns, showing the performation process of hyphae from soft-rot in cell walls of coniferous wood were published by Ünligil and Chafe (1974).

Several authors (Savory and Pinion 1958) reported that soft-rot fungi mainly degrade the cellulose part of the plant materials. According to Haider and Domsch (1969) soft-rotters seem to attack lignin more effectively than it was considered before. But it could not yet be decided wether these fungi are able to assimilate lignin as a carbon source or they only depolymerize it.

In order to ascertain whether soft rot fungi actually utilize lignin, experiments were conducted by us, where radioactive, labelled phenols and polymers were used. The compounds were labelled specifically in methyl, carboxyl, side chains or rings.

Studies were made also with polymers of radioactive coniferyl alcohols, synthesized *in vitro* or *in vivo.*

The dehydropolymers (DHP) were prepared according to Freudenberg and Neish (1968), by oxidation of coniferol by peroxidase.

The native lignin in living plants was labelled specifically using radioactive ferulic acid as a precursor of lignin synthesis. (The synthesis of radioactive labelled compounds was described by Haider and Lim (1965) and Haider (1966).

In the studies presented here $^{14}CO_2$-evolution was used as a criterion for the degradation of lignin and lignin models, or monomers. The release of CO_2 was measured each day over a period of 9 days.

The soft-rot strains isolated from soil (Haider and Domsch 1969) were used.

The next tables indicated the release of $^{14}CO_2$ from several specifically labelled groups of the applied substances. The summation values are indicated in per cent of the applied radioactivity.

Table 1 shows the release of $^{14}CO_2$ from the methyl groups. More CO_2 was released from compounds with free OH-groups, (vanillic acid, coniferyl alcohol), than from those where the hydroxyl groups were *etherified*. There was a higher release of 4–CH_3 from veratric acid than from the 3-position.

Table 2 shows the release of the carboxyl groups. The carboxyl groups from compounds with free OH were rapidly released, but much less from compounds with *etherified* OH. It could be expected that release of COOH occurred as a result of ring cleavage (deoxygenation process).

Experiments with ring-labelled phenolic compounds are summarized in Table 3. Only *Preussia* could not degrade anisic acid but this is in agreement with the low rate of demethylation by this fungus. Catechol, as compared to vanillic acid, was not so rapidly degraded to CO_2. Therefore, catechol does not seem to be an intermediate during ring degradation of these compounds by soft-rot fungi. Protocatechuic acid might be considered as a probable intermediate before ring splitting.

Table 4 indicates the degradation of the side-chain carbons from cinnamic acid derivatives. A rapid degradation of C–2 and C–3 position to CO_2 was observed.

Table 1
$^{14}CO_2$-release from $O^{14}CH_3$-labelled benzoic acid compounds and from coniferyl alcohol, added to shaken cultures of soft-rot fungi

	$^{14}CO_2$-release in per cent of the applied activity			
	anisic acid	vanillic acid	benzylvanillic acid	3–$O^{14}CH_3$-veratric acid
Preussia fleischhakii	0.1	52.8	ˎ2.5	0.2
Chaetomium piluliferum	46.8	76.7	0	1.9
Stachybotrys chartarum	12.8	3.1	0	0.2

	$^{14}CO_2$-release in per cent of the applied activity			
	4–$O^{14}CH_3$-veratric acid	3,5–$O^{14}CH_3$-syringic acid	3,4,5–$O^{14}CH_3$-trimethoxybenzoic acid	coniferyl alcohol
Preussia fleischhakii	0.2	0.9	0	43.0
Chaetomium piluliferum	4.7	26.3	0	44.9
Stachybotrys chartarum	2.2	0.2	0	0.9

Table 2
$^{14}CO_2$-release from ^{14}C-carboxyl-labelled benzoic acid compounds, added to shaken cultures of soft-rot fungi

	$^{14}CO_2$-release in per cent of the applied activity					
	benzoic acid	p-hydroxy-benzoic acid	vanillic acid	benzylvanillic acid	veratric acid	syringic acid
Preussia fleisch-hakii	66.0	83.0	98.5	6.8	0.2	77.2
Chaetomium piluliferum	65.0	89.1	99.2	0.4	8.0	82.5
Stachybotrys chartarum	0.8	83.0	74.0	0	10.2	2.4

Table 3
$^{14}CO_2$-release from ^{14}C-ring-labelled benzoic acid compounds and from catechol, added to shaken cultures of soft-rot fungi

	$^{14}CO_2$-release in per cent of the applied activity				
	benzoic acid	anisic acid	vanillic acid	veratric acid	catechol
Preussia fleisch-hakii	43.7	0	48.6	0.3	6.0
Chaetomium piluliferum	34.9	25.1	59.3	3.5	4.7
Stachybotrys chartarum	0.6	39.3	43.5	7.0	7.3

Table 4
$^{14}CO_2$-release from side-chain-labelled cinnamic acids and cinnamyl alcohols, added to shaken cultures of soft-rot fungi

	$^{14}CO_2$-release in per cent of the applied activity			
	$^{14}C_3$-p-hydroxy-cinnamic acid	$^{14}C_3$-ferulic acid	$^{14}C_2$-coniferyl alcohol	$^{14}C_2$-p-coumar alcohol
Preussia fleischhakii	10.6	9.2	30.4	22.5
Chaetomium piluliferum	91.7	56.4	22.2	31.8
Stachybotrys chartarum	83.2	82.9	2.8	19.4

Table 5
Comparison of the $^{14}CO_2$-release from several labelled phenolic compounds by shaken and stationary cultures of soft-rot fungi

| | $^{14}CO_2$-release in per cent of the applied activity | | | | | | | | | |
| | benzoic acid $^{14}COOH$ | | anisic acid $O^{14}CH_3$ | | vanillic acid $O^{14}CH_3$ | | vanillic acid ^{14}C-ring | | ferulic acid $^{14}C_3$ | |
	shaken cultures	station. cultures	shaken cultures	station. cultures	shaken cultures	station. cultures	shaken cultures	station. cultures	shaken cultures	station. cultures
Chaetomium piluliferum	65.0	58.3	46.8	25.1	76.7	20.3	59.3	41.2	56.4	59.4
Stachybotrys chartarum	0.8	0.5	12.8	7.3	3.1	0.6	43.5	26.0	82.9	30.1

Table 6
CO_2-release from dehydropolymers (DHP's) of coniferyl alcohol labelled by ^{14}C in the methoxyl group, the 2—C-carbon of the side-chain or in the ring Carbons, respectively. CO_2-release from maize plant material labelled by incorporation of methoxyl and 3—C-side-chain labelled ferulic acids, respectively

| | $^{14}CO_2$-release in per cent of the applied activity | | | | | | |
| | coniferyl alcohol DHP's | | | | | plant materials | |
	$O^{14}CH_3$–DHP (shaken cult.)	$2-^{14}C$–DHP (shaken cult.)	ring-^{14}C–DHP (shaken cult.)	$O^{14}CH_3$–DHP (stat. cult.)	$2-^{14}C$–DHP (stat. cult.)	$O^{14}CH_3$ (shaken cult.)	$2-^{14}C$ (shaken cult.)
Preussia fleischhakii	7.8	2.3	3.8	2.8	1.1	1.9	2.3
Chaetomium piluliferum	1.8	1.5	3.0	2.2	0.9	3.5	5.7
Stachybotrys chartarum	0.5	1.4	1.9	0.3	0.7	4.0	5.3

Table 5 shows some experiments on $^{14}CO_2$ release after incubation in shaken and stationary cultures, respectively. Generally it can be concluded that soft-rot fungi release more $^{14}CO_2$ from phenolic compounds on incubation in shaken cultures. This is in agreement with the experiments reported by Walsh and Stewart (1971); they found an increasing cellulolytic activity of soft-rot fungi with increasing oxygen tension.

Table 6 indicates the release of $^{14}CO_2$ from coniferyl alcohol dehydropolymers (DHP) and from maize plant material labelled specifically. The DHP's were better degraded by soft-rot fungi in shaken cultures. The labelled lignin fraction in plant material was degraded to a similar degree.

SUMMARY

The experiments showed that soft-rot fungi were able to release CO_2 from methoxyl and carboxyl groups, side-chains and ring structures of several lignin monomers and polymers. Therefore it can be concluded, that soft-rotters can not only depolymerize the *beta*-linkages in lignin polymers, but also assimilate the ring structures and hence carry out a thorough degradation of the lignin.

REFERENCES

Freudenberg, K. and Neish, A. C. (1968): *Constitution and biosynthesis of lignin.* Springer-Verlag. Berlin, Heidelberg. New York.

Haider, K. (1966): *J. Labell. Comp.* **2,** 174–183.

Haider, K. and Domsch, K. H. (1969): *Arch. Mikrobiol.* **64,** 338–348.

Haider, K. and Lim, S. U. (1965): *J. Labell. Comp.,* **1,** 294–299.

Savory, J. G. (1954a): *J. Appl. Bact.* **17,** 213–218.

Savory, J. G. (1954b): *Ann. Appl. Biol.* **41,** 336–347.

Savory, J. G. and Pinion, L. C. (1958): *Holzforsch.* **12,** 99–103.

Únligil, H. H. and Chafe, S. C. (1974): *Wood Sci. and Technol.* **8,** 27–32.

Walsh, J. H. and Stewart, C. S. (1971): *Trans. British Mycol. Soc.* **57,** 75–84.

CHITINOLYTIC ACTIVITY IN SOILS

by

J. FARGUES[1], G. KILBERTUS[2], O. REISINGER[2], and G. M. OLÁH[3]

[1] I. N. R. A. Station de Recherches de Lutte Biologique,
  Versailles, France
[2] Université de Nancy I. Laboratoire de Microbiology,
  Nancy, France
[3] Université Laval, Laboratoire de Mycologie,
  Quebec, Canada

Chitin appears in soil during the biodegradation of primary products of terrestrial ecosystems, and is associated with arthropod exoskeletons and fungal cell walls. It is always complexed with other materials which, together with its highly polymerised state, make chitin resistent to microbial attack. Therefore, in any particular microhabitat, chitin, by acting as a nutrient source, can bring about the development of a specialised microflora. This flora has been studied using classical microbiological methods (Okafor 1967) but its activity on different chitin sources has not been the object of a comparative ultrastructural investigation. Here we report our initial observations on the colonisation of three materials containing chitin, fungi, insect cuticles and commercial chitin. In addition, we propose an experimental procedure for comparing the chitinolytic activities of the isolated microorganisms.

MATERIAL AND METHODS

The materials used (fungi, insect cuticles and commercial chitin) have different chitin concentrations. Their lysis is studied by the "traps" method (Reisinger and Kilbertus 1974, Mourey et al. 1974), where traps containing the material are buried in soil. At various times they are collected, the loss in weight recorded, and the contents subjected to microbiological and ultrastructural investigation (Fig. 1).

For Scanning Electronmicroscopy (SEM), samples are dried by the critical point method and coated with gold-palladium.

For Transmission Electronmicroscopy (TEM), samples are osmium fixed (OsO_4 2%, 90 min.), dehydrated and Epon impregnated. Serial sections, cut with diamond knife, are contrasted with lead citrate (Reynolds 1963) or stained for polysaccharides (Thiery 1967).

Analysis of microbial colonisation is performed using conventional methods (Reisinger and Kilbertus 1975). The results, given below, include only those microbes which are associated with the degradation of the "chitin fraction" of the materials studied.

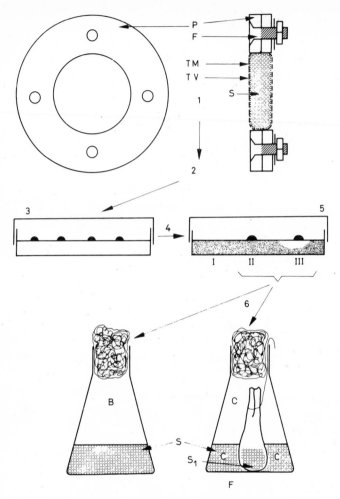

Fig. 1. 1 – Incubation of material S under analysis, in traps:
Plastic rings, F = fixation, TM = metallic (stainless
steel) network, TV = glass fibre tissue; 2 – Dilution;
3 – plating on nutrient agar; 4 – Transfer of obtained
microorganisms (solid medium containing a suspension
of material S) allowing the diagnosis of chitinolytic organism (5); 6 – B = medium for bacteria, C = medium
for fungi; S_1 – Known amount of material submitted to
the enzymic action of the fungus. Only the medium in
the flask is inoculated with the fungus. The content of
the bag is sterile. Enzymes diffuse through the pores of
the bag

RESULTS

A) FUNGI

The degradation of mycelium of *Pyrenochaeta lycopersici*, and conidia from *Drechslera spicifera (= Helminthosporium spiciferum)* and both the dematiaceous and the "albino" forms of *Drechslera sorokiniana* has been followed by TEM and SEM. The ultrastructural localisation of the chitin fraction is at present being studied using chemical methods (unpublished results and work in progress).

1) *Pyrenochaeta lycopersici*

This fungus is the agent of "Corky Root" disease of tomato. Its wall is made up of an external mucilaginous layer (A) covering a fibrillar layer (B) containing chitin Plate I (1). The two layers react differently when stained for polysaccharides (2).

One month after burial in soil. EM shows complete lysis of the fibrillar layer (B layer) whilst the A layer (= interhyphal mucus) remains. This can only be due to the action of bacterial enzymes (3).

The developmental cycle of *P. lycopersici* includes the formation of mycelium in the roots of the tomato. Here hyphae are degraded by the soil microflora in a manner, similar to that found for mycelium buried in traps, although after one month's degradation, differences in the structure of the mucilaginous layer may be seen (4).

In both cases the mycelium has been buried in soil, naturally infected for several years with *P. lycopersici*. In such a soil, a microflora will be present that is able to degrade the mycelial cell-wall. We suggest that the type of microhabitats of the mycelium, within the roots or in the traps, may be the cause of qualitative and quantitative differences in the microfloral colonisation pattern. This could produce the different sorts of A layer decomposition described above (3, 4).

2) *Drechslera sorokiniana* and *D. spicifera*

In the genus *Drechslera* the conidial wall consists of four layers (Reisinger 1972), and the ultrastructure of conidia from *D. sorokiniana* has been described (Cole 1973). Using the albino mutant of *D. sorokiniana*, we find that the mucilaginous layer C_1 is completely lysed after one month's incubation of conidia in soil. In addition, the initially compact structure of the chitin containing B-layer is replaced by a sparse frame of fibrils. The rapid lysis is due to the absence of dark pigments which usually reduce the speed of fungal cell-war degradation (Reisinger 1972, Reisinger and Kilbertus 1973).

The protective nature of the melanic components of fungal cell-walls is shown by the action of helicase on isolated *D. spicifera* walls. The non-melanised part of the B-layer disappears after a 2 hr. incubation with the enzyme and N-acetyl-glucosamine is released. However, the melanised part of the B-layer liberates N-acetyl-glucosamine, only after drastic chemical treatment (7, 8). This demonstrates the resistance of the chitin-melanin complex to decay (Berthe *et al.* 1976).

B) INSECT CUTICLES

Mainly pupal (9, 10) and larval (11, 12) exuvial cuticles of *Oryctes rhinoceros* were used. Transverse sections and SEM micrographs of the internal part of the cuticle are shown (9, 10). The external part of the larval cuticle is characterised by numerous spines of various sizes (12), and transverse sections show that, in contrast to the internal part, it has a smooth surface and numerous canaliculi (11).

As in the case of the fungi, the biodegradation of cuticles seems to be due solely to procaryotes. Their action is seen in TEM as a zone of lysis together with modification of the original material (13, 14).

C) COMMERCIAL CHITIN

This is very variable in TEM, but a fibrillar framework with numerous cavities is always sivible (15, 16). After four months' incubation in soil, many characteristic zones of lysis are seen, caused predominantly by procaryotes (17). Alternatively the fibrillar frame may collapse and be replaced by an electron-dense mass (18) or by dark granules.

Plate I.   *Pyrenochaeta lycopersici*
1 – (2 weeks' incubation). The fibrillar components of the mucilaginous layer (A) and striated layer (B) probably containing chitin; 2 – (2 weeks' incubation). Thiery coloration showing polysaccharides; 3 – (1 month's incubation). Bacterial degradation of B layer. Only remmants of the mucilaginous layer are still visible (M); 4 – (1 month's incubation of parasitised roots). Complete lysis of the B layer of intracellular hyphae. Only the fibrillar fraction of the mucilaginous layer remains visible

Plate II.   *Drechslera sorokiniana* (5, 6) and *Drechslera spicifera* (7, 8)
5 – (albino mutant, 1 month's incubation) lateral wall of a conidium. Notice the partial lysis of the chitinaceous layer (B); 6 – (albino mutant, 1-month incubation) lateral wall and septum (S) of a conidium. B and C_1 layers are lysed (ly). The C layer is mucilaginous and probably contains very little chitin; 7 – Purified walls, treated for 9 hours with helicase. The residual melanised fraction contains typical chitin, protected by dark pigments (B_2); 8 – Purified wall made of a striated partially melanised layer (B_1 non pigmented, B_2 melanised)

Plate III.   *Oryctes rhinoceros*
9 and 10 – pupal cuticles internal side; 11, 12 – larval cuticles, external side; 13, 14 – pupal cuticles after a two-months' incubation (Ba = bacteria)

Plate IV.   Commercial chitin
15, 16 – general appearance of the used material; 17, 18 – alterations after a four months' incubation. Lysis zones (ly) and electron-dense byproducts (D)

254

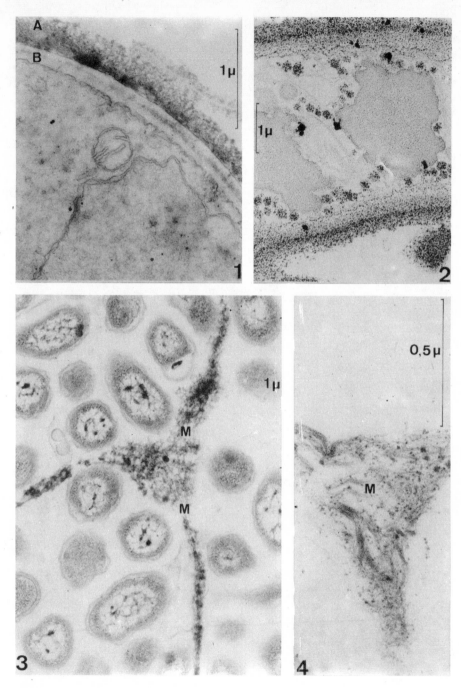

Plate I.

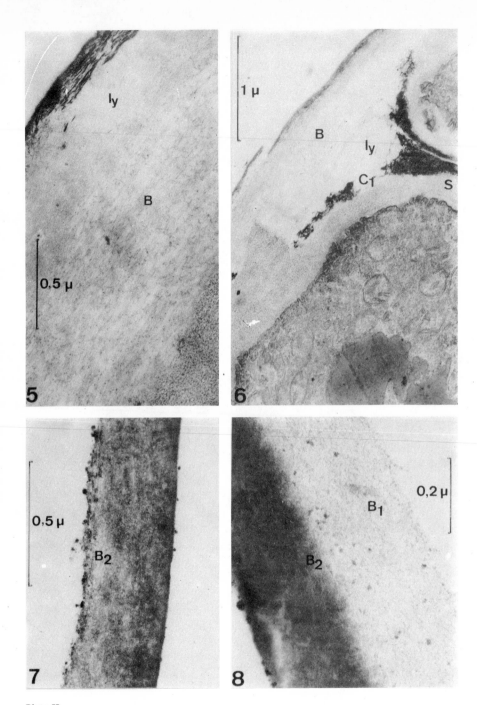

Plate II.

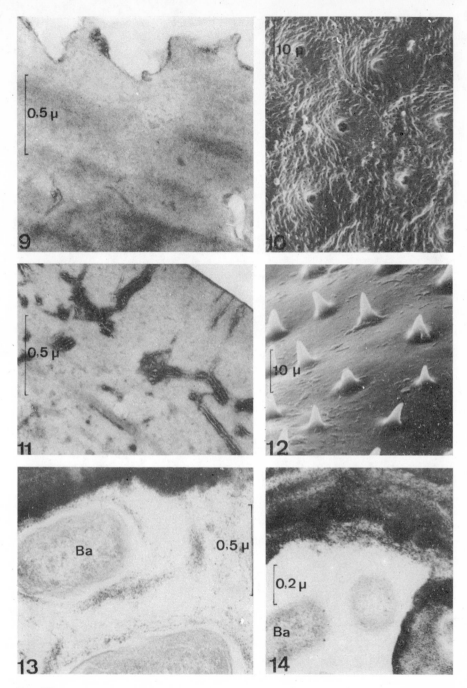

Plate III.

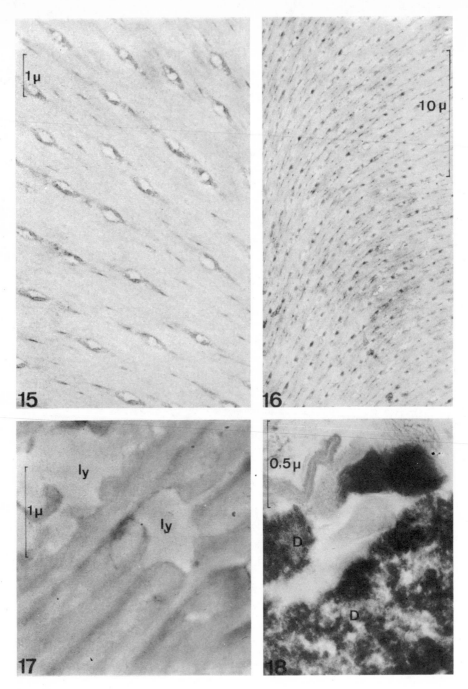

Plate IV.

D) MICROBIOLOGICAL STUDY

Since we isolated a similar microflora from traps containing degraded fungi, insect cuticles and commercial chitin, we shall give only a general outline of the flora.

The bacterial flora is dominated by two actinomycetes, including a *Streptomyces sp.* The non-filamentous species are those given as frequent in soil by Clark (1967); mainly *Arthrobacter spp.,* and *Bacillus spp.,* and *Bacillus spp.,* and sometimes a *Pseudomonas sp.,* and a *Flavobacterium sp.*

Fungi isolated from the traps are often found in soil; *Trichoderma viride, Penicillium spp., Humicola nigrescens,* etc.

Probably none of these species are specialised for chitin degradation, and for this reason we propose, in our conclusion, an experimental procedure for evaluating the enzymatic capabilities of each microbe in this micro-association.

CONCLUSIONS

Ultrastructural study of the biodegradation of various chitin-containing materials demonstrates the essential role of procaryotes. Indeed, in our study, we rarely saw any development of fungal species *in situ.* In order to evaluate the activity of each isolated microbe, we propose the experimental procedure pictured in schema I.

Micro-organisms of group I, which lack lytic ability are considered as forming a secondary flora which develops on byproducts of metabolism of groups II and III.

Micro-organisms of groups II and are able to lyse the component under study. To compare the activities of each member of this microflora, we use two methods, according to their bacterial or fungal nature.

With bacteria, where autolysis does not liberate N-acetyl-glucosamine, this component may be titrated directly in the filtrate taken from a culture where the bacterium has been growing in a liquid medium composed of inorganic salts, water, and commercial chitin.

This method is difficult to use with fungi, because the autolysis of their mycelium may liberate N-acetyl-glucosamine or other byproducts of the fungal wall. It is necessary to use another method, already applied to the study of cellulolytic activity (Kilbertus *et al.* 1973). A liquid medium containing salts and a small amount of the required substrates (chitin, cuticles or fungal walls) is inoculated with the fungus. A small glass fibre paper bag containing a known amount of the substrate S, is immersed in the culture medium. Lytic activity of the fungus is evaluated by the rate of weight loss of the substrate within the bag.

The ultrastructural modifications that occur may be assessed with TEM.

Comparative studies *in situ* and experiments *in vitro* should be useful in drawing up a general scheme for the microbial lysis of chitin in a given soil. The study of the specific ultrastructural modifications produced *in vitro,* should also make it possible to localise some of the micro-organisms *in situ* and with greater accuracy.

ACKNOWLEDGEMENTS

We thank the governments of France and of the Province of Quebec, who, under the patronage of Co-operation Franco-Québecoise, have made this work possible. We are deeply indebted to Prof. G. Grignon, Director, Laboratoire de Microscopie Electronique de l'Université de Nancy I for his help and authorisations and to Mrs. Desbiens and Mrs. Simonetti for their technical assistance.

SUMMARY

For this study, shedding of an insect coat: and other substance containing N-acetylglucosamine polymers: the fungal wall, is used. Commercial chitin is taken as reference material. These substances are incubated in nature.

Periodically samples are investigated in order to isolate chitinolytic micro-organisms and to study them with electronmicroscope. Experimental processes *in vitro* are proposed to restore trophic chains and to observe the activity of each micro-organism.

REFERENCES

Berthe, M. C., Bonaly, R. and Reisinger, O. (1976): *Can. J. Microbiol.* (In press).

Clark, F. E. (1967): *Bacteria in soil.* In *Soil Biology.* A. Burges and F. Raw (Eds), Academic Press, London and New-York, 15–49.

Cole, G. T. (1973): *Can. J. Bot.* 51, 629–638.

Gray, T. R. G. and Baxby, P. (1968): *Trans. Br. mycol. Soc.* 51, 293–309.

Kilbertus, G., Mangenot, F. and Reisinger, O. (1973): *Mycopathol. Mycol. appl.* 49, 101–107.

Mourey, A. (1973): *Etude de la lipolyse dans quelques sols forestiers et caractères d'une préparation enzymatique d'origine bactérienne. Thèse de spécialité.* Université de Nancy I, France.

Mourey, A., Kilbertus, G. and Mangenot, F. (1974): *Bull. Ecol.* 5, 351–356.

Okafor, N. (1967): *An ecological study of microbial chitin decomposition in soil, in Progress in soil biology.* O. Graff and J. E. Satchell (Eds), Friedr. Vierveg and Sohn GmbH, Braunschweig, 440–454.

Reisinger, O. (1972): *Contribution à l'étude ultrastructurale de l'appareil sporifère chez quelques Hyphomycètes à paroi mélanisée. Genèse, modification et décomposition. Thèse Sciences Naturelles.* Université de Nancy. France.

Reisinger, O. and Kilbertus, G. (1973): *Soil Biol. Biochem.* 5, 187–192.

Reisinger, O. and Kilbertus, G. (1974): *Can. J. Microbiol.* 20, 299–306.

Reisinger, O. and Kilbertus, G. (1975): *Documents de T. D. de Microbiology.* Université de Nancy, I, 500 pp.

Reynolds, E. S. (1963): *J. Cell. Biol.* 17, 208–212.

Thiery, J. P. (1967): *J. Microsc.* 6, 987–1018.

LINKAGE OF ANTHRAQUINONES TO A FUNGAL HUMIC-TYPE POLYMER

by

C. SÁIZ-JIMÉNEZ
Centre of Soil Science and Applied Biology,
Sevilla, Spain

McGrath, in 1972, extracted several anthraquinones in amounts up to 120 ppm from a variety of Irish and Canadian soils. Chrysotalunin, a hydroxybianthraquinone derived from chrysophanol, was more prominent than monomer anthraquinones such as physcion and chrysophanol. These anthraquinones could be of plant or microbial origin. Their occurrence, however, under heath or grass suggests a microbial origin.

Numerous soil fungi synthesize anthraquinones and the possibility that these and other quinones in addition to simple phenolic compounds are important constituent units in the formation of soil humus is receiving more consideration (Sáiz-Jiménez *et al.* 1975).

In this paper, the linkage between anthraquinones and a humic-type polymer synthesized by a fungus, is studied.

MATERIAL AND METHODS

The isolation and characteristics of the fungus *Eurotium echinulatum* Delacr. and the methods for cultivation have been described by Sáiz-Jiménez (1975).

The fungus was cultured in glucose-asparagin medium. A dark-coloured humic acid-type pigment was isolated after 3 months and treated as usual for soil humic acids.

Separation of anthraquinones from pigment was achieved by two methods: gel filtration according to Swift and Posner (1971), and chemosorption by baryte (Schnitzer and Gupta 1965).

Anthraquinones were detected with UV-light at 366 nm and by spraying with 24 per cent NaOH or with 0.5 per cent Mg-acetate the thin layer chromatograms. Agreement of Rf-values, colour reaction and spectra in the UV and visible light range of extracted spots with the pure anthraquinone were used as criteria for identification.

RESULTS AND DISCUSSION

Eurotium echinulatum cultured on glucose as a carbon source synthesized numerous phenols and anthraquinones. During the period of pigment formation the phenols and anthraquinones largely disappeared from the medium. It is highly probable that these phenols and anthraquinones were linked to the developing pigment (Sáiz-Jiménez *et al.* 1975).

Reduction of the pigment with Na-amalgam yielded namely phenols and anthraquinones, while Na-dithionite treatment releases largely anthraquinones (Sáiz-Jiménez and Haider 1975).

Table 1
Weight distribution, K_{av} and MW of fractions

fractions	weight distribution (%)	K_{av}	MW
I.	23	0.2	~ 73,000
II.	68	0.5	~ 28,000
III.	9	>1	~ 300

The elution of the pigment through Sephadex G-100 showed three peaks (Fig. 1). In accordance with the boundaries of exclusions of this Sephadex, the fractions representing peaks I and II have a molecular weight in the range of 100,000–1,000, while peak III, retained by the column, has lesser MW.

Table 1 shows weight distribution of fractions, K_{av} and molecular weight obtained by interpolation of these in the calibration curve of Cameron *et al.* (1972).

Peak III, with a scarlet-pink colour, was eluted from the column, acidified and extracted with ether. Thin-layer chromatography from the extract showed anthraquinones distribution identical to those obtained from culture media or Na-dithionite degradation by Sáiz-Jiménez *et al.* 1975 (Fig. 2).

Elution of pigment through Sephadexes G-25 and LH-20 with TRIS, dimethylformamide or dimethylsulphoxide also separate peak III.

The exhaustive treatment of pigment with $Ba(OH)_2$ releases anthraquinones, showing the supernatant the same colour as peak III. Ether extraction gives the anthraquinone distribution referred to above, excepting a non-identified fluorescent compound under 254 nm light.

These results show that the anthraquinones are physically adsorbed to the pigment by hydrogen bonds, which are broken by elution through Sephadexes or treatment with baryte. The linkage of anthraquinones can occur during the polymer formation, through co-precipitation in the extraction of pigment cannot be neglected.

The significance of fungal polymers with respect to soil humus formation under natural conditions must be more extensively studied to solve the origin of humic substances.

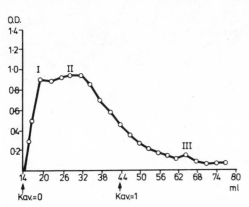

Fig. 1. Gel filtration with Sephadex G–100 of pigment

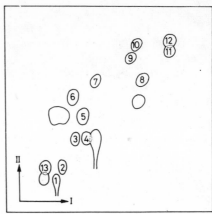

Fig. 2. Two dimensional thin-layer chromatogram showing anthraquinones extracted from peak III. The developing solution for the first direction (1) was benzene–ethylformate–formic acid (75:24:1) and for the second (II) dibutylether–acetic acid (10:1). The specific anthraquinones were: 1. dermocybin, 2. questinol, 3. fallacinol, 4. questin, 5. demolutein, 6. endocrocin, 7. parietinic acid, 8. fallacinal, 9. emodin, 10. catenarin, 11. physcion, 12. erythroglaucin, 13. dermoglaucin

SUMMARY

Eurotium echinulatum synthesizes a humic acid-type polymer, whose structural units are phenols and anthraquinones. When the polymer is extracted from a glucose-asparagine medium, almost 10 per cent of total molecules is constituted by physically adsorbed anthraquinones. These can be separated from the pigment by gel filtration or by a chemosorption method using 0.1 N Ba(OH)$_2$.

REFERENCES

Cameron, R. S., Swift, R. S., Thornton, B. K. and Posner, A. M. (1972): *J. Soil Sci.* **23**, 342–349.
McGrath, D. (1972): *Geoderma.* **7**, 167–176.
Sáiz-Jiménez, C. (1977): *Microbiol. Esp.*
Sáiz-Jiménez, C. and Haider, K. (1975): *An. Edaf. Agrobiol.* **34**, 959–969.
Sáiz-Jiménez, C. Haider, K. and Martin, J. P. (1975): *Soil Sci. Soc. Amer. Proc.* **39**, 649–653.
Schnitzer, M. and Gupta, U. C. (1965): *Soil Sci. Soc. Amer. Proc.* **29**, 274–277.
Swift, R. S. and Posner, A. M. (1971): *J. Soil Sci.* **22**, 237–249.

STUDIES OF PIGMENT FORMATION BY *ACTINOMYCETES*

by

F. GULYÁS
Research Institute for Soil Science and Agricultural Chemistry, of the Hungarian Academy of sciences
Budapest, Hungary

Among actinomycetes, a number of dark-coloured species is known. The often diffusible pigments formed in tyrosine-containing synthetic media are melanins or melanin-like compounds; their biosynthesis, physical and chemical properties have been extensively studied (Douglas and San-Clemente 1956, Frommer 1956, Krassilnikov 1938, Krassilnikov and Vinogradova 1960, Mencher and Heim 1962, Raper 1927, Waksman 1961). The chromogenic precursor is transformed to DOPA, DOPA--quinone then, via oxidative polymerization, to melanins. These steps are catalyzed partly by enzymes, while certain reactions are non-enzymatic. The second group of pigments is formed in protein- or peptone-containing media. Tyrosine and tyrosyl groups are oxidized to quinones by tyrosinase, then the products polymerize non-enzymatically (Skinner 1938). The third group of pigments is formed in synthetic media from unknown precursors. According to Gregory and Vaisey (1956), these pigments might also be formed from tyrosine, deliberated from proteins by autolysis during ageing of cultures. Other extracellular pigments may be formed from antibiotics having quinoidal structures or from aromatic monomers of lignin (Küster 1953, Waksman 1967).

MATERIAL AND METHODS

Strains of two *Streptomyces* sp. (No. 1–56, Series *Chartreusis* and No. 4–10, Series *Violaceorectus*) were used in this study. The strains were inoculated into 25 ml liquid medium containing glucose as carbon and asparagine as nitrogen source (Martin *et al.* 1967). On the seventh day of incubation protocatechuic acid or yeast extract was added aseptically to the cultures in a final concentration of 0.1 mg/ml.

Cultures were analyzed weekly for pH, glucose, optical density and for extracellular phenoloxidase activity. Ether extractable aromatic compounds of the media were separated by paper chromatography. The pigment in the culture liquid was precipitated with HCl. Pigments were dissolved in 0,2 n NaOH and U.V. absorption spectra recorded with U.V. spectrophotometer.

Glucose utilization of the two strains (Table 1) was different. Strain No. 1–56 utilized more than 50% of the glucose added within the first two weeks of incubation. In the later periods the rate of glucose consumption decreased. Utilization of glucose by strain No. 4–10 became intensive only in the second half of the incubation period and 5–24% of glucose remained in the media at the end of incubation.

Table 1
Changes of glucose content in the culture solution during incubation period.
(Glucose content in mg/25 ml culture medium)

	Treatments	1. day	7. day	14. day	21. day	35. day	49. day
Streptomyces sp. N° 1–56	I. Basal medium	750	540	250	155	105	70
	II. Basal medium + PA	750	570	356	120	55	0
	III. Basal medium + Y	750	560	318	90	30	0
	IV. Basal medium + Y + PA	750	540	265	120	58	0
Streptomyces sp. N° 4–10	I. Basal medium	750	655	600	520	380	180
	II. Basal medium + PA	750	670	610	490	310	180
	III. Basal medium + Y	750	650	570	470	310	40
	IV. Basal medium + Y + PA	750	650	530	450	350	75

Y = Yeast extract
PA = Protocatechuic acid

The pH of the cultures of strain No. 1–56 decreased quickly in the first period of incubation (down to pH 5), afterwards, parallel with the depletion of glucose supply, gradually increased again (Table 2). In the cultures of strain No. 4–10 the decrease of pH was slower; pH value was lowest (depending on the media) at the 3rd–5th weeks of incubation. In cultures containing yeast extract the final pH value was above 7.

As data of Table 3 show, intensive formation of pigments occurred only after the third week. Before this period the amount of pigments precipitable by HCl was negligible.

From the second week onwards, presence of **phenoloxidases** in the culture filtrates could be detected by specific reactions. On the basis of substrate specificity, these were **p-phenoloxidases** reacting with o- and p-diphenols, resulting in formation of quinones. Reaction with monophenols could not be observed except in the case of p-cresol which yielded a whitish precipitate. Generally, phenoloxydase activity was highest during the fourth week of incubation, then decreased gradually.

Table 2
Changes of pH in the culture solution during incubation periods

	Treatments	1. day	7. day	14. day	21. day	35. day	49. day
Streptomyces sp. N° 1–56	I. Basal medium	7.34	5.05	5.10	5.25	5.40	5.85
	II. Basal medium + PA	7.34	5.00	5.05	5.20	6.45	7.74
	III. Basal medium + Y	7.34	5.00	5.20	5.45	7.58	7.35
	IV. Basal medium + Y + PA	7.34	5.00	5.15	5.30	5.85	7.89
Streptomyces sp. N° 4–10	I. Basal medium	7.34	7.26	7.06	6.45	6.10	6.35
	II. Basal medium + PA	7.34	7.18	6.90	4.60	5.90	6.20
	III. Basal medium + Y	7.34	7.18	6.98	4.65	5.75	7.49
	IV. Basal medium + Y + PA	7.34	7.15	6.40	4.85	5.80	7.54

Y = Yeast extract
PA = Protocatechuic acid

Table 3
Changes of optical density in the culture solution during incubation periods

	Treatments	1. day	7. day	14. day	21. day	35. day	49. day
Streptomyces sp. N° 1–56	I. Basal medium	0.0	0.006	0.025	0.070	0.095	0.154
	II. Basal medium + PA	0.0	0.006	0.040	0.038	0.230	0.376
	III. Basal medium + Y	0.0	0.006	0.030	0.080	0.254	0.338
	IV. Basal medium + Y + PA	0.0	0.006	0.060	0.075	0.150	0.428
Streptomyces sp. N° 4–10	I. Basal medium	0.0	0.010	0.045	0.068	0.085	0.144
	II. Basal medium + PA	0.0	0.010	0.060	0.048	0.160	0.208
	III. Basal medium + Y	0.0	0.010	0.050	0.050	0.086	0.485
	IV. Basal medium + Y + PA	0.0	0.010	0.065	0.058	0.158	0.466

Y = Yeast extract
PA = Protocatechuic acid

Ether extracts of cultures — as it was detected by paper chromatography — contained aromatic carbonic acids, aromatic mono- and diphenols. The quantity, as well as number of detectable compounds increased continuously during incubation. In media containing protocatechuic acid, the amount of this compound slowly decreased with time, however, it was detectable even at the end of incubation.

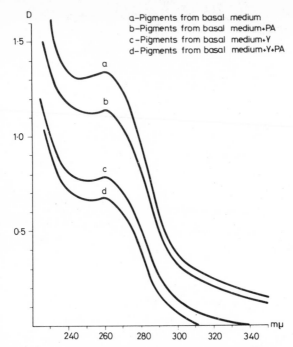

a–Pigments from basal medium
b–Pigments from basal medium+PA
c–Pigments from basal medium+Y
d–Pigments from basal medium+Y+PA

Fig. 1. UV absorption spectra of pigments of *Strepto-myces sp.* (series: *Chartreosus,* strain N° 1–56)

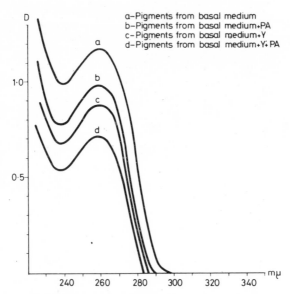

a–Pigments from basal medium
b–Pigments from basal medium+PA
c–Pigments from basal medium+Y
d–Pigments from basal medium+Y+PA

Fig. 2. UV absorption spectra of pigments of *Strepto-myces sp.* (series: *Violaceorectus,* strain N° 4–10)

UV spectra of pigments isolated from the cultures are presented in Figures 1 and 2. Independently from the composition of culture media, shape of the curves is almost identical. Maxima are at 258 nm (strain No. 1—56) and at 260 nm (strain No. 4—10).

DISCUSSION

The investigated strains formed extracellular pigments in liquid medium containing glucose as carbon and asparagine as nitrogen source. Chromogenic substrates probably were synthesized by the strains in their intermediary metabolism. Aromatic carbonic acids, mono- and dihydroxy phenols were isolated from the media; quantity and number of these compounds increased in the second half of the incubation period. This suggests that — at least partially — they might be formed during autolysis. Addition of small amounts of protocatechuic acid and yeast extract increased the production of pigments, therefore, these compounds are chromogenic substrates of pigment production. Optical properties of pigments isolated from different media were almost identical, suggesting that extraneously added precursors are more or less transformed to other compounds before utilization in pigment synthesis. Transformations to quinones are catalyzed by laccase-type polyphenoloxidases; these enzymes were detectable in the media of the two strains. Laccases are bifunctional enzymes having mono- and polyphenoloxydase activity centres. Generally, the polyphenoloxidase activity dominates, but lignin-monomer monophenols are also oxidized by these enzymes. On the other hand, cresol is not oxidized. According to Küster (1953, 1963), laccases and/or tyrosinase play an important role in the pigment formation of *Actinomycetes*.

Polymerization and condensation of quinones via autooxidation also occurs; amount of pigments increased in the media even in the period of decreasing phenoloxidase activity. Similar observations are recorded by Martin *et al.* (1967), in experiments with fungi. As data show, pigments are formed during the period of intensive growth and there is an apparent correlation between pH of the medium and pigment formation: extracellular pigments are produced intensively above pH 6.

The pigments formed by the strains investigated show properties of melanins. These compounds (according to Zenova, 1965, 1968) show peaks in the region of 240—280 nm of their UV spectra. In the case of the strains investigated, the corresponding peaks were at 258 nm (strain No. 1-56) and at 260 nm (strain No. 4—10).

SUMMARY

Pigment production in a liquid medium by two *Streptomyces sp.* was studied by the author. Pigments were produced without addition of tyrosine or tyrosine-containing proteins, from aromatic chromogenic substances synthesized by the strains. Addition

269

of protocatechuic acid or yeast extract was stimulatory. Laccase-type polyphenoloxidases were present in the culture media. Intensive pigment production began after considerable consumption of glucose followed by the increase of pH to values above pH 6. Pigments formed were melanins with peaks in their UV spectra in the region of 255—265 nm.

REFERENCES

Douglas, R. J. and San-Clemente, C. L. (1956): *Canad. J. Microbiol.*, 2, 407—415.
Frommer, W. (1956): *Arch. Microbiol.* 23, 385—399.
Gregory, K. F. and Vaisey, E. B. (1956): *Canad. J. Microbiol.* 2, 65—71.
(Krassilnikov, N. A.) Красильников, н. А. (1958): *Лучистые грибки и родственные им организмы.* АН СССР, Москва—Ленинград.
(Krassilnikov, N. A., and Vinogradova, К. A.) Красильников, Н. А., Виноградова, К. А. (1960): *Труды ин-та Микробиол.*, 8, 202.
Küster, E. (1953): *Ztbl. Bakt. I.* 160, 207—213.
Küster, E, (1963): *Phenol oxidases in Streptomycetes.* In: Enzyme Chemistry of Phenolic compounds. Ed. Pridham, Pergamon Press, London, 81—86.
Martin, J. P., Richards, S. J. and Haider, K. (1967): *Soil Sci. Soc. Amer. Proc.* 31, 657—662.
Mencher, J. R. and Heim, A. H. (1962): *J. Gen. Microbiol.* 28, 665—670.
Raper, H. S. (1927): *Fermentforschung.* 9, 206—212.
Skinner, C. E. (1938): *J. Bacteriol.* 35, 415—424.
Waksman, S. A. (1961): *The Actinomycetes, vol. II.* Classification, identification and description of genera and species. Baltimore.
Waksman, S. A. (1967): *The Actinomycetes.* A summary of current knowledge. New York.
(Zenova, G. M.) Зенова, Г. М. (1965): *Микробиол.* 34, 276—283.
(Zenova, G. M.) Зенова, Г. М. (1968): *Микробиол.* 27, 454—459.

EFFECT OF BENTONITE ON THE SUBSTRATE STABILIZATION

by

Jitka NOVÁKOVÁ
University of Agriculture, Department of Microbiology,
Prague-Suchdol, Czechoslovakia

Bentonite occurring in Czechoslovakia consists mostly of montmorillonite. That is why a series of pronounced effects have been observed on the soil processes, particularly on the microbiological and biochemical processes. Different kinds of montmorillonite effects on the substrate stability have been reported also. The direct stabilization of substrates (Pinck and Allison 1951, Pinck *et al.* 1954, Lynch *et al.* 1957, Lynch and Cotnoir 1956, Greenland 1965a, b, Nováková 1974, 1975), as well as the enhanced substrate mineralization (Estermann and McLaren 1959, Stotzky and Rem 1966, Kunc and Stotzky 1974, Kubista 1969, 1972, Nováková 1972, Sörensen 1965, Zvigaintsev and Velikanov (1968) was studied by authors in different experiments. The aim of the present communication is to contribute to the understanding of the clay effect on the substrate stabilization.

MATERIAL AND METHODS

Sandy river levee (the portion that passed through 2 mm siéve) was amended with 1 per cent starch and with 0, 3, 8 and 13 per cent bentonite, moistened to 20% humidity and incubated for 23 days at 30 °C.

The laboratory refuse composts were prepared from the solid crushed town refuses (45%), semi-liquid sewage sludges (20%), peat (15%), lignite (10%), and crushed rind (10%); 0 or 10% bentonite were added.

The respiration test was carried out in appropriate time intervals using the method of Novák and Apfelthaler (1964).

RESULTS AND DISCUSSION

The employed soil samples respired very actively under laboratory incubation conditions. On the average, 1.28 mg CO_2 was evolved by 100 g soil in an hour during the initial phase of the experiment (the first two days) and 0.92 mg CO_2 after three

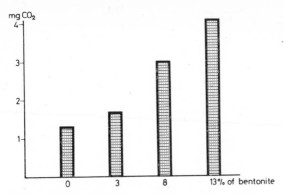

Fig. 1. The effect of added bentonite on initial respiration (B) of soil samples at the start of experiment

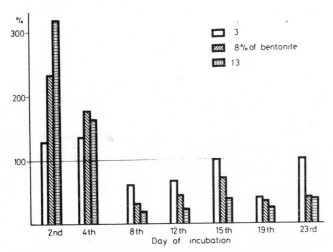

Fig. 2. Relative effect of bentonite addition on the initial respiration during the experiment (control soil = 100)

weeks of incubation. The addition of bentonite (Fig. 1) increased the organic matter mineralization. The higher bentonite doses had a greater effect. This stimulative effect of bentonite gradually decreased (Fig. 2). After a week of bentonite action, all the bentonite variants mineralized less organic substances than the control variant. Similarly to the bentonite effect on the stimulation of the substrate mineralization when added freshly, the higher doses of bentonite stabilized the substrate to a higher degree than the lower ones.

Earlier findings on the clay effect demonstrating the stimulation of microbial transformation of substrate, and the increased stability of the clay adsorbed organic

272

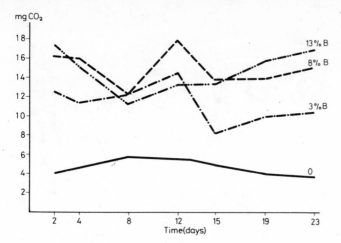

Fig. 3. Effect of bentonite addition on the potential soil respiration (NG)

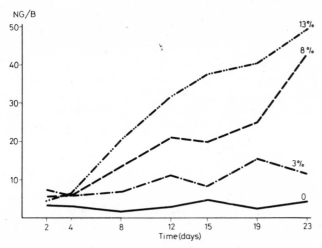

Fig. 4. The course of the soil organic matter stabilization due to the effect of increased doses of bentonite — indicated by the NG + B ratio

substances could explain these experiments. The stability of the organic matter has been gradually established, evidently due to the soil processes influenced by clays.

The alteration of the soil properties as a result of the clay action and/or the clay affected substrate transformations may be the cause of the substrate stabilization.

The validity of the second explanation seems to be much more probable considering the results of the glucose + nitrogen amended soil respiration (Fig. 3). The freshly

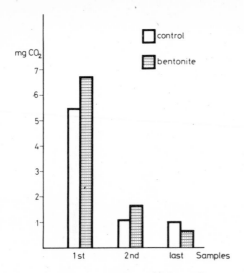

Fig. 5. Initial respiration of the refuse compost samples during the ripening

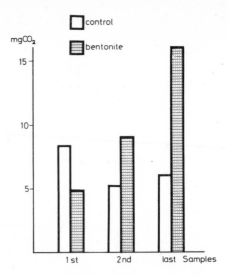

Fig. 6. The changes in the organic matter stability during the refuse compositing under the influence of bentonite

added glucose is metabolized in the individual variants to the same degree regardless of the time when bentonite was added to the soil previously. The stability of the soil organic matter rose steadily, nevertheless, during the experiment (Fig. 4).

Similar results (Figs 5 and 6) were achieved in the compost experiments. The bentonite addition did not change the organic matter mineralization in the initial stage of composting, but the indicated stability (NG : B ratio) was diminished. As the compost ripening proceeded, the stability of the bentonite amended compost increased compared to the initial stage and to the control as well.

There is no doubt of the direct effect of clays on the nutritional availability of some substrates to soil microflora. Nevertheless, the metabolic effect seems to be more common and, consequently, more particular.

SUMMARY

The effect of bentonite on the substrate stabilization was examined in model experiments. The organic substances of the starch-amended soil samples and of the fresh refuse composts were mineralized more rapidly if bentonite was added. The bentonite caused gradual substrate stabilization due to the effect of the metabolic processes.

REFERENCES

Estermann, E. F. and McLaren, A. D. (1959): *J. Soil Sci.* 10, 64–78.

Greenland, D. J. (1965a): *Soil and Fertilizers.* 5, 415–424.

Greenland, D. J. (1965b): *Soil and Fertilizers.* 6, 521–532.

Kubista, K. (1969): *Rostlinná Vyroba (Praha).* 15, 221–228.

Kubista, K. (1972): *Symp. Biol. Hung.* 11, 229–235.

Kunc, F. and Stotzky, G. (1974): *Soil Sci.* 118, 186–195.

Lynch, D. L. and Cotnoir, L. J. (1956): *Soil Sci. Soc. Amer. Proc.* 20, 367–370.

Lynch, D. L., Wright, L. M., Hearne, E. F. and Cotnoir, L. J. (1957): *Soil Sci.* 84, 113–126.

Novák, B. and Apfelthaler, R. (1964): *Rostlinná Vyroba.* 10, 145–150.

Nováková, J. (1972): *Symp. Biol. Hung.* 11, 159–165.

Nováková, J. (1974): *Rostlinná Výroba.* 20, 813–816.

Nováková, J. (1975): *Studies about Humus.* Trans. Int. Symp. Humus et Planta VI, Prage, 235–240.

Pick, L. A. and Allison, F. E. (1951): *Science.* 114, 130–131.

Pick, L. A., Dyal, R. D. and Allison, F. E. (1954): *Soil Sci.* 78, 109–118.

Sörensen, H. (1965): *Nature.* 208, 97–98.

Stotzky, G. and Rem, L. T. (1966): *Canad. J. Microbiol.* 12, 547–563.

(Zviagintsev, D. G. and Velikanov, L. L.) Звягинцев, Д. Г. и Великанов, Л. Л. (1968) : *Микробиол.*, 37, 1017–1021.

UTILIZATION OF POPLAR WOOD BY *PLEUROTUS OSTREATUS* (JACQ. EX FR.) KUMMER IN THE PRESENCE OF THIAMINE, UREA AND LIME

by

T. TAKÁTS
University of Forestry and Timber Industry,
Sopron, Hungary

Depending on the kind of wood and fungus, wood-decaying fungi are able to utilize wood, directly in various forms and at various rates, but relatively slowly (Rypacek (1966), Igmándy and Pagony (1966, 1967) Cowling (1961)). In this study, the (poplar) wood-decaying properties of *Pleurotus ostreatus* were studied. It was supposed that N-content of the wood plays a limiting role in the utilization of wood by the fungus.

In the present work we are reporting on how much — in one of our experiments *in vitro* — a certain strain, used in industrial production, of *Pleurotus ostreatus* [(Jacq. ex Fr.) Kummer]; register number in our laboratory: 77/5) decayed the wood of the sawdust made from the log of a poplar *(Populus × euramericana* cv., *robusta)* prepared for industrial purposes, when thiamine hydrochlor, carbamide and $CaCO_3$ or one of their combinations was added to the wood moistened previously with salt solution.

By analysing the results of this experiment we tried to find out the role of these materials and their combinations in speeding up the wood decay.

MATERIAL AND METHODS

1.5 g of air-dry sawdust was put into 180×18 mm test-tubes. This wood was moistened with 6 ml total volume of nutrient solution. 12 combinations of substrates were prepared, which are shown in Table 1.

Five cultures of each treatment were analyzed on the first, 30th and 60th days of incubation. For each test-tube the aqueous pH, the absolute and relative extract contents of the cultures were determined. The decay of wood was determined from the decrease in the extract content of the cultures. The experimental results were evaluated biometrically (Table 2).

Table 1
Combinations of thiamine, urea and $CaCO_3$ in the media used

Combination	Thiamine	Urea	$CaCO_3$
	μg	g	
	in 100 g of wood		
O	–	–	–
M	–	–	0.8
MM	–	–	4.0
V	40	–	–
K	–	0.5	–
VM	40	–	0.8
VMM	40	–	4.0
VK	40	0.5	–
KM	–	0.5	0.8
KMM	–	0.5	4.0
VKM	40	0.5	0.8
VKMM	40	0.5	4.0

RESULTS

The inocula began to grow within 1–2 days. The properties of the cultures varied according to the treatments, and changed during incubation. In the presence of urea, with small dosage of $CaCO_3$, a denser mycelial mat was observed, than in –k combinations. As it is shown, in treatment VK the weight loss was over 14% on the 30th day. In treatment KM the cultures reached this level only on the 60th day. By the 60th day the weight loss of the dry material rose over 10% in almost every + k combinations. In + k combinations the losses were generally higher even on the 30th day, than in the other variants.

On the 30th day treatments VK and KM while on the 60th day treatments VK, KM and K were the most effective. The reduction in extract content rose in control treatment to 2.8–5.4%, in the other treatments to 10.9–14.9%. Urea alone was rather successful, particularly if thiamine or small amount of $CaCO_3$ was also added. In the presence of a large dose of $CaCO_3$ the loss of wood was generally less, while in combination with urea the reduction in dry weight was the same as that of the control. The depressive effect, however, apparently ceased in the triple combination by the 60th day.

It could be observed that with higher losses of wood, a denser mat of mycelium was associated.

The data of the loss of wood added to the cultures are collected in Tables 2–3. In Table 3 the effect of urea is shown. Up to the 30th day thiamine, urea and small dose of $CaCO_3$ were effective alone. Only the effect of urea added alone is detectable up to the 60th day (Table 4). In combinations, only the effect of thiamine and carbamide was favourable, the large $CaCO_3$ dose was depressive. In combinations free of $CaCO_3$ thiamine and urea was always effective. Thiamine in combination with large $CaCO_3$ dose + urea in combination with small $CaCo_3$ dose showed a favourable effect. Small amounts of $CaCo_3$ were effective in combinations free of thiamine. The depressive effect of the large $CaCo_3$ dose appears frequently, but not in every case, only in combination with urea. Otherwise, there is (though to a smaller extent) a depressive combination of both carbamide and $CaCO_3$. Such effect was not found in the case of thiamine. Ineffective combinations were found in certain cases in all the three materials.

The experimental results (Table 2) showed that the best utilization of wood was found in the treatments with two components. However, not every combination was equally favourable. Treatments $+ v + k - m$ (VK) and $- v + k + m$ (KM) were the most effective; urea was present in both treatments. (Up to the 30th day the results of the two combinations differed significantly from each other to the advantage of VK.) Combinations VM, VMM, KMM were not favourable. The advantage of combinations thiamine-urea and urea-small $CaCO_3$ dose was demonstrated by processing the data for the two components separately. Combinations $+ v + k$ (Table 5), were the most favourable; on the basis of the averages combination $+ v + k$ showed a prominently high average. Combination $+ k + m$, however, did not differ significantly from $+ k - m$.

In Table 2 we tried to show what interrelationship exists between the compounds tested. Except for three cases, the calculated values do not reach the value of $SD_5\%$. The measure of the mutual effect between treatments with two components was significant and contractive in treatment urea-large $CaCO_3$ dose. A remarkably great synergistic effect was detected in the combination of thiamine-urea-large doses of $CaCO_3$. In the other cases the synergistic effects are negligible.

The pH values of the cultures were also followed (Table 2). Significant difference was demonstrated between the effects of the treatments at $P = 5\%$ on both the first and 60th days. On the first day, pH ranged from 4.65 to 6.18. The average pH values of the cultures with single components are collected in Table 6. The averages of the urea, as well as $CaCO_3$ groups reflect the alkalifying effect of these compounds. The culture in the group with the larger doses of $CaCO_3$ had the least acidic reaction. In Table 7, the average pH values of treatments with two or three components are collected.

On the 30th day, no significant difference was found between the pH values, although the average pH of almost every treatment changed more or less towards acidity. Comparing the pH values measured on the 60th day to those measured on the first day it is apparent that during incubation pH values below 5 were shifted towards the alkaline side and, pH values above 5 towards acidity. Because of the rather large differences between the initial pH values of the cultures the question arises what the role of pH is in the wood utilization of the fungus.

279

Table 2'
Utilization of poplar wood by *Pleurotus ostreatus* in the presence of thiamine, urea and calcium carbonate

Combination	Marked as	Concentration of			Decrease of dry weight, in percent		pH of the substrate on the			Percentage effect of the treatment on the	
		thiamine	urea	CaCO$_3$				days of incubation			
		μg	g	g	30th	60th	1st	30th	60th	30th	60th
		per 100 g of wood			$\bar{x}$ %		pH			$\bar{x}$ %	
1.	2.	3.	4.	5.	6.	7.	8.	9.	10.	11.	12.
						Control					
– v – k – m	φ	–	–	–	2.845	5.413	4.65	4.64	4.66	100.00	100.00
						Combinations with one variable					
+ v – k – m	V	40	–	–	5.410	6.845	4.65	4.80	4.74	90.15	26.45
– v + k – m	K	–	0.5	–	7.947	11.788	5.00	4.66	4.82	179.33	117.77
– v – k + m	M	–	–	0.8	7.837	6.942	5.48	4.74	4.90	175.47	28.25
– v – k + mm	MM	–	–	4.0	4.277	6.809	5.24	4.74	4.96	50.33	25.79

Combinations with two variables

+ v + k – m	VK	40	0.5	–	14.926	14.796	4.72	4.72	4.78	57.57	20.19
+ v – k + m	VM	40	–	0.8	7.136	9.073	5.20	4.76	4.92	– 43.22	23.61
+ v – k + mm	VMM	40	–	4.0	7.553	6.640	5.46	4.78	4.94	17.79	– 56.61
– v + k + m	KM	–	0.5	0.8	10.898	13.960	5.22	4.64	4.82	– 20.22	8.16
– v + k + mm	KMM	–	0.5	4.0	2.624	3.340	5.92	5.08	4.86	–103.38	–126.68

Combinations with three variables

+ v + k + m	VKM	40	0.5	0.8	9.469	11.138	5.42	4.65	4.72	– 42.70	– 53.29
+ v + k + mm	VKMM	40	0.5	4.0	8.114	11.030	6.18	4.66	4.84	– 29.45	943.39
$LSD_{5\%}$			–	–	2.129	3.416	0.145	–	0.156	74.83	63.11

– not measured, + present, – absent, v = thiamine, k = urea, m = small doses of $CaCO_4$, mm = large doses of $CaCo_3$, x = mean

Table 3

Effects of urea on the production of dry matter in the cultures

Combination	At the 30th day				Combination	At the 60th day			
	−k	+k	LSD$_5$%	d		−k	+k	LSD$_5$%	d
	variants $\bar{x}$%		%	%		variants $\bar{x}$%		%	%
+ v − m	5.41	14.93	2.13	9.52	+ v − m	6.84	14.80	3.42	7.24
− m	4.12	11.44	2.15	7.32	− m	6.12	13.29	2.90	7.17
− v − m	2.84	7.95	2.13	5.11	− v − m	5.41	11.79	3.42	6.38
+ v	6.70	10.84	2.26	4.14	− v + m	7.96	13.96	3.42	6.00
Total	5.84	8.99	1.61	3.15	+ v	7.52	12.32	2.66	4.80
− v + m	7.84	10.90	2.13	3.06	+ v + mm	6.64	11.02	3.42	4.38
+ m	7.50	10.18	2.15	2.68	+ m	8.51	12.55	2.90	4.04
+ v + m	7.14	9.47	2.13	2.33	Total	7.12	10.91	2.04	3.79
− v	4.99	7.16	2.26	2.17	− v	6.73	9.51	2.66	2.78
+ v + mm	7.55	8.11	2.13	0.56	+ v + m	9.07	11.14	3.42	2.07
+ mm	5.91	5.36	2.15	−0.55	+ mm	6.72	6.90	2.90	0.18
− v + mm	4.28	2.62	2.13	−1.66	− v + mm	6.81	2.78	3.42	−4.03

Table 4
Effects of the compounds added in various combinations

Compound added	Days of incubation			
	30th		60th	
	advantageous	depressive	advantageous	depressive
Thiamine + v	alone generally − m + mm		+ k + mm	
Urea + k	alone generally − m + m		alone generally − m − v + m	− v + mm
small dosis of CaCO₃ + m	alone − v	+ v + k		+ v + k
large dosis of CaCO₃ + mm	+ v − k	generally + k alone generally − v		generally + k generally − v + k
CaCO₃ + m and + mm	− v − k	+ v + k	− v − k	+ v + k

As it is shown in the table, the initial pH values of the cultures did not influence the results systematically. The greater loss in wood may rather be due to urea than the pH because apart from one combination of urea, the level of wood utilization in every culture with urea was higher than those in combinations free of urea. Under the conditions applied in our experiments the most favourable pH range for wood utilization by the fungus is between 4.72 and 4.84. For *Pleurotus ostreatus* this range in agar-agar or liquid cultures is usually unfavourable being excessively acidic.

SUMMARY

On moistened wood meal decayed by one strain *Pleurotus ostreatus* (Jacq. ex Fr.) Kummer adapted in plant production we investigated the rate of wood decay and the protein yield with and without addition of thiamine, urea, lime and their combinations *in vitro*. The wood meal used as a substrate was prepared from the stem of poplar *(P.* × *euramericana, robusta).*

Table 5
Weight losses of wood in the different treatments

Combination	Mean loss of (dry) weight at the	
	30th	60th
	days of incubation	
− v − k	4.99	6.73
+ v − k	6.70	7.52
− v + k	7.16	9.51
+ v + k	10.84	12.31
LSD$_5$%	2.26	2.66
− v − m	5.40	8.60
− v + m	9.37	10.96
− v + mm	3.45	4.80
+ v − m	10.17	10.82
+ v + m	8.30	10.10
+ v + mm	7.83	8.81
LSD$_5$%	2.30	3.23
− k − m	4.13	6.13
− k + m	7.49	8.52
− k + mm	5.92	6.73
+ k − m	11.44	13.29
+ k + m	10.18	12.55
+ k + mm	5.37	6.90
LSD$_5$%	2.15	2.90

The combination of thiamine and urea produced the most successful wood decay in the applied fungal strain. On addition of urea the wood decay was increased and large amounts of lime were moderated.

In the single factor combination the rate of wood decay decreased as follows: urea, small dose of lime, thiamine large dose of lime.

In the double-factor combinations:

1) the combination of thiamine and urea, as well as of thiamine and large dose of lime were of synergical effect and later the combination of thiamine and small dose lime as well as of urea and small dose of lime showed a similar effect.

2) the combination of urea and large dose of lime was of contradictory effect and later the combination of thiamine and small dose lime and of urea and small dose lime as well as of thiamine and large dose lime were of similar effect.

The three-factor combinations produced contradictory results and later a synergical interaction was shown by addition of the combination of thiamine urea and large dose lime.

Table 6
The pH of cultures with single additives

Combination	pH at the		
	1st	30th	60th
	days of incubation		
– v	5.25	4.75	4.84
+ v	5.24	4.73	4.82
LSD$_{s}\%$	–	–	–
– k	5.08	4.74	4.85
+ k	5.41	4.74	4.81
LSD$_{s}\%$	0.33	–	–
– k	5.08	4.74	4.85
+ k	5.41	4.74	4.81
LSD$_{s}\%$	0.33	–	–
– m	4.75	4.70	4.75
+ m	5.28	4.70	4.84
+ mm	5.70	4.81	4.90
LSD$_{s}\%$	0.17	–	0.07

Table 7
The pH of various combination groups
at different stages of incubation

Combination	pH at the		
	1st	30th	60th
	days of incubation		
+ v + k	5.44	4.78	4.78
– v + k	5.38	4.79	4.83
– v – k	5.12	4.71	4.84
+ v – k	5.04	4.78	4.87
LSD$_{s}\%$	0.18	–	–
+ v + mm	5.82	4.72	4.89
– v + mm	5.58	4.91	4.91
– v + m	5.35	4.69	4.86
+ v + m	5.22	4.71	4.82
– v – m	4.82	4.69	4.86
+ v – m	4.68	4.76	4.76
LSD$_{s}\%$	0.20	–	0.12

Table 7
(contd)

Combination	pH at the		
	1st	30th	60th
	days of incubation		
+ k + mm	6.05	4.87	4.85
− k + mm	5.35	4.76	4.95
+ k + m	5.32	4.65	4.77
− k + m	5.25	4.75	4.91
+ k − m	4.86	4.69	4.80
− k − m	4.62	4.72	4.70
LSD$_5$%	0.28	−	0.09
+ v + k + mm	6.18	4.66	4.84
− v + k + mm	5.92	5.08	4.86
+ v − k + mm	5.46	4.78	4.94
+ v + k + m	5.42	4.65	4.72
− v + k + m	5.22	4.64	4.82
+ v − k + m	5.20	4.76	4.92
+ v + k − m	4.72	4.72	4.78
LSD$_5$%	0.145	−	0.156

REFERENCES

Cowling, E. B. (1961): *Techn. Bull. No 1258, U. S. Dep. Agric.* Forest Service. Washington.
Igmándy, Z. and Pagony, H. (1966): *Erdészeti Kutatások.* 1–3, 269–277.
Igmándy, Z. and Pagony, H. (1967): *Erdészeti és Faipari Egyetem Tudományos Közleményei.* 1–2, 85–94.
Rypaček, V. (1966): *Biologie holzzerstörender Pilze.* Gustav Fischer Verlag, Jena.

CHEMICAL TEST OF POPLAR SAWDUST DECAYED
BY *PLEUROTUS OSTREATUS* (JACQ. EX FR.) KUMMER

by

Ildikó KOVÁCS-LIGETFALUSI
University of Forestry and Timber Industry,
Sopron, Hungary

The effect of the various additives added to the substrate on protein output was clarified by experiments *in vitro* of microbial protein production taking place directly on waste wood inoculated with *Pleurotus ostreatus* (Takáts 1975). However, it was also necessary to determine chemically, to what extent and in what way (i.e. according to what decomposing mechanism) the fungus — in an advanced stage of the biological process — utilizes the main constituents of wood, lignin and carbohydrate as sources of energy. According to its decaying mechanism, *Pleurotus ostreatus* is placed among the white-rot fungi by Rypacek (1966) as well as by Cowling (1961).

MATERIAL AND METHODS

As test material the samples of the experiments by Takáts (1975) were used. The additive agents, well proved during the preliminary experiments, were used in amounts most intensively enhancing the wood utilization of the fungus, in the following combination: Carbamide + large dosage of $CaCO_3$ (0.5 g + 0.8 g/100 g of wood), and carbamide + vitamin B_1 (0.5 g + 40 μg/100 g of wood) respectively. Lignin and total carbohydrate content was determined with the standard hydrolytic method elaborated by the Forest Products Laboratory, America (Moore and Johnson 1967). The lignin content was determined gravimetrically after sulphuric acid hydrolysis, the mono-saccharides, i.e. the total carbohydrate content with Somogyi-Shaffer's titrimetric method from the hydrolysate. The pentose content was also determined from the hydrolysate with spectrophotometry, on the basis of colour reaction specific to the pentose (Kakac and Vejdelek 1974).

The chemical analyses were made from 3 representative samples arbitrarily selected from 5 repetitions of each treatment in the experiment. The samples were tested in air-dry condition. Two parallel analytical determinations were made from each of the samples selected.

RESULTS AND DISCUSSION

The analysed data from the samples taken on the zero, 30th, 60th, 90th days of the incubation period are shown in Table 1. These values give the composition data of the sawdust hydrolysed with sulphuric acid, interwoven by mycelium, in 100 g of the air-dry material weighed. In order to characterize the time process of the biological activity, the percentage composition derived on the basis of weight loss of the decayed wood has been calculated and it is shown in a graph too (Fig. 1, Table 2 respectively).

Table 1
Data of chemical analysis of poplar sawdust decayed by *Pleurotus ostreatus*

Treatment	Incubation time (day)	Results of sulphuric acid hydrolysis %		
		Lignin	Total carbohydrate	Pentose
Control	0	21.94	72.18	13.74
	30	21.02	74.48	14.86
	60	21.82	65.94	13.97
	90	22.00	66.55	14.04
Carbamide + + CaCO₃	0	22.65	71.92	12.28
	30	21.34	76.26	12.60
	60	20.51	61.88	12.63
	90	20.93	62.44	10.80
Carbamide + + vitamin	0	22.62	71.95	14.07
	30	21.32	74.63	14.10
	60	21.34	60.52	13.88
	90	21.60	61.42	13.88

In the initial stage of the biological activity, until the 30th day, there was no significant change. The amounts of the single wood constituents and their proportion in each treatment were approximately the same as the amounts and their proportion in the counter-sample. In the later stage of decay, from the 30th day on the loss in weight increased under the influence of the additive agents. As a matter of course, the total carbohydrate, lignin and pentose contents, calculated for loss in weight, decreased, but the proportion of the wood constituents, utilized by the fungus, did not change as compared with that of the counter-sample. The rapidity of decay increases to a lesser extent with carbamide + $CaCO_3$ dosage, to a larger extent with carbamide + vitamin dosage. As for the degree of decay the most significant change takes place between the 30th and 60th days of the process. With carbamide + vitamin treatment on the 60th day, a degree of decay was found which did not appear with carbamide + $CaCO_3$ treatment until the 90th day. The biological activity of the fungus practically came to an end on the 60th day, at least under special laboratory conditions.

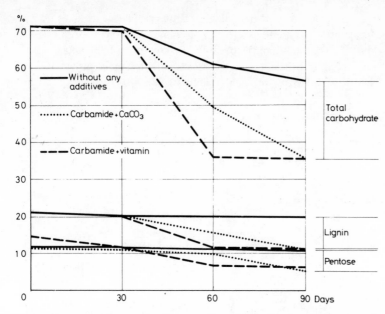

Fig. 1. Evolution of composition of the decayed wood in the single stages of decay, under the influence of different additive agents

Table 2
Single wood constituents in the decayed wood

Treatment	Incubation time (day)	Average weight loss %	Percentage of the single wood constituents in the decayed wood		
			Lignin %	Total carbohydrate %	Pentose %
Control	0	0.00	21.94	72.18	13.74
	30	2.80	20.43	72.31	14.44
	60	5.97	20.49	62.00	13.14
	90	13.31	19.07	57.70	12.17
Carbamide + + CaCO$_3$	0	0.00	22.65	71.92	12.28
	30	4.30	20.42	72.98	12.06
	60	20.83	16.24	48.99	9.98
	90	41.16	12.31	36.74	5.88
Carbamide + + vitamin	0	0.00	22.62	71.95	14.07
	30	5.32	20.19	70.66	13.35
	60	38.52	13.12	37.21	8.53
	90	41.08	12.72	36.19	8.18

It may be stated that in the course of its biological activity, the fungus takes up the wood constituents proportionately with the loss in weight, and what is decomposed will be utilized. There is no accumulation, because the amounts of the single wood constituents decrease according to the degree of loss in weight. This is proved by the proportional numbers obtained from the calculations (Table 3). These numbers are

Table 3

Change in proportion of lignin – carbohydrate, under the influence of additive agents in the single stages of decay, compared with the counter-sample

Treatment	Incubation time (day)	Lignin	Total carbohydrate
Control	30	0.9990	0.9985
	60	0.9983	1.0002
	90	0.9988	0.9995
Carbamide + + CaCO$_3$	30	1.0003	1.0031
	60	1.0004	1.0004
	90	0.9996	1.0001
Carbamide + + vitamin	30	0.9996	0.9992
	60	1.0001	0.9999
	90	1.0020	1.0029

obtained from the average losses of the utilized wood constituents and from the percentage of the average loss in weight. These proportional numbers show an approximately constant value in the single treatments and in the single stages of decay as compared with the counter-sample.

As it can be seen, under the influence of the additive agents the biological activity increased, but the proportion of lignin and carbohydrate does not change with the speeding up of and increase in the decomposing activity of the fungus.

The conclusion may be drawn that the additive agents increase the decomposing activity of the fungus on the whole, they do not shift it to one of the wood constituents.

The fact that without additive agents in the white-rot fungi – and *Pleurotus ostreatus* is one of them – the proportion of the decayed wood constituents does not change in the course of decay, has already been known from the work by Cowling (1961), dealing with the comparative biochemistry of white-rot and brown-rot fungi. Cowling's results are confirmed by the results of the present study, and complemented by the statement that the proportion of the decayed wood constituents does not change even in the course of more intensive biological activity caused by additive agents, further that *Pleurotus ostreatus* can be classified as white-rot fungus defined by Cowling.

SUMMARY

In the course of experiments *in vitro* on the wood decay of *Pleurotus ostreatus* the chemical analysis of inoculated sawdust was also made. The total carbohydrate and lignin content of the substrate interwoven by mycelium was determined by applying sulphuric acid hydrolysis. The analyses were made on the zero, 30th, 60th, 90th days of the incubation period. It has been stated that the additive agents added to the wood (carbamide, vitamin B_1) accelerate the decay process, and the presence of these materials does not alter the decomposing mechanism of the wood destroying fungus mentioned.

REFERENCES

Cowling, E. B. (1961): *Techn. Bull. No 1258,* U. S. Dep. Agric. Forest Service, Washington.
Kakac, B. and Vejdelek, Z. J. (1974): *Handbuch der photometrischen Analyse Organischer Verbindungen.* Band II, Verlag Chemie, Weinheim.
Moore, W. E. and Johnson, D. B. (1967): *Procedures for the chemical analysis of wood and wood products.* Forest Products Laboratory, Forest Service U. S. Department of Agriculture, Madison, Wisconsin.
Rypaček, V. (1966): *Biologie holzzerstörender Pilze.* Gustav Fischer Verlag, Jena.
Takáts, T. (1975): *Utilization of Poplar Wood by Pleurotus Ostreatus (Jacq ex Fr) Kummer in Presence of Thiamine, Carbamide and CaCO₃.* VIIth Scientific Session of Soil Biology, 2–4 September, Keszthely, Hungary.

THE ROLE OF BACTERIA IN THE PREPARATION
OF SUBSTRATE FOR PRODUCTION OF OYSTER FUNGUS

by

P. GYURKÓ
University of Forestry and Timber Industry,
Sopron, Hungary

We started studying oyster fungus thoroughly as early as the beginning of the sixties. Our objective was to elaborate an intensive production procedure of oyster fungus. For the production of fungus we wanted to utilize waste material of agricultural plants scarcely or not at all used before. From results of more than ten years' research, only broad outlines will be presented here. Mainly results related to microbiology, which throw light on the interrelationships between higher fungus decaying vegetable fibre and the other micro-organisms, especially mould fungi and bacteria living in the substrate will be dealt with.

Already in the first year, the excellent cultivation properties of the fungus were recognized. It turned out, that the wood decaying *Pleurotus ostreatus* grows well and more quickly on the waste material of agricultural plants with soft stalk, than on its natural nutrient substrate, on wood. For example, on wood of deciduous trees, such as poplar, the total yield obtained within three years, amounted to 18–20% (weight) of the original woody material, whereas 40–45 kg of fungus was produced on 100 kg of maize-cob under laboratory conditions within 9–10 weeks, i.e. roughly within 2 and a half months. The shortening of the production period and the increase in yields have led to elaboration of an intensive production procedure. At that time the substrate for production, e.g. ground maize-cob had not been prepared. It was simply moistened and – placed into chests covered with foil – inoculated with inoculum made also on ground maize-cob, but under sterile circumstances. When the maize-cob was not moudly and it was kept in a dry place, the interweaving was successful. Keeping maize-cob dry, however, particularly on a large scale, caused a lot of trouble. Utilization of more or less mouldy, bin-burned maize-cob or corn-straw was not successful. Such material became mouldy soon after inoculation, and the inoculated fungus was suppressed by moulds.

Oyster fungus belongs to the fungi producing fruit bodies even on sterile substrates. However, production on sterile substrates is very expensive. For the sake of feasibility non-sterile circumstances, should be used but for the sake of safety and so that the more or less mouldy material should also be usable, new ways had to be found. Several observations, to be mentioned below, showed the necessity of microbiological examinations.

Material interwoven by oyster fungus never becomes mouldy. Consequently, the critical period for oyster fungus lasts from the moistening and inoculating of the material up to the complete interweaving.

Another observation was that the pH value of the mouldy maize-cob was always higher, than that of the non-mouldy maize-cob, and this higher pH value (about 7.5) was unfavourable for oyster fungus. We tried to adjust the pH value (optimum for oyster fungus, is 5.8—6.0), but this was not useful for moulds. A lot of moulds grow excellently at this pH value. Examining mouldy maize-cob, it turned out that in mouldy maize-cob water-soluble materials, particularly carbohydrates are always present in larger amounts, than in healthy ones. Their amount may even reach 1.5%. As the complementary experiments showed, if monosaccharides or some other easily utilizable carbonhydrates were added to the healthy maize-cob, kept dry, (3.5—4.0% of weight of the dry substrate), moulds irreparably covered the healthy maize-cob. Consequently, easily utilizable carbohydrates are relatively more favourable for moulds, than for *Pleurotus*.

Perhaps the most useful method and conclusions drawn from it were as follows: healthy, non-mouldy, not bin-burned maize-cob was interwoven by fungus under non-sterile circumstances. When the maize-cob sterilized and inoculating with oyster fungus was kept under non-sterile conditions, the reinfecting organisms became dominant rapidly and suppressed the oyster fungus. Consequently, in the non-sterilized material there must have been micro-organisms inhibiting moulds, but they were destroyed by sterilization. From experiments with various disinfectants and heat it became obvious that the protective micro-organisms must be thermophilic or at least thermotolerant ones. This supposition was supported by the good results achieved at that time in the Cooperative Danube, Csepel where heat-treatment, well-known from cultivation of mushroom was applied during preparation of substrate for oyster fungus. According to recent results, heat-treatment applied in the cultivation of mushroom is effective not only against pests, mites and nematods, but it is also important in the final stage of composting, when humic materials and lignin-protein complex assuring selectivity are accumulated in the compost and microflora having a protective effect also develops.

Further quantitative microbiological experiments have revealed, that under the influence of a 24 hours' heat-treatment at about 50 °C, the number of bacteria near the well-aerated surface, at a depth of 5 cm, increased by a factor of $3 \cdot 10^5$. The pH in this layer had not changed. The original number of micro-organisms in 25—30 cm depth (with less air), increased only by a factor of $2 \cdot 10^3$ and pH-value was reduced from the original 6.7 to 5.1—5.2.

From the material which had been heat-treated about 350 strains of micro-organisms were isolated without selection; 20 strains (about 6%) were actinomycetes, 40 strains (about 12%) belonged to moulds while the majority (about 82%) represented bacteria.

Antagonistic properties of the isolates were tested on malt- and maize-cob extract plates, in order to determine the effects of these organisms on the growth of *Pleurotus*.

Without exception oyster fungus was strongly inhibited by all moulds. The relatively weakest inhibitory effect was exhibited by some strains of *Mucor*.

The actinomycetes were partly stimulative, partly inhibitory but, because of their low number, they were considered unimportant.

From the bacteria isolated, 15 strains stimulated the growth of *Pleurotus*, 8 strains inhibited it considerably and the majority — 92% — showed only slightly inhibitory effect. In our opinion, the protective bacteria must be among these isolates.

The bacteria were arranged into 11 groups on the basis of their morphological, and physiological properties, but no identification was done. The following experiment was carried out with two representative strains of each group.

The ground maize-cob, put into five-litre glasses, was sterilized then inoculated with the bacteria to be examined and incubated at 50 °C for 24 hours. After this treatment, *Pleurotus* and two kinds of aggressive moulds, selected previously, were inoculated. As a control, pots were used in which no bacteria had been cultivated before, only *Pleurotus* and moulds were inoculated. In such arrangement, a distinct protective effect was found in the case of several groups of bacteria. In the case of one group, complete protection against moulds was found and, at the same time, good growth of *Pleurotus* was also observed. In our opinion, these results support the hypothesis that protection of oyster fungus against moulds is caused by thermophilic-thermotolerant bacterial flora, developed after heat-treatment of the material.

According to our experiments, the protective effect has two components. Firstly the bacteria produce antibiotics effective against moulds and, secondly, the bacteria — during their rapid multiplication — consume the readily utilizable carbohydrates of the substrate, causing unfavourable circumstances for the moulds.

Taking into consideration the requirements of bacteria, i.e. by providing the temperature, pH and aeration necessary for their multiplication, the protective effect in the substrate may be developed even on a large scale.

SUMMARY

Moulds are the most dangerous competitors of oyster fungus propagated artificially on maize-cob.

It was experimentally proved that the thermophilic bacteria in a warm, aerated environment — during their rapid multiplication — consume the readily utilizable carbohydrates of vegetable waste-material necessary for the moulds, furthermore, they also produce antibiotics effective against moulds. Competition of the moulds might be eliminated almost completely by heat-treatment of substrate and thereby it may be possible to produce oyster fungus safely.

INVESTIGATION OF SOME FREE AND BOUND AMINO ACIDS IN THE FRUIT BODIES OF *PLEUROTUS OSTREATUS* (JACQ. EX FR.) KUMMER

by

P. VARJÚ
University of Foresty and Timber Industry,
Sopron, Hungary

The presence of free basic and aromatic amino acids, in addition to some neutral ones (Val, Ala, Leu) occurring in considerable quantities is characteristic in the extracts of well-developed, sound fruit bodies of *Pleurotus ostreatus*. Investigations described below were carried out for five amino acids as follows: Arg, His, Lys, Phe, Tyr. The flow of amino acids to the fruit body was traced and the building up proteins in it during fructification.

MATERIAL AND METHODS

Two strains with considerably different cultural properties were compared. The main difference between the two was that one of them marked Plo NTT required an impact of cold before fructifying. The other strain marked Plo Flo, originating from North America, produces fruit bodies spontaneously. Fruit bodies of Plo Flo are white or cream coloured, and those of Plo NTT are ash-blue.

The fungi were allowed to interweave rough-ground corn cob in five-litre bottles under sterile conditions. It lasted for 3—5 weeks. During the following incubation period of 3 weeks, the cultures of the Plo Flo strain started to fruit. The cultures of the other strain were turned to fructification by being kept for four days at 5 °C.

The age of a fruit body or the stages of fruiting can hardly be defined. Fruit bodies at the same stage of development may have various sizes and weights, and under different conditions the development of fruit bodies takes place at different rates. Four stages of fruit body production were arbitrarily differentiated. Initial fruit bodies with a not totally spread head of max. 30—40 mm in diameter on the 5th—7th day after emerging were called young fruit bodies. The head and stem had almost the same weights. The well-developed fruit body before spore dusting was the second stage. It is the full-spread head that is characteristic of this stage. The head of the mushroom was 4—8 times heavier than its stem. The fruit body just dusting spores was defined the third stage, and the last stage was a fruit body on the third day after spore dusting. By this time withering was usually observed on the edge of the head, and generally the moisture content of the mushroom was considerably lower than before.

Picked fruit bodies were cut to heads and stems, lyophilized, and pulverized. The nitrogen content was determined by Kjeldahl's method. Weighed quantities of powder samples were extracted with a known quantity of 0.01 M solution of hydrochloric acid in ethanol by shaking at room temperature. The free amino acids were determined from the clear liquid after centrifugation. Other parts of the samples were hydrolyzed by heating with 6 N hydrochloric acid for 48 hours at 105 °C. The sum of the amounts of free and bound amino acids was determined from the hydrolysate. Aromatic and basic amino acids were separated by Fixion 50 X 8 strongly acidic cation exchanger thin layer chromatographic plates (manufacturer: Chinoin, Nagytétény). Development was made according to Dévényi (1970) by sodium citrate buffer (pH 5.23, 0.35 M for Na^+). Amino acids were detected by spraying with ninhydrin reagent containing Cd^{2+} ions. Plates were kept in the dark at room temperature overnight. Quantitative evaluation was carried out by a densitometer (type: ERI 65 M, Carl Zeiss, Jena). A filter of 560 nm was used. It was previously found that samples developed on different plates could not be compared directly. Moreover the linearity of the densitometer was not guaranteed at the sensitivity range used. For these reasons an internal standard mixture was developed on every plate in three different quantities. Peaks recorded by the densitometer were integrated, and the quantity of each amino acid was determined on the basis of peak areas by interpolation between two appropriate standards. It was found, in accordance with data in the literature, that the error of the method was 5–20% depending on the absolute values. That is why all the results are given as only one- or two-digit numbers.

RESULTS

Total protein contents of the samples, calculated on the basis of nitrogen contents are shown in Table 1. Tables 2 and 3 contain the sum of free and bound quantities of amino acids investigated in per cent of the total protein content of the samples. Data related to the heads of fruit bodies are especially noteworthy, because (except the first stage of development) the head of a mushroom is heavier than the stem, and the protein content of a head is about twice as much as that of a stem. There is a difference between data of the two strains. In the case of Plo NTT the amino acid contents of mushrooms of various stages of development vary within the limits of error. In the case of Plo Flo, the quantity of basic amino acids is higher at the beginning and at the end of the fruiting period than in the period of quick increase of weight and during spore dusting. In order to characterize the changes of the quantities of free amino acids in the fruit bodies, the proportions in weight of free and bound amino acids are shown in Tables 4 and 5.

Table 1

Total protein contents in fruit bodies of *Pleurotus ostreatus* at various stages of development in per cent of the air-dry samples

Sample		Stage of development*			
		1.	2.	3.	4.
Plo Flo	head	25.5	23.9	18.2	20.5
	stem	12.9	10.6	7.0	9.3
Plo NTT	head	35.0	24.3	17.4	18.2
	stem	20.6	10.0	8.6	7.4

*see definitions in the text.

Table 2

Quantities of free and bound amino acids in fruit bodies of Plo NTT at various stages of development in per cent of total protein

Stage of development	Sample from	Amino acids				
		Arg	His	Lys	Phe	Tyr
1.	head	7.7	3.1	6.9	4.3	3.1
	stem	12.1	1.6	15.0	3.9	1.9
2.	head	7.8	2.5	6.7	5.3	2.8
	stem	6.3	1.7	14.0	4.9	2.3
3.	head	8.0	2.3	7.5	4.4	1.8
	stem	6.6	2.3	8.0	6.0	3.6
4.	head	8.2	2.7	7.7	4.4	1.9
	stem	5.4	2.0	7.3	4.5	2.3

DISCUSSION

Young fruit bodies have higher protein content. In well-developed fruit bodies a large part of skeletal substances, carbohydrates, lipids, ash constituents, and other substances can be found. In accordance with its function, the stem contains a smaller part of protein in every sample. In the young fruit body of Plo NTT the head and stem were not totally differentiated. Surely it was the reason for the relatively high protein content found in the stem. Only a short time passed between the 2nd and 3rd stages. Differences in protein contents of the two stages were certainly caused by losses of nitrogenous substances through spore dusting. The exhaustion of non-nitrogenous

Table 3
Quantities of free and bound amino acids in fruit bodies of Plo Flo at various stages of development in per cent of total protein

Stage of development	Sample from	Amino acids				
		Arg	His	Lys	Phe	Tyr
1.	head	10.0	3.1	11.0	5.5	2.7
	stem	6.2	3.1	6.3	5.4	1.6
2.	head	2.9	2.5	8.4	4.2	2.1
	stem	8.5	4.7	13.2	4.7	2.8
3.	head	6.0	2.7	6.6	4.9	3.3
	stem	7.1	2.9	8.6	4.3	2.9
4.	head	11.0	3.9	8.8	4.4	2.4
	stem	5.4	2.1	7.5	6.5	3.2

Table 4
Proportion in weight of some free and bound amino acids in fruit bodies of Plo NTT at various stages of development

Stage of development	Sample from	Amino acids				
		Arg	His	Lys	Phe	Tyr
1.	head	0.02	0.05	0.07	0.04	0.09
	stem	0.01	0.04	0.04	0.03	0.09
2.	head	0.13	0.17	0.12	0.13	0.23
	stem	0.44	0.56	0.17	0.53	1.15
3.	head	0.04	0.04	0.04	0.03	0.40
	stem	0.02	<0.02	0.05	0.10	0.12
4.	head	0.13	0.06	0.04	0.08	0.38
	stem	0.04	0.07	0.04	0.05	0.13

substances may be the reason for the N content being relatively high at the stage after spore dusting. The fact is that different fruit bodies were attached to different stages. It was not possible to determine the earlier protein contents of fruit bodies representing the 4th stage.

The proportional changes of free amino acids to bound ones reflect fairly well the course of development of a fruit body. A slow growth is characteristic of the first

Table 5
Proportion in weight of some free and bound amino acids in fruit bodies of Plo Flo
at various stages of development

Stage of development	Sample from	Amino acids				
		Arg	His	Lys	Phe	Tyr
1.	head	<0.01	0.01	<0.01	0.02	0.03
	stem	<0.01	0.01	0.03	0.02	0.04
2.	head	0.10	0.06	0.05	0.14	0.54
	stem	0.09	0.03	0.19	0.23	0.63
3.	head	0.14	0.08	0.11	0.20	0.29
	stem	0.03	0.09	0.16	0.38	0.32
4.	head	0.06	0.02	<0.01	0.04	0.07
	stem	0.02	0.01	0.01	0.03	0.06

period of 5—7 days, the quantity of free amino acids is not significant. The usually much shorter next period is characterised by the quick increase in weight. Amino acids flow in large quantities from the mycelia to fruit body. After spore dusting the flow of amino acids, weight increase, and the building up of proteins of the fruit body slow down and stop. The difference between the two strains at the 3rd stage can be ascribed to the fact that in the case of Plo NTT, sampling was carried out at the end of the period of spore dusting. The state of the 3rd sample was closer to the 4th stage than in the case of Plo Flo.

On the basis of these findings optimal picking time is the stage before dusting. At this stage the fruit body has nearly its final dry weight, and using free amino acids as a foodstuff (present in 3—20 per cent) certainly adds considerably to its peculiar taste and aroma by condensation or other reactions.

Having divided a well-developed fruit body of Plo NTT strain before spore dusting in the direction of its lamellas into three parts, differences of samples lyophilized at once, lyophilized after deep freeze of 48 hours, and dried by infrared lamp with air ventilation were investigated. No difference could be observed between the first two samples after lyophilization. Samples dried by infrared lamp became brown and hard, and contracted. In spite of the possibility that free basic amino acids probably played a role in browning by condensation reactions significant differences in the quantities or proportions of free and bound amino acids of the samples were not found by the semiquantitative analytical method applied.

It is known that in a fruit body stored in a dry place at room temperature the same changes accompanied by decrease in the quantity of free amino acids take place as in fruit bodies on their stem. Picking the fruit body, the amino acid supply ceased to exist, but enzymes soon became inactive under the infrared lamp.

SUMMARY

As part of a comprehensive investigation of the nitrogenous substances in the mushroom, the quantities of some free and bound — aromatic and basic — amino acids were determined in the fruit bodies of *Pleurotus ostreatus*.

Fruit bodies of the mushroom cultivated on corn cob substratum were studied at various stages of the fructification from a few days after coming out of the first initial fruit bodies to the stage after spore dusting. Samples were quickly and carefully dried and ground. The free amino acids extracted with an appropriate solvent, and the bound ones deliberated by hydrochloric hydrolysis were separated by ion exchange thin-layer chromatography. These quantities were determined by densitometry. The relation between the quantity and proportion of the free and bound amino acids and the age of the fruit body was studied. The possibility of the determination of the optimal picking time and the effect of storage conditions on the studied properties were also studied.

REFERENCES

Dévényi T. (1970): *Acta Biochem. Biophys. Acad. Sci. Hung.* 5, 435.

SOIL ORGANISMS AS COMPONENTS
OF THE SOIL ECOSYSTEM

THE GEOGRAPHICAL FACTOR IN RELATION
TO SOIL TYPES AND THEIR MICROBIAL POPULATION

by

E. N. MISHUSTIN
Institute of Microbiology of the Academy of Sciences of the USSR,
Moscow, USSR

In his classical works, V. V. Dokuchayev developed a doctrine of natural zones and elucidated the distributive patterns of soil types on the Earth's surface.

Dokuchayev worked during a period of enhanced interest in microbiology stemming from the great discoveries by Louis Pasteur, when many scientists carried out a number of important studies that demonstrated an immense role of micro-organisms in soil and plant life. Being well aware of those studies, Dokuchayev became greatly preoccupied with microbiology.

Many years have elapsed since that time. Our knowledge of the soil population and its activities has grown tremendously. Nevertheless, many of the fundamental aspects of soil microbiology still remain poorly known. This applies, in particular, to the relationship between soil type and soil micropopulation.

Having duly appreciated Dokuchayev's doctrine of soil zonality, many researchers attempted to demonstrate a specificity of the microflora of particular soil types. However, they failed to reveal any essential differences among micropopulations of different types of soil. An impression was created that the ecological factors had a greater effect on the composition of soil micropopulation than did the geographic factors (Severin, 1909; Kriss, 1947; Krassilnikov, 1958; and others). For instance, Krassilnikov held that the greatest influence on soil microflora was exerted by higher plants.

Generally, many Soviet microbiologists had, until quite recently, denied that the geographical factor had a decisive role in the formation of microbial associations in soils. The same is true of foreign investigators who were much less preoccupied with questions of microbial geography than their Soviet counterparts. The overall results obtained in the studies carried out thus far favour the conclusion that different soil types are distinguished only by microbial numbers present in them, while the composition of microbial species is more or less similar whatever the soil type, and that the ratios among the different members of microbial coenoses mainly change under the effect of ecological conditions. We think, however, that such concepts are based on erroneous premises.

A number of investigations (*e.g.* Mishustin and Timofeeva, 1944; Krassilnikov and Nikitina, 1945) have demonstrated that different microbial coenoses are involved at different stages of organic matter decomposition. For that reason, the geographical environment, which abruptly changes the rates of organic refuse decomposition and of soil processes, should call into play quite different associations of soil micro-organisms, notably because of temperature differences which strongly affect the microbiological processes. The ecological conditions, of course, have also a big role to play in each zone in addition to the geographical factor, as will be shown later in this paper.

Thus, basing oneself on general considerations, one should expect that, while soil micro-organisms do show wide ranges of distribution, the zones of their optimal growth should be limited for a number of reasons, particularly geographical ones. It is in this sense that one should interpret the concept of geographical distribution of soil micro-organisms, i.e. that their distribution is naturally and organically linked to the geography of soil types.

It should be noted that this view is fully consistent with that of Kluyver who wrote, in his article entitled "Microbial Metabolism and the Energy Basis of Life" (1956) that "...experience has shown that an overwhelming majority of microbes may be considered to be ubiquitous. This does not imply, however, that they occur everywhere and are present in large numbers but merely that a few individuals manage to maintain the species in quite different locations of the globe, either in a state of anabiosis or by way of short-term and local bursts of multiplication succeeded by a slow diminution of the population formed".

Using the evidence presented below, we strive to show that the geographical factor does exert a powerful influence on the composition of soil micropopulation, causing marked differences in microfloral composition between different soil types which, in turn, are highly dependent on the geographical environment. And this is only natural, since the distribution of micro-organisms in soils is a highly sensitive indicator of the properties of the environment under consideration. Back in 1924, V. L. Omeliansky in his paper "Micro-organisms as Chemical Reagents" called attention to microbes as very sensitive indicators of the composition of the substrate on which they reproduced.

A question arises why no substantial differences can be detected, in certain cases, among the microbial coenoses of different soils? We believe that the main reason why microbiologists tend to reach erroneous conclusions regarding the composition of soil micropopulation is the inadequate choice of investigative techniques. While soil microbiologists have a diversity of methods at their disposal, particular methods can be employed to the best advantage only for specific purposes. Unfortunately, this simple fact is often forgotten and inadequate methods are frequently used. Thus, for instance, when in determining the composition of soil micropopulation, it is a common practice to limit oneself to determinations of total numbers of soil micro-organisms growing on particular nutrient media, or to ascertain the physiological status of particular microbial groups. However, overall determinations of microbial numbers in a soil cannot make a substantial contribution to the characterization of that soil. Also, physiological groups are extremely wide and include not only members of different

306

species but also of different classes. The only exceptions are narrowly specialized microbial groups, such as the group of nitrifiers for which the concepts of function and species are practically equivalent. Therefore, by revealing only certain physiological groups of micro-organisms without resorting to a detailed study of their function it is impossible to take account of highly important re-groupings occurring in the soil micropopulation. A change in environmental conditions may entail a change of some particular microbial species for others, although the former do not disappear entirely from the soil micropopulation.

The foregoing does not deny the usefulness of determining the overall quantitative composition of soil microflora, including the identification of physiological groups of micro-organisms. We think, however, that the most promising approach is to conduct deep-going studies into the state of individual microbial species. Such studies should be undertaken in conjunction with those of the physiology of those microbial species that make up a coenosis, for it is only on this basis that more or less complete conclusions can be made regarding the state of the substrate.

As concerns the procedures to be used in those studies, it should be noted, that the commonly employed media provide only for the growth of a relatively limited set of micro-organisms, and the task is to diversify both the composition of such media and the procedures used to detect micro-organisms.

For a number of years, the Department of Soil Microbiology, Institute of Microbiology, of the Academy of Sciences of the USSR, has been engaged in studies of soils in different climatic zones of the USSR. In their experimental studies, the workers of our Laboratory have analyzed thousands of soil samples collected throughout the Soviet Union (both its European and Asian parts). In most cases, longitudinal studies were carried out lasting throughout the warm period of the year. In comparing the microfloras of soils, all the way from the polar deserts of the Far North through to the deserts of Central Asia, we strove to establish characteristic differences among the micropopulations of different soil types. Before proceeding to discuss the results obtained in these studies, it is appropriate to emphasize that the status of soil microfloras is subject to considerable change, depending on a number of factors, including soil moisture content and temperature, supply of organic compounds, etc.

For quite obvious reasons, the numbers of non-spore-bearing bacteria are subject to the greatest seasonal change. Bacteri show less marked fluctuations with time. The above factors also affect the numbers of *Actinomycetes* and microscopic fungi.

It is important that a change in microbial numbers in a soil does not entail disappearance of the specific signs characterizing the microbial make-up of particular soil types. The averaged results of large numbers of analyses enable quite definite conclusions to be made regarding the micropopulation of different soil types. A tentative characterization of the microflora of the A horizon for several virgin soils is presented in Figure 1. Soil cultivation usually increases the total microbial number without, however, altering in any substantial degree the proportions of individual microbial groupings.

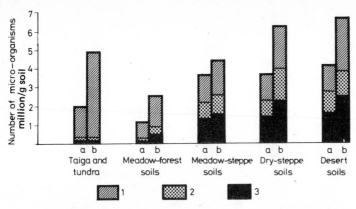

Fig. 1. Relationship between common groups of micro-organisms of
different soil types.
a. Virgin soil, b. cultivated soil
1. *Asporogenous* bacteria, 2. *Actinomycetes*, 3. *Bacilli*

As can be seen from this figure, southern soils are richer in micro-organisms, that is they display greater biogenicity. The fact that the virgin soils of the Far North have somewhat increased microbial numbers is accounted for by the accumulation on their surface of slightly decomposed plant residues which provide a good food supply for micro-organisms, notably. fungi and non-spore-forming bacteria, during the warm season.

Further south, bacteri and *Actinomycetes* come to play increasing roles in the microbial coenoses. As our model-experiments have indicated, these micro-organisms come into play at later stages of decomposition of organic residues. Possibly, this is due to the fact that they (notably *Actinomycetes*) are provided with a more powerful enzyme apparatus and also that they (bacteria) require additional growth factors. Because in warm climates plant residue is decomposed faster, more favourable conditions are created for the reproduction of bacteria and *Actinomycetes*. In more southern zones, fungal numbers decreased, apparently due to increased competitive activities of bacteria and *Actinomycetes*.

It is noteworthy that the relative proportions of microbial groups in different soils can be determined only tentatively: mycelial fragments and fungal and actinomycete spores recorded with plating methods, differ considerably in their mass and functions in soils. Therefore, our data are only rough estimates, marking out only the general trends in microbial re-groupings in different soil types.

We believe it more reasonable to calculate bacterial numbers per gram of humus, rather than per gram of soil, since the saprophytic micro-organisms are active mainly in soil organic matter rather than in the entire soil mass. With this approach, the great biogenicity of southern soils is made more apparent.

That southern soils contain more micro-organisms is suggested by the results of studies using a variety of methods, such as direct counts according to Winogradsky,

Table 1
Microbial numbers in soils of the USSR as revealed by direct counts
(millions/g)

Soil	Soil status	Per g of soil	Per g of humus
Podzol	Virgin	300– 600	9.000– 18.000
Soddy podzol	Virgin	600–1000	18.000– 30.000
	Cultivated	1000–2000	30.000– 60.000
Chernozem	Virgin	2000–2500	30.000– 37.000
	Cultivated	2500–3000	37.000– 45.000
Sierozem	Virgin	1200–1600	60.000– 80.000
	Cultivated	1800–3000	90.000–150.000

Novogrudsky's method (1948), plating micro-organisms on solid nutrient media, etc. As known, direct soil microscopy yields much higher values than the plating methods. So, while the absolute microbial numbers recorded with different methods are different, the general conclusions reached, are similar.

Table 1 presents results of studies devoted to the quantitative estimation of microbial numbers using the direct count method, most of which were carried out by workers of the Institute of Agricultural Microbiology of the Lenin All-Union Academy of Agricultural Sciences (Lazarev, 1949; and others).

So far, soils of several of the mountain ranges of Caucasus and Central Asia have been explored. The vertical zonation has been found to affect the composition of soil microflora in the same way as the latitudinal zonality. With increasing altitude and decreasing mean annual soil temperatures, bacterial numbers diminish and the proportion of bacteria decreases. This is particularly well marked when the soil micropopulation is recalculated per gram of humus.

An increase in microbial numbers in a soil, including increases in bacterial and antinomycete numbers, provides an indication of enhancement of mobilization processes. A direct proof of this is the increase of the nitrification energy. Several decades ago, Kostychev and his co-workers found that the nitrification energy progressively increased from northern to southern soils, and this has been confirmed by our studies. Thus, Tepliakova who studied the microbiology of the A horizon in soils of the vertical zones of the Zailüsk Alatau, came to the conclusion that the nitrifying capacity of soils rich in micro-organisms was much higher in warm climates than in cold ones. Calculations of nitrification energy in per cent of humus indicate that, for three weeks, a mountain meadow soil accumulates 1.2 mg NO_3 per 1 kg of soil, a chernozem soil, 6.9 mg, and a sierozem soil, 62.9 mg (Table 2). Those soils richer in microbial mass thus have greater supplies of mineral nitrogen compounds (Table 2).

It should be noted that a very important practical implication of differences in the mobilization processes in different soils is a more effective action of mineral fertilizers in the north than in the south (Anikst, 1969). This is a result of a lesser accumulation of nutrient materials in soils of the nothern zone.

Table 2
Nitrification energy in different virgin soils of Zailüsk Alatau
(Tepliakova, 1961)

Soil type	Depth (cm)	Increment of NO_3^- (mg 1 kg of soil)	Amount of NO_3^- per 1% of humus
Mountain meadow	0–10	12.8	1.2
Mountain forest	0–12	85.6	2.9
Chernozem	0–13	64.8	6.9
Dark chestnut	0– 9	102.7	26.5
Sierozem	0– 6	138.9	62.9

With respect to the make-up of the bacterial population of different soils, the dominating species are those from the genera *Pseudomonas, Bacterium* and *Mycobacterium,* as judged from the records obtained on generally used nutrient media. However, it has not been possible, until now, to determine reliably the differences in the proportions of spore-forming bacteria in different types of soil. Possibly, no significant differences exist here at all. Non-spore-bearing bacteria have been found to be pioneers in the digestion of organic residues. Since all soils have fresh organic matter (mainly plant residues) which do not differ greatly in their chemical make-up, it is quite possible that identical bacterial species which do not form spores, develop in different soils. Our studies have clearly demonstrated the existence, in a number of widely distributed bacterial species, of ecological races differing in their physiological and certain cultural characters. It is of particular importance that a large proportion of soil bacteria display adaptive responses to climatic changes (Mishustin, 1947).

As already mentioned, spore-forming bacteria are associated with the more strongly decayed soil organic matter, and the composition of these bacteria may be expected to reflect the features of the soil type in question. Our studies have confirmed that assumption. There is a large body of evidence to show that each soil type has a quite characteristic composition of bacterial species. Associations of spore-bearing soil bacteria are exceedingly well-demonstrable using the medium which we have proposed, consisting of a mixture of equal volumes of meat-infusion agar and must agar. The medium should have a neutral reaction.

It has been our usual practice, in identifying bacterial species, to culture a soil suspension pasteurized at 70 °C for 5 minutes. Figure 2 presents data on the groupings of spore-forming bacteria peculiar to different soil types. A great diversity of bacterial species can of course be found in any soil but only a few of them are important as indicators. These data show that the *B. agglomeratus–B. cereus* grouping is very characteristic for soils of the Far North. The podzols of the middle part of the USSR are abundant in *B. mycoides* and *B. cereus* chernozems contain large numbers of *B. idosus* and *B. megaterium,* while chestnut and sierozem (brownish grey) soils are rich in *B. subtilis.* In addition, these soils usually contain large numbers of embryos of

Soils	Bac. agglomeratus	Bac. cereus	Bac. adhaerens	Bac. mycoides	Bac. virgulus	Bac. idosus	Bac. megaterium	Bac. mesentericus	Bac. gasificans
Gleic–podzolic	▨								
Podzolic	▨	▨		▨	▨				
Podzolic under grass		▨							
Chernozems						▨	▨		▨
Solonetz			▨			▨	▨		
Chestnut brown						▨	▨	▨	
Sierozems						▨	▨	▨	

Fig. 2. Dominant *Bacillus* spp. of different soils occurring in the Soviet Union

B. megaterium. Apart from the above-mentioned bacteria, certain numbers of embryos of other species can be found in any soil.

The foregoing information on the bacillary make-up of microflora refers to virgin soils. Cultivation makes a soil more similar to more southern soils with respect to bacterial composition.

The distributive pattern of a microbial group is associated with the physiological features of the latter. Those soils where mobilization processes are strongly marked are dominated by bacteria which are capable of utilizing mineral nitrogen. Conversely, those soils with weak mobilization processes are best suited for those spore-formers which need organic nitrogen.

Similar variations in bacterial forms exist in soils of vertical zones, although these soils show some differences. Thus, for instance, mountain meadow soils, while being poor in *B. mycoides* as well as tundra soils, are abundant in *B. cereus* and *B. idosus*. Mountain chernozem soils support *B. mycoides* which are virtually absent from ordinary chernozems.

That bacterial species vary in a consistent manner from one soil to another has been demonstrated by many published studies.

A large number of investigations have shown that the geographic factor influences the distribution of microscopic fungi, and general agreement has been reached concerning certain features of fungal distribution in soils. Thus, for example, the diversity of soil fungi is generally known to increase in southern soils although their total numbers noticeably decrease. Fungi from the genus *Aspergillus* have been found to be virtually absent from soils of the North and to be abundant in southern soils (*Waksman, 1927;* and others).

Our Laboratory has accumulated a large body of evidence related to the ecology of a number of fungi.

Analyses were performed following inoculation of soil on solid nutrient media. Cultivation somewhat altered the composition of soil fungi.

These analyses have revealed consistent patterns in fungal distribution. Thus, those soils in which mineralization processes are weak, contain increased proportions of fungi belonging to the genera *Penicillium* and *Mucor*. Further south, *Penicillium* progressively decrease to give way to those from the genus *Aspergillus*. This is due to the fact that *Aspergillus* is able to take up more complex organic compounds. It is of interest that soloñetz soils which occur within the chernozem zone, frequently exhibit increased numbers of fungi belonging to the genus *Aspergillus*.

Soils of different climatic zones are different not only with respect to numbers of members of the genus *Penicillium* but also in the proportions of members of different sections of that genus. It is of interest that soils in which biological processes are less intensive show a predominance of biochemically less active members from the genus *Penicillium*. Those soils in which conditions for fungal development are less favourable, such as solonetzes, solonchaks and takyrs, are dominated by fungi from the section *Monoverticillata*. Forest soils are rich in fungi from the section *Biverticillata*. Without dwelling, for lack of space, on the species composition of *Penicillium* in particular soils, we shall confine ourselves to pointing out that different soils contain species with limited distributive ranges along with those having wide-range occurrences (*Penicillium canescens, P. cyclopium, P. thomii*, etc.).

We may state that members of the genus *Fusarium* tend to occur in soils supporting grasses, while forest soils are virtually free of these fungi. Chernozem, chestnut and sierozem soils are the richest in *Fusarium* fungi.

Mucor sp., which prefer organic nitrogen, are common in the upper layers of virgin soils containing large amounts of undecomposed plant residues. *Mucor ramannianus* is demonstrable only in forest soils.

Our results, as well as those obtained by Pumpianskaya (1932) indicate that yeasts are abundant in soils rich in slightly decomposed organic compounds. This is quite understandable because yeasts use only simple sugars and organic acids as the source of carbon, and so are widely distributed in northern soils.

The study by Babaieva and Golovieva (1963) devoted to yeast ecology deserves special mention. The authors made a comprehensive study of a variety of soils, all the way from tundra to dry steppe and confirmed the presence of large amounts of yeasts in soils rich in slightly decomposed plant remains, with acid reactions, and considerable moisture levels. Other soils contain less yeast. It is noteworthy that the particular soil types have particular sets of yeast species. Thus, the genus *Candida*, which has a mycelial stage in its developmental cycle is predominant in acid podzolic and soddy-podzolic soils. Capsulated yeasts from the genus *Cryptococcus* are found in large numbers in gley tundra and bog soils. Members of the genus *Lypomyces* are consistently found in forest soils and chernozems. Chernozems frequently contain pink yeasts *(Rhodotorula)*. Particularly diverse yeasts are found in bog soils in which *Torulopsis* yeasts are commonly found along with other species. These yeasts are not found in other soils.

While rather little information on yeast ecology has been accumulated, the evidence which is available clearly demonstrates differences among soils in yeast distribution.

Concerning actinomycetes, their distributive patterns have been delineated rather clearly by our studies as well as those of other investigators (Tepliakova, 1961).

Table 3
Percentages of pigmented versus non-pigmented Actinomycetes in soils
of Kazakhstan

Soil	Actinomycetes	
	Pigmented	Non-pigmented
Mountain meadow, alpine	21.0	79.0
Mountain chernozem, virgin	43.4	56.6
Mountain chernozem, cultivated	51.4	48.6
Sierozem, virgin	46.0	54.0
Sierozem, cultivated	51.2	48.8

The accumulated evidence indicates that northern soils are poor both in actinomycete numbers and diversity, and these progressively increase in a north-to-south direction.

Some actinomycetes are wide-ranging while others can multiply in significant numbers only in particular soils. The distributive pattern of actinomycetes is thus similar to those of bacteria and fungi shown above.

The difficulties involved in actinomycete identification are generally known, and considerable work has to be done if the ecology of actinomycetes is to be elucidated. Possibly the best way to proceed towards this goal is to begin with a study of the distribution in soils of individual actinomycete groups (series) which may provide a first scheme of their distributive patterns. Tepliakova (1961) noted decreases in pigmented forms of actinomycetes with increased absolute altitudes of soil occurrence (Table 3).

A few words should be said about the free-living fixers of molecular nitrogen. Recent studies have considerably broadened our knowledge of this highly important group of micro-organisms which has been shown to include a great diversity of forms (*Mycobacterium, Clostridium, Azotobacter, Azotomonas, Derxia, Bejerincka*, etc.). But only a few of them have been studied in detail from the ecological viewpoint. This mainly applies to *Clostridium* and *Azotobacter* whose distributive patterns are rather well-known.

Until quite recently, nitrogen fixers of the genus *Clostridium* were thought to be ubiquitous. The studies of Emtsev (1966), however, make it necessary to modify this view. Evidence shows that *Cl. pasteurianum* occurs in large numbers in podzolic and soddy-podzolic soils, while in the southern zone (chestnut and sierozem soils) it is largely succeeded by *Cl. acetobutilicum*. The soil type thus influences actinomycete distribution as well.

There is extensive literature devoted to *Azotobacter* and its distribution in soils of the USSR and many other countries. The information on *Azotobacter* biology and ecology has been summarized in monographs by Sushkina (1949) and Blinkov (1959). Experimental evidence and critical reviews of some studies have also been published by the present author (Mishustin *et al.* 1968).

Azotobacter is an organism very exacting to the environment. It develops in soils rich in available phosphorus compounds, giving a reaction close to neutral, containing organic substances, having a sufficient water supply, etc. Clearly, such requirements are not always met even by rich soils such as chernozems. In podzolic and soddy podzolic soils *Azotobacter* occurs mainly in more neutral areas of floodplains and heavily farmed lands. In chernozems and more southern soils it is constantly found only in irrigated or sufficiently moistened soils. In non-irrigated soils, *Azotobacter* usually reproduces as an ephemeral only in springtime. This appears to be mainly due to its increased requirements in water supply.

The foregoing makes it clear why adequate knowledge of *Azotobacter* ecology can be gained only through studies conducted over time. Analyses that do not take account of the soil status result in incorrect conclusions regarding the ecology of *Azotobacter*.

Generally, *Azotobacter* distribution is not associated with any particular soil-climatic zone: it occurs both in the north and in the south but only in highly fertile soils. The presence of *Azotobacter* is a good indicator of valuable agronomic properties of the soil.

Cellulose is known to be broken down by both bacteria and fungi. Different cellulose-decomposing organisms show considerable differences in their substrate requirements, notably in their need of available nitrogen. Of all fungi, the least exacting are those from the genus *Dematium*, which therefore dominate in those soils where mobilization processes are slight. Nitrogen requirements are higher in such cellulose decomposers as *Chaetomium, Fusarium,* etc. Bacteria have need for even more nitrogen than fungi, so that soils with a more favourable nitrogen balance support large numbers of myxobacteria *(Polyangium, Myxococcus)* and, with further improvement of environmental conditions, also vibrios *(Cellvibrio)* and myxobacteria from the genus *Cytophaga.*

While all these bacteria and fungi may be present in soils of the same zone, soils of warmer zones contain many more cellulose-decomposing bacteria than fungi because of increasing energy of mobilization processes in a north-to-south direction.

The foregoing discussion warrants the conclusion that species may be singled out among soil micro-organisms which characterize the type of soil-forming process as well as those which are indicative of the agronomic properties of soils.

In the foregoing characterization of different soils, we made use of data relating only to the A horizon of virgin soils and to the ploughed-layer of cultivated soils. Different soils, however, strongly differ in the depth of their microbiological profiles, and the microbial composition of soils changes with depth. There is, however, no direct correlation between humus content in a soil and microbial numbers in it. With increasing depth, microbial numbers fall rather abruptly both in virgin and cultivated soils. Microfloral composition likewise changes with depth. Deeper soil layers are relatively richer in bacteria and not infrequently, also in *Actinomycetes,* particularly in chernozem and sierozem soils where these microbial groups are more abundant.

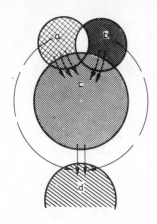

Fig. 3. Schematic structure of a microbial coenosis
a. zymogenic, b. humus-decomposing,
c. other forms, d. autotrophic

The changes in the species make-up of micro-organisms that take place with increasing depth can be illustrated by chernozem soils. Some spore-forming bacteria, such as *B. idosus* are found deep in the soil, while others, such as *B. megaterium* and *B. mycoides,* tend to inhabit the topsoil. The same is true for fungi. *Penicillium sp.* are the main representatives of microflora in deeper soil layers. *Mucor, Fusarium* and *Trichoderma* mainly occur in the upper layers.

A question arises as to which soil layers should be sampled in studying differences between micropopulations of different soils? We think that the most representative in this respect is the upper soil layer, i.e. the A horizon of virgin soils and the ploughed-layer of cultivated soils. In our ecolo-geographic correlations we base ourselves on these layers.

The ecological factors disturb the analysis of the effect of the geographic factor on the composition of soil microflora. While ecological conditions do play a large role and at times may mislead the investigator (notably those working with a limited set of soils) into believing that their effects are greatest, there can be no doubt that the most powerful influence on the composition of soil microflora is exerted by the geographic factor.

Recently, the use of new methods of investigation, such as capillary microscopy (Perfiliev and Gabe, 1961; Aristovskaya, 1965; and others) and electronmicroscopy (Nikitin and co-authors, 1966) have greatly expanded our knowledge of soil microflora and have demonstrated immense stores of micro-organisms in soils. And the question arises whether the concepts of coenoses of soil microflora should be reviewed.

Our findings indicate that the commonplace, well-studied microflora comprises the main mineralizers of organic matter, i.e. it is the zymogenous microflora. Some of these organisms (*Pseudomonas, Nocardia,* etc.) can decompose humus, i.e. perform the function of autochthonous microflora.

The bulk of "Newly discovered" organisms requires low concentrations of organic substances, and appears to mineralize the remnants of decomposed organella. These organisms may be collectively called the "dispersion microflora" (Zavarzin, 1970).

315

In summary, the following scheme of the composition of a soil microbial coenosis may be proposed (Fig. 3) bearing in mind, however, that the make-up of dominating organisms may strongly vary for reasons referred to above.

CONCLUSIONS

1. The composition of soil micro-organisms is subject to strong changes with soil type and status. These changes depend on ecological and geographic factors, as well as on weather conditions and human activities.

2. The geographic factor, which is critical for the soil-forming process, acts specifically on the formation of microbial coenoses in soils. This effect can be recorded, and so it is possible to differentiate between the effects of geographic and other factors on the composition of soil micropopulation.

3. While microbes have wider distributive ranges than other organisms, mass-scale multiplication of particular microbial groups occurs in particular zones. As a result, the microbial associations of particular soil types have a characteristic composition. Soil cultivation does not change the distributive patterns of micro-organisms although it does alter soil microflora.

4. Soils formed in warmer climates have more diversified and numerous microbial populations. The content of microbial mass in soil organic matter increases from northern to southern soils. Hence soils of the southern zone exhibit more vigorous biological processes.

5. The proportions of different microbial groups strongly vary from one soil type to another. Northern soils have few spore-forming bacteria and actinomycetes, and these generally tend to increase in number and diversity in a north-to-south direction.

6. Different soil types are characterized by distinctive microbial groups. This has been particularly well-demonstrated for spore-forming bacteria and fungi but there is also some evidence to suggest that this is also true for actinomycetes.

REFERENCES

(Anikst, D. M.) Аникст, Д. М. (1969) : *Агрохимия,* **10**, 37.
(Aristovskaya, T. V.) Аристовская, Т. В. (1965) : *Микробиология подзолистых почв,* Изд. "Наука"
(Babaieva, J. P. and Golovieva L. A.) Бабаева, Ю. П. Головева Л. А. (1963) : *Сборник "Микроорганизмы в сельском хозяйстве",* изд. МГУ.
(Blinkov, G. N.) Блинков, Г. Н. (1959) *Азотобактер и его значение в сельском хозяйстве.* Изд. Томского У-та.
(Dokuchayev, V. V.) Докучаев, В. В. (1899) : *К изучению о зонах природы* СПБ.
(Emtsev, V. T.) Емцев, В. Т. (1966) : *Сборник ,,IX Международной микробиологический конгресс".* 286.
Kluyver, A. (1956): *The microbial contribution to biology.* Harvard Univ. Press.

(Krassilnikov, N. A.) Красильников, Н. А. (1958): *Микроорганизмы почвы и высшие растения*. Изд. АН СССР.

(Krassilnikov, N. F. and Nikitina N. I.) Красильников, Н. А., Никитина,Н. И. (1945): *Почвоведение, №2,* 132.

(Kriss, A. E.) Крисс, А. Е. (1947): *Микробиол.* **16,** 437.

(Lazarev, N. M.) Лазарев, Н. М. (1949): *Труды Ин-та с. х. микробиологии ВАСХНИЛ за. 1941—45 г. г.,* 23.

(Mishustin, E. N.) Мишустин, Е. Н. (1947): *Эколого-географическая изменчивость почвенных бактерий.* Изд. АН СССР.

Mishustin. E. N. (1975): *Microbial ecology.* **2,** 97.

(Mishustin, E. N. and Shilnikova, V. K.) Мишустин, Е. Н., Шильникова, В. К. (1968): *Биологическая фиксация молекулярного азота.* Изд. ,,Наука''.

(Mishustin, E. N. and Timofeeva A. G.) Мишустин, Е. Н., Тимофеева, А. Г. (1944): *Микробиол.* **13,** 272.

(Nikitin, D. I., Vasilieva, L. V. and Lochmatcheva, R. A.) Никитин, Д. И., Васильева, Л. В., Лохмачева, Р. А. (1966): *Новые и редкие формы почвенных микроорганизмов.* Изд. Наука.

(Novogrudsky, D. M.) Новогрудский, Д. М. (1948): *Известия АН СССР.* сер. биол., 8, 214.

(Omeliansky, V. L.) Омелянский, В. Л. (1924): *Микроорганизмы, как химические индикаторы.* Изд. АН СССР.

(Perfiliev, B. V. and Gabe, D. R.) Перфилев, Б. В., Габе, Д. Р. (1961): *Капиллярные методы изучения микроорганизмов.* Изд. АН СССР.

(Pumpianskaya, L. V.) Пумпиянская, Л. В. (1932): *Доклады ВАСХНИЛ.* 1—2, 41.

(Severin, S. A.) Северин (1909): *Вестник Бактериолого-агрономической станции,* **15,** 116.

(Severin, S. A.) Северин, С. А.: (1909): *Вестник Бактериолого-агрономической станции,* 15, 116.

(Sushkina, N. N.) Сушкина, Н. Н. (1949): *Эколого-географическое распространение азотобактера в почвах СССР.* Изд. АН СССР.

(Tepliakova, Z. F.) Теплякова, З. Ф. (1961): *Труды Ин-та микробиологии и вирусологии АН КазССР,* 5, 129.

(Zavarzin, G. A.) Заварзин, Г. А. (1970): *Журнал общей биологии, №4,* 386.

(Winogradsky, S. N.) Виноградский, С. Н. (1952): *Микробиология почвы.* Изд. АН СССР.

SOME OBSERVATIONS ON THE LITTER BREAKDOWN
BY MESO- AND MACROFAUNA
IN A HORNBEAM-OAK MIXED FOREST

by

J. CSUTÁK and M. B. BAYOUMI
Eötvös Loránd University, Department of Systematic Zoology and Ecology,
Budapest, Hungary

In the framework of "Man and Biosphere" programme, intensive studies have been undertaken on the litter production and decomposition in certain Hungarian hornbeam-oak mixed forest since 1970. These studies have been carried out by the Soil Zoology Research Group of the Hungarian Academy of Sciences, the workers of the Department of Systematic Zoology of the Eötvös Loránd University, in addition to the Research Group of the Botanical Garden of the University. Considerable data have been published on these investigations (Csuták 1975, Gere and Hargitai 1971, Isépy 1974, Loksa and Zicsi 1972).

The rate of litter decomposition in the ecosystem of the investigated area was studied by Isépy (1974), who concluded that the annually produced hornbeam litter disappears in mid-summer. He also found that 87% of the total litter disappeared within half a year. In this connection, Zicsi (1974) pointed out that earthworms, particularly the litter-consuming large-bodied species, play an important role in the breakdown process.

The present investigation aimed to assess the role of meso- and macrofauna in the process of litter breakdown during a course of seven months (from February till August) in 1974. This period was selected due to the fact mentioned previously that litter produced annually ($350-400 \text{ g/m}^2$) in the area under investigation completely disappeared at the and of August (Isépy 1974).

MATERIAL AND METHODS

The study was conducted in a 60 year-old hornbeam-oak forest (*Querco robori–Carpinetum* association) near Szendehely (about 50 km North-east of Budapest). The forest slopes moderately, and is about 250 metres above sea level. The trees are about 18 metres high with a canopy covering 80% of the total surface area of the locality. Hornbeam *(Carpinus betulus),* predominates in the area constituting about 80% of the standing crop, in addition to red oak *(Quercus robur)* which forms about 15%, while the remainder is occupied by cherry, lime and maple trees. After leaf fall, the forest floor is covered with approximately 75% of hornbeam leaves and 25% of oak leaves (Isépy 1974).

Brown leaves collected from the forest floor were airdried, and 5 g of the selected kinds of leaves (hornbeam and oak leaves) were placed into a series of unglazed earthen pots (7 cm in diameter and 7 cm deep). The pots were then covered with nylon nets of three different mesh apertures, viz., small mesh (175 micron aperture diameter) to permit only the entrance of micro-organisms and microfauna, medium mesh (2 mm aperture diameter) to permit the previously mentioned group in addition to mesofauna as *Collembola*, mites, etc., and large mesh (7 mm aperture diameter) to allow for all the above mentioned groups as well as for the macrofauna as *Isopoda, Diplopoda,* large-bodied *Enchytraeidae,* etc.

The leaves were collected at the end of December, 1973, and in February 1974, the pots were buried in the forest soil so that their openings lay on the same level as the soil surface, then were covered with litter. Every two months, three pots of different meshes containing hornbeam leaves, and others containing oak leaves were dug up and brought to the laboratory. The animals were recovered from the pots using Balogh-Loksa funnel extractor, and then counted. After the complete extraction of the animals, the leaves were cleaned by means of a brush under a binocular microscope, air-dried and weighed. Leaves were also oven-dried at 105 °C to estimate their dry weight.

To estimate the percentage of litter loss due to the activities of the different groups of the edaphon under investigation, Wood's method (Wood 1971) was adopted using the following formulae: Percentage loss weight due to:

1. Leaching + microflora + microfauna: C

$$C = (c_1 - c_2) \ \frac{a_1 + a_2}{c_1 + c_2}$$

2. Mesofauna: B

$$B = (b_1 - b_2) \ \frac{a_1 + a_2}{b_1 + b_2} \ - C$$

3. Macrofauna: A
$$A = (a_1 - a_2) - (C + B),$$

where a_1, a_2, b_1, b_2, c_1, c_2 are the per cent dry weights of litter remaining in the large, medium and small mesh pots respectively at times t_1 and t_2.

RESULTS

Table 1 indicates the amount of litter produced between 1971—1973 (after Isépy 1974). The weights of the remaining litter in the pots every two months can be seen in Table 2; while Table 3 represents the effect of leaching + micro-organ-

Table 1
Litter produced between 1971–1973
(after Isépy, 1974)

Year	Total litter g/m²	Carpinus betulus g/m²	Quercus robur g/m²
1971	396.10	310.50	85.60
1972	350.40	266.50	83.90
1973	354.94	253.23	101.71

Table 2
The weight of litter remaining in the pots

Sampling time 1974.	175 μ		2 mm		7 mm	
	air dried	dried at 105 °C	air dried	dried at 105 °C	air dried	dried at 105 °C
Carpinus betulus						
13 Feb.	5.00	4.60	5.00	4.60	5.00	4.60
18 April	4.52	4.02	4.44	3.95	3.95	3.49
	4.45	3.96	4.25	3.78	4.02	3.55
	4.33	3.85	4.40	3.91	4.05	3.57
mean:	4.43	3.94	4.36	3.88	4.00	3.54
5 June	3.57	3.08	3.60	3.11	3.30	2.85
	4.00	3.45	3.88	3.35	2.30	1.98
	4.25	3.66	4.03	3.47	3.40	2.93
mean:	4.43	3.94	3.89	3.31	3.01	2.59
14 Aug.	3.10	2.65	2.20	1.88	0.58	0.49
	3.30	2.82	2.29	1.96	0.70	0.59
	3.20	2.74	1.87	1.60	0.75	0.64
mean:	3.20	2.74	2.12	1.81	0.68	0.57
Quercus robur						
13 Feb.	5.00	4.25	5.00	4.25	5.00	4.25
18 April	4.38	3.98	4.51	4.01	4.35	3.74
	4.52	4.11	4.60	4.10	4.40	3.78
	4.52	4.11	4.60	4.10	4.30	3.75
mean:	4.47	4.06	4.57	4.06	4.35	3.76
5 June	4.40	3.76	4.00	3.42	3.50	3.00
	4.45	3.80	4.30	3.68	3.48	2.98
	4.50	3.88	4.60	3.93	3.59	3.08
mean:	4.45	3.78	4.30	3.68	3.53	3.02
14 Aug.	3.60	3.36	3.25	3.03	2.42	2.07
	3.80	3.54	3.50	3.26	2.44	2.09
mean:	3.72	3.47	3.46	3.23	2.42	2.07

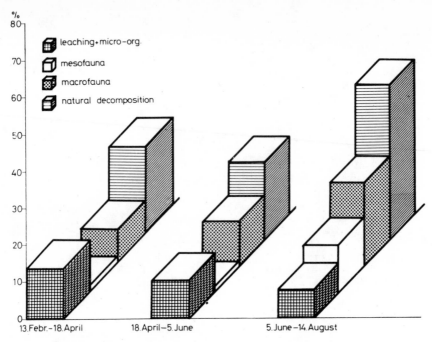

Fig. 1. The percentage of different edaphic groups participating in the decomposition of *Carpinus betulus* leaves

isms + microfauna, in addition to that of meso- and macrofauna on litter breakdown. It appears from Table 3 and Figures 1 and 2 that the macrofauna has the greatest effect in the breakdown process, while the loss in litter weight due to leaching + microorganisms + microfauna is of a moderate degree, and still the mesofauna has only a small part in this process. It is clear from the data presented in Figures 3 and 4 that the rate of hornbeam breakdown is much faster than that of the oak leaves. This might be indicated by comparing weight losses of the two kinds of leaves during the whole experimental period (see Table 3) as the hornbeam lost about 87.61% of its original weight, while the oak leaves lost only 51.3%

In both kinds of leaves the greatest loss occurred between June and August. This might be ascribed to the physical and chemical changes in the leaves that render them more palatable for soil organisms.

Table 4 represents the mean numbers of the most important mesofaunal groups, mainly *Collembola* and *Oribatida*, extracted from the pots. Of the *Collembola*, *Folsomia quadrioculata* Tullb., and of the *Oribatida*, *Oppia ornata* (Oudms.) were the most dominant species recovered. It is worth while noting that the Collembolan families *Onychiuridae* and *Hypogastruridae* were found in large numbers in some

322

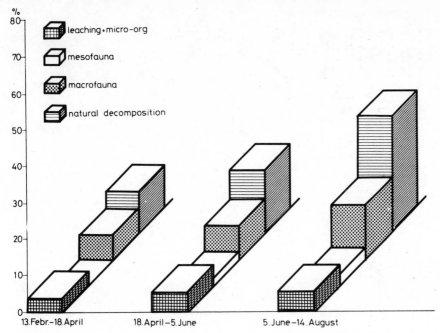

Fig. 2. The percentage of the different edaphic groups participating in the decomposition of *Quercus robur* leaves

Table 3
Effect of different biotic factors on litter disappearance

Biotic factors	13 Feb.—18 April	18 April—5 June	5 June—14 Aug.	13 Feb.—14 Aug.
Carpinus betulus				
Leaching + Micro-org. + Microfauna	13.67	9.80	7.39	30.86
Mesofauna	1.35	0.68	12.77	14.80
Macrofauna	8.03	10.17	23.75	41.95
Total	23.05	20.65	43.91	87.61
Quercus robur				
Leaching + Micro-org. + Microfauna	4.31	5.60	5.12	15.03
Mesofauna	0.00	2.24	2.67	4.91
Macrofauna	7.22	9.58	14.56	31.36
Total	11.53	17.42	22.35	51.30

Table 4
The mean numbers of *Collembola* and *Oribatida* revealed from the pots in 1974

Mesofaunal groups	*Carpinus betulus*						*Quercus robur*					
	18 April		5 June		14 Aug.		18 April		5 June		14 Aug.	
Nets covering pots	2 mm	7 mm	2 mm	7 mm	2 mm	7 mm	2 mm	7 mm	2 mm	7 mm	2 mm	7 mm
F. 4-oculata	306	173	356	440	261	93	86	199	156	269	125	58
Collembola	474	426	834	889	677	361	198	425	405	547	285	170
F. 4-oculata D%	64.55	40.61	42.68	49.49	38.55	25.76	43.43	46.82	38.52	49.18	43.86	34.12
Oppia ornata	161	22	605	104	387	103	335	204	396	203	346	103
Oribatida	259	65	705	147	607	164	439	292	500	324	442	195
O. ornata D%	62.16	33.84	85.81	70.75	63.10	62.80	76.31	70.10	79.20	62.65	78.28	52.82
Collembola Oribatida Total	733	491	1539	1036	1284	525	637	717	905	871	727	365

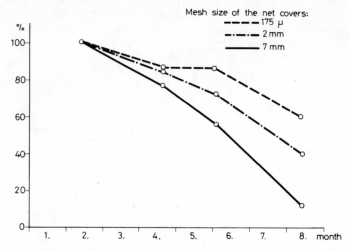

Fig. 3. Rate of disappearance of *Carpinus betulus* leaves

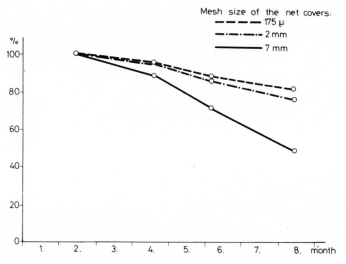

Fig. 4. Rate of disappearance of *Quercus robur* leaves

pots. Also it was observed that the number of mesofauna in pots of medium-sized mesh nets was much greater than in other kinds of pots. Again, it was revealed that the number of mesofaunal individuals extracted from hornbeam pots exceeded that in oak pots.

It was not possible to assess completely the number of macrofaunal individuals because of the high activity of these animals escaping when the pots are dug out from the field. It is interesting to note here that only the small species of earthworms as well as their *young forms* were commonly found in the large-mesh pots, whereas the large-bodied species were unable to go into these kinds of pots as their body diameters exceed 1 cm (Zicsi 1974).

DISCUSSION

The small contribution of the mesofauna in the breakdown process could be explained on the basis that these animals frequently consume microfungi, bacteria and animal excrements. This was confirmed by Csuták (1975) from his feeding biological experiment on some *Collembola* collected from the locality of the present investigation. Also, many authors (Bödvarrson 1970, Hartenstein 1962, Poole 1959, Shereef 1970, Singh 1969) agree that mites and *Collembola* consume mainly micro-organisms. Poole (1959) reports that the feeding preference of *Collembola* changes throughout the year. This tendency has been also observed in the present experiment as the mesofauna was responsible for the breakdown of only 2.03% of hornbeam leaves till the end of June, thereafter this quantity was increased to 14.80% at the end of the experiment (see figures). This was not the case for oak leaves, where the breakdown process was going on slowly and without such a marked difference.

The predominance of mesofauna in pots of medium-sized mesh nets could probably be explained in terms of the "litter bag effect" of Crossley and Hoglund (1963), in addition to the good microclimate inside these pots, and also due to their unavailability for the large-bodied predators. All these factors render a more suitable niche inside these pots.

No relationship between the number of mesofaunal individuals and the rate of litter breakdown was observed during the course of the present work, as the mesofauna prefers feeding on micro-organisms than on litter leaves.

Our data dealing with the percentage of litter disappearance are in harmony with those obtained by Isépy (1974). He estimated the loss to range between 67.83–100.00% for hornbeam, and between 59.2–86.34% for oak leaves depending on the water conditions of the locality in addition to the activities of the large-bodied earthworms.

In conclusion, the macrofauna plays the most significant role in the process of litter breakdown, which may be attributed to its high activities. Besides, the good role of leaching and micro-organisms was observed, while the mesofauna participates very little in the process of breakdown.

SUMMARY

The role played by meso- and macrofauna in the process of litter breakdown was assessed in the field by placing known weights of hornbeam and oak leaves into unglazed earthen pots. The pots were covered with nylon nets of three different mesh apertures, and then buried in the forest. Every two months the percentage of litter disappearance was estimated.

It was concluded that the hornbeam leaves disappeared more rapidly than oak leaves which is attributed to the palatability of hornbeam leaves for soil animals. The macrofauna plays the most significant role in this process, while the mesofauna has a very small contribution which may be explained by its feeding habits.

REFERENCES

Bödvarsson, H. (1970): *Ent. Scand.* 1, 74–78.
Crossley, D. A. Jr. and Hoglund, M. P. (1963): *Ecology.* 43, 571–573.
Csuták, J. (1975): *Opusc. Zool.* 13,
Gere, G. and Hargitai, L. (1971): *Erd. Kut.* 67, 21–28.
Hartenstein, R. (1962): *Annal. Entom. Soc. Amer.* 55, 202–206.
Isépy, I. (1974): *Bot. Közlem.* 61, 205–216.
Loksa, I. and Zicsi, A. (1972): *MTA. Biol. Oszt. Közlem.* 15, 45–50.
Poole, T. B. (1959): *Proc. Zool. Soc. London,* 132, 71–82.
Shereef, G. M. (1970): *Observations on the feeding, reproduction and faces obtained from Oribatids fed on different species of Penicillium* and *Aspergillus.* Organismes du sol et production primaire. IV. Coll. Pedobiol. Dijon, 14/19. IX. 163–177. 1971.
Singh, S. B. (1969): *Rev. Écol. Biol. Sol.* 6, 461–467.
Wood, T. G. (1971): *The effects of soil fauna on the decomposition of Eucalyptus leaf litter in the snowy mountains, Australia.* Organismes du sol et production primaire. IV. Coll. Pedobiol. Dijon, 14/19 IX. 1970. 349–361.
Zicsi, A. (1974): *A struktúra és funkció kapcsolata teresztrikus ökoszisztémák földigilisztáinak tükrében.* Thesis, Budapest. 1–303.

FACTORS DETERMINING THE RATE OF LITTER DECOMPOSITION IN SOME MEADOW ECOSYSTEMS

by

Marta TESAŘOVÁ
Botanical Institute of the Czechoslovak Academy of Sciences
Brno, Czechoslovakia

Alluvial meadows situated in the vicinity of the village Lanžhot, southern Moravia — Czechoslovakia, were subjected to a detailed study concerning the main structures and functions at the levels of the primary producers and decomposers (for bibliography see Rychnovská 1972). As a part of these researches a study of litter decomposition was carried out in the meadow with dominant plant species of *Festuca sulcata* (*Festuca* site), *Alopecurus pratensis* (*Alopecurus* site), and *Glyceria maxima* (*Glyceria* site) respectively. The rate of litter decomposition in these sites is essentially different (Tesařová 1975); it amounted during the growing season to 3.7–9.3 mg/g per day in *Festuca* site, 6.2–16.1 mg/g per day in *Alopecurus* site, and 8.6–15.4 mg/g per day in *Glyceria* site. The causes of these differences were investigated in a series of experiments under field conditions. The dependence of litter decomposition rate on the chemical quality of litter, litter moisture and temperature, and composition of litter decomposers were studied.

CHARACTERISTICS OF STUDY SITES

The meadows under study form a part of a flooded meadow complex situated in the alluvia of the rivers Morava and Dyje. The meadow dominated by *Festuca sulcata* can be found on local elevations and it is flooded only rarely. The meadow predominant with *Alopercurus pratensis* is flooded regularly. These two meadows are cut once or twice a year. The meadow having mainly *Glyceria maxima* is situated at the base of a depression flooded with water for a relatively long period of time. This meadow is uncut. The meadows under study essentially differ in the amount and chemical composition of litter (Table 1).

METHODS

Litter bag method was used for study of litter decomposition under field conditions. The bags were 12×18 cm in size with 0.5 mm pore size. Litter was deposited in the bags in amounts of 5 g in *Festuca* and *Alopecurus* sites, and 15 g in

Table 1
Amount and chemical composition of litter in the meadows under study

	Festuca site	*Alopecurus* site	*Glyceria* site
average amount g · m $^{-2}$	142.4	176.0	796.8
* content of nutrients as a sum of N + P + K + Na + + Ca + Mg mg/g	25.6	34.0	30.5
C/N	31.4	25.0	24.9

* according to Jakrlová (1972)

the case of *Glyceria* site. In each site, bags containing litter collected from *Festuca* site (30 bags), *Alopecurus* site (30 bags), and *Glyceria* site (30 bags), respectively were exposed on the soil surface from 9 December 1971 to 21 June 1973 — i.e. for about 19 months. During this period the bags were successively removed (5 April, 4 July, 26 October 1972, 17 March and 21 June 1973) and analyzed for weight loss after drying at 60 °C. For expressing rates of decay, the Olsen's equation was used: $X/X_0 = e^{-kt}$, where X/X_0 is the fraction of weight remaining at time t_1, e is the base of natural logarithm, and k is the decomposition constant. The expression of dry weight loss as a negative exponential function permits the calculation of litter "half-life" (0.69315/k) and the time required for loss of dry weight (5/k).

The litter bag method was used also for estimation of micro-organisms, meso- and macrofauna participation in litter decomposition. Litter bags with pore size 0.003 mm, 1.5 mm and 7—8 mm were placed on soil surface of the *Festuca*, *Alopecurus* and *Glyceria* sites respectively, for the period of 17 March — 25 October 1972. After this period, the dry weight loss of litter was estimated. Initial amounts of litter in bags were the same as in the previous experiment.

The influence of temperature and moisture on the litter decomposition rate (= LDR) was recorded in the field during the study of litter production and disappearance (Tesařová 1975).

RESULTS AND DISCUSSION

The amount of litter decomposed in the meadows is influenced to a much higher degree by the ecological conditions, than by the chemical composition of litter. As shown in Table 2 the decomposition of the same kind of litter on different sites showed considerable variations (data in lines). All tested values were significantly different (P < 0.05). However, the differences in decomposition of various kinds of litter on the same site were statistically not significant (P < 0.05). Any sort of litter was decomposed at the highest rate on the *Glyceria* site, and at the lowest rate on the *Festuca* site.

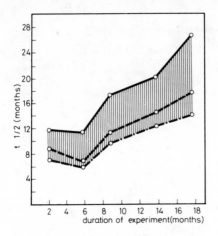

Fig. 1. Changes of half-life values during the 19 months of litter decomposition on the *Festuca* site (——), *Alopecurus* site (– – –) and *Glyceria* site (–.–.–).

In Figure 1, the half-lives (in months) for individual phases of decomposition of various kinds of litter placed on *Festuca, Alopecurus* and *Glyceria* sites are shown. After about 7 months of exposition, the more readily available plant substances had been used up. This period is characterized by low half-life values. Subsequently the decomposition of the hardly available plant substances takes place, which can be recognized by a rapid increase of half-life values. The differences between the values of half-lives of litter exposed on sites under study were small during the decomposition of more resistant substances, but they increased significantly during the decay of substances more resistant to decomposition. It can be concluded from the results that the different ability of decomposers to destroy the relatively resistant substances like the cellulose and lignin is one of the main reasons of different litter decomposition rates on the sites under study. The lowest capacity for decomposing the resistant substances was found at the *Festuca* site, the highest one at the *Glyceria* site. This sequence is in agreement with data on cellulose decomposition in the soil of meadows under study; the rate of cellulose decomposition reached on an average 6.5 mg/g per day in the soil of *Festuca* site, 7.7 mg/g per day in the *Alopecurus* site and 10.2 mg/g per day in the *Glyceria* site (Tesařová 1971). From the results obtained, it is possible to calculate the time required for the decomposition of 99% dry weight of litter. It corresponds to 7.4 years in case of litter from the *Festuca* site, to 6.1 years for *Alopecurus* site, and 4.4 years for litter from the *Glyceria* site. However, it is necessary to take in to account that the respective times were calculated from data on litter decomposition in bags (Table 2), where

331

Table 2
Loss of dry weight of litter (in %) after a 19 months' exposition period.
($\bar{X} \pm 2$ S. E., N = 6–8)

Litter collected from	Litter placed on the soil surface at the		
	Festuca site	*Alopecurus* site	*Glyceria* site
Festuca site	62.0 ± 3.7	72.5 ± 3.4	78.2 ± 1.8
Alopecurus site	67.0 ± 2.6	72.0 ± 3.4	87.0 ± 1.6
Glyceria site	66.7 ± 2.1	72.7 ± 2.1	87.0 ± 1.5

the decomposition proceeds at least twice as slowly as under natural conditions (Tesařová 1975).

The rate of litter decomposition is in all sites significantly affected by the moisture content of the litter (Figs 2a–c). The relatively low moisture content of litter (20% on the average) is probably one of the factors retarding the litter decomposition at the *Festuca* site. A significant increase of litter decomposition rate (LDR), i.e. about 70%, took place between 30 and 40% moisture content of the litter as can be seen in Figure 2a. However, such a moisture content was found only in 7% of all samples. At the *Alopecurus* site the litter moisture increase from 10 to 40% does not appear to affect the LDR markedly. A sudden drop occurs at the moisture range 40 to 50% when the LDR increases by about 60%. Considering that more than one half of all the cases tested within the moisture range of 40–70%, the litter moisture content can be regarded as restricting the LDR also at the *Alopecurus* site. The LDR increases steadily with the rise in litter moisture at the *Glyceria* site. The averages of litter moisture as well as of LDR here are the highest of the three sites.

The relationships between the LDR and litter temperature as estimated in our experiments under field conditions are more complicated (Figs 3a–c). In the 8–16 °C, temperature interval the relationship does not deviate very much from linearity. However, the LDR is strongly variable at temperatures higher than 16 °C. It means that the LDR is controlled by other significant factors besides temperature. The variation of LDR at temperatures above 16 °C may also result from varying litter moisture, as can be deduced from Figs 3a–c. A high temperature acting concurrently with a low litter moisture resulted in a relatively low LDR in all cases, as indicated especially in the *Festuca* and *Alopecurus* sites. Similar relationships between the litter moisture and the CO_2 output from litter of individual plant communities were described by Tesařová and Gloser (1975).

Some information on participation of macrofauna, mesofauna and micro-organisms in litter decomposition were obtained by the litter bag technique. Great differences among the sites were found with respect to the decomposing activity of micro-organisms (Table 3). If the amount of litter decomposed by combined action

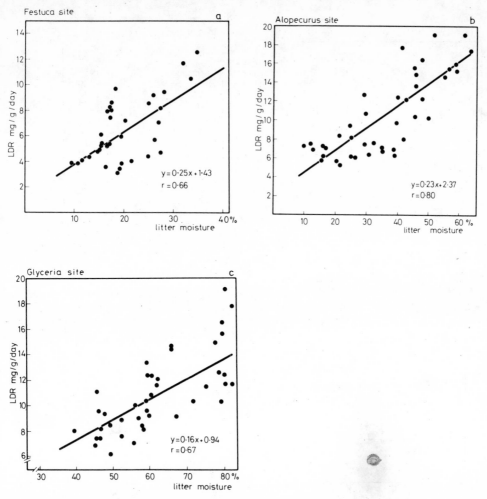

Fig. 2. The dependence of litter decomposition rate (LDR) on litter moisture for the *Festuca* site (Fig. 2a), *Alopecurus* site (Fig. 2b) and *Glyceria* site (Fig. 2c)

Table 3
Litter decomposition in bags with various pore size
($\bar{x} \pm 2$ S. E., N = 5)

	Pore size		
	0.003 mm	1.5 mm	7—8 mm
	loss of dry weight in %		
Festuca site	18.42 ± 2.07	36.50 ± 5.96	53.17 ± 9.71
Alopecurus site	28.60 ± 3.05	64.17 ± 4.10	75.62 ± 10.91
Glyceria site	49.30 ± 5.43	73.80 ± 5.79	84.63 ± 7.75

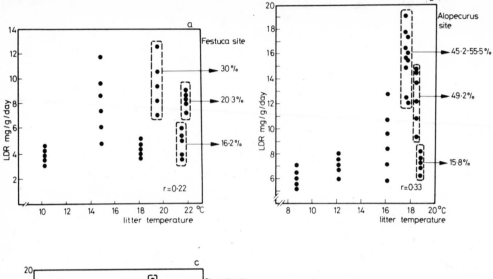

Fig. 3. The dependence of litter decomposition rate (LDR) on litter temperature for the *Festuca* site (Fig. 3a), *Alopecurus* site (Fig. 3b) and *Glyceria* site (Fig. 3c). Data on litter moisture are given on the right side

of macrofauna, mesofauna and micro-organisms (bags with mesh size of 7–8 mm) is taken as 100%, then the micro-organisms (bags with pore size of 0.003 mm) decomposed 35% of litter in the *Festuca* site, 37% of litter in the *Alopecurus* site, and 58% of litter in the *Glyceria* site, where the highest litter moisture (70% in average) was estimated. This points to the important role played by micro-organisms in the decomposition processes in wetlands. Similar conclusions were reached by Pieczynska (1972) and Úlehlová (1975) from the studies on decomposition processes in reed ecosystems.

SUMMARY

It was pointed out that the litter decomposition rate in three meadow ecosystems (differing in vegetation composition and in primary production) was quite different. The causes of these differences were investigated in a series of experiments under field and laboratory conditions. The relations between the litter decomposition rate and quality of litter, its moisture and temperature, and composition of litter decomposers were studied. Special attention was paid to the participation of micro-organisms in litter decomposition.

REFERENCES

Jakrlová, J. (1972): *Mineral nutrient uptake by four inundated meadow communities.* – In: Rychnovská, M, (ed.): Ecosystem Study on Grassland Biome in Czechoslovakia. – Czechoslov. IBP/PT-PP Report No. 2. Brno, 51–54.

Olsen, J. S. (1963): *Ecology.* **44**, (2), 322–331.

Pieczyńska, E. (1972): *Ekologia Polska 204.* **44**, 637–732.

Rychnovská, M. (Ed.) (1972): *Ecosystem Study on Grassland Biome in Czechoslovakia.* – Czechoslov. IBP/PT-PP Report No. 2. Brno.

Tesařová, M. (1971): Intensita rozkladu celulosy v půdách některých lučních společenstev. Thesis, Botanical Institute CAS, Brno.

Tesařová, M. (1975): *Litter disappearance in alluvial plant communities.* – In: Kilbertus G., et al. (Eds.): Biodegradation et Humification. Rapp. 1er Coll. Inter., Nancy, 255–266.

Tesařová, M. and Gloser, J. (1975): *Pedobiologia* (in press).

Úlehlová. B. (1975): *Rozpravy ČSAV,* (in press).

EFFECT OF SOME ECOLOGICAL FACTORS
ON SOIL BACTERIA OF THE GENUS *ARTHROBACTER*

by

Z. BUKOWSKI
Agricultural Academy, Department of Soil Science and Microbiology,
Krakow, Poland

Species of the genus *Arthrobacter* represent a characteristic group of the autochthonous microflora of soil. Their proportion in the soil bacterium population amounts to more than 60%. Not only their quantity is high but they have an important role too, since these bacteria take part in synthesis and conversion of several organic and inorganic compounds. Bacteria of this genus are able to synthetize certain vitamins of the group B, amino acids and growth substances, which are utilized by the other soil bacteria and the higher plants. *Arthrobacters* decompose proteins, lipids and carbohydrates, promote the solution of carbonates and phosphates, and fix nitrogen from the atmosphere. Hence, *Arthrobacter* species are very important members of the soil micro-organisms association.

The role and the proportion of the *Arthrobacters* in the soil depend on different ecological factors. During a three years' study, the effect of some ecological factors, i.e. the season (temperature), the active acidity of the soil, plants cultivated and the nitrogen content of soil (fertilization), on *Arthrobacters* was investigated.

Arthrobacter seem to be less sensitive towards the low temperature. Many of the *Arthrobacter* species and strains are psychrophylic. The maximum number of the living *Arthrobacter* cells was observed during the winter and the spring. In summer, these bacteria decrease to minimum (while *Bacillus* species occur in the highest number).

Arthrobacters are also resistant to low pH. The optimum pH for these species is about 6–7, but they can be frequently isolated from forest soil (pH 4–5), too. However, their quantity is low in acid soil.

As it is known, the composition of the vegetation modifies the composition of the micro-organism population. The highest quantity of arthrobacters is found in the grassy ecosystems ($1-10 \times 10^5$ cells per 1 g soil). Less cells ($6-300 \times 10^3$) are present in cultivated soil, and the lowest *Arthrobacter* quantity can be detected in forest soil. A very high *Arthrobacter* cell number can be found in the soil of grasslands of the *Valeriano- Caricetum flavae* and *Molinietum coerulae typicum* types. The widest species range of the genus *Arthrobacter* was observed in soil of the Penin and Tatra reserves. *A. ramosus* and *A. tumescens* were the predominant species here.

Arthrobacters belong to the ologonitrophylic bacteria, therefore, their nitrogen requirement is low. 90% of the strains studied were oligonitrophylic, and 60% of those were able to fix the nitrogen from the atmosphere.

Investigations were carried out in order to determine the effect of the nitrogen fertilization on arthobacters. In the experiments ammonium-nitrate and urea fertilizers were used at dosages of 60, 120, 180 and 240 kg nitrogen per hectare. The nitrogen surplus results in the decrease of arthrobacters. Small dosages of the nitrogen fertilization stimulate the growth of these bacteria, but at high concentrations (180 and 240 kg per hectare) their quantity is depressed (the so-called "zymogenic" bacteria of the genus *Bacillus* were increased with the increase of the nitrogen). It must be emphasized, that the disappearance of arthrobacters and the rapid increase in the proportion of *Bacillus* species indicate the disturbance of the biological balance in the soil.

As can be concluded, arthrobacters are resistant to the unfavourable ecological factors and are sensitive to human influences, consequently show an imbalance in the life of the soil.

BIOLOGICAL CHARACTERIZATION OF A TROPICAL GLEY SOIL AT THE RICE EXPERIMENTAL STATION OF JUCARITO, ORIENTE, CUBA

by

María RODRIGUEZ, Neredia CORTÉS and Miriam FERNÁNDEZ
University of Oriente, School of Biological Sciences Santiago, Cuba

Human activities influence the composition and number of soil micro-organisms. Root excretions and crop residues are a nutrient supply and its decomposition rate by the microflora depends mainly on soil air conditions (Macura 1965, Sorokina 1965, Tardieux and Roche 1964).

The purpose of this report is to determine quantitative and qualitative variations of total microflora and inorganic phosophorus solubilizers in a Tropical Gley soil. Influence of water-logged conditions during crop development of *Oriza sativa*, var. IR-8, and of crop residue incorporation into soil were observed.

MATERIAL AND METHODS

The Rice Experimental Station of Jucarito lies between the cities of Bayamo and Tunas.

This soil belongs to the Great Group of Tropical Gley, deep medium-developed gley, according to the I. S. A. C. C. (Soil Institute of the Cuban Science Academy) System. In 1966, these soils were classified by Prof. S. V. Zonn as grey plastic, alitic-sialitic; humic gley alitic-sialitic, etc. and in 1969, by G. Tatevosian in the Oriente Province as dark-grey plastic gleyized and grey plastic gleyized.

In other regions of the world those soils have been classified as Gleisoles, Grumosoles or Vertisoles. In French classification they are known as Paravertizoles or Vertic soils.

Five samples from soil surface 0—20 cm were taken aseptically during the periods and conditions given in Table 2. The first sample was taken in an area left undisturbed under grass vegetation, for 5 years.

Samples were homogenized. Dilutions from 10^{-1} to 10^{-8} were made. The microflora was determined quantitatively and qualitatively by the dilutions-plate method. Heterotropic soil micro-organisms were studied in the following media: nutrient — broth—agar, Czapek—Dox—agar, starch—minerals—agar (Gause's agar). Medium for *Clostridium*, as anaerobic representation was used by the McCrady's Method inoculating 1 ml. per tube, 3 tube per dilution.

Table 1
Soil analysis data*

	Depth, cm	
	0–30	30–60
	1	2
pH (ClK)	6.4	6.6
Organic matter %	1.92	0.28
Nitrogen (N) ppm.	19	2.8
Phosphorus (P_2O_5) ppm.	6.41	5.60
Calcium (Ca^{++}) ppm.	23.95	19.31
C.E.C., Meq/100 g.	35.62	34.37

* From Central Laboratory of Soil Analysis, INRA.

Table 2
Sampling

Sample	Date	Conditions	Field humidity (%)
1	2	3	4
I	XII – 72	Natural conditions under grass vegetation	20
II	III – 73	Ploughed field	30
III	IV – 73	Germinated field	80
IV	VIII – 73	Crop maturity	water-logged
V	X – 73	After harvest	50

Table 3
Quantitative composition of soil microflora (counts/g.)

Sample	Bacteria	Fungi	*Actinomycetes*	*Clostridium*	Phosphorus solubilizers
I	87.9×10^4	70×10^4	85.5×10^4	30×10^4	Not determined
II	73×10^4	42×10^4	8×10^4	1.1×10^4	6×10^4
III	50×10^4	22×10^4	4×10^4	1.5×10^4	1.6×10^4
IV	60×10^4	2×10^4	1.2×10^4	1.1×10^4	1.9×10^4
V	541×10^4	10.2×10^3	70.4×10^4	15×10^8	80×10^3

For inorganic phosphorus solubilizers, Pikovskaya medium was used with superficial and deep seeding. Readings were made at 24, 48 and 72 hours. Phosphorus solubilization was assayed in liquid medium and determined by the Osmond method, modification I as is described by Jackson (1964).

All samples were incubated at 28 °C and bacteria, actinomycetes and fungi were isolated and determined in suitable media.

Table 4
Qualitative composition of soil microflora

Sample	Bacteria	Fungi	*Actinomycetes*	Phosphorus solubilizers
1	2	3	4	5
I	*Bacillus mycoides* *B. subtilis* *Clostridium* *Pseudomonas*	*Penicillium* *Aspergillus* *Curvularia* *Trichoderma*	*Streptomyces* *S. albus* Group	Not determined
II	*Bacillus* *Azotobacter*	*Aspergillus*	*S. albus* Group *S. griseus*	*Bacillus* *A. niger* *Streptomyces*
III	*Bacillus* *Azotobacter*	*Monilia* *Curvularia*	*S. albus* *S. griseus* *S. azureus*	*Bacillus* *Aspergillus* *Mucor*
IV	*Bacillus* *Azotobacter*	*Monilia*	*S. albus* *S. griseus*	*Aspergillus* *Penicillium*
V	*B. mycoides* *B. cereus* *Pseudomonas* *Azotobacter*	*Aspergillus* *Mucor*	*S. albus* *S. griseus*	*Mucor* *A. niger* *A. terreus* *A. flavus*

RESULTS

The number of micro-organisms is given in Table 3. Group balance of micro-organisms on each sample is given in Table 4.

DISCUSSION

The results obtained about number and balance of micro-organisms during crop development express three main tendencies:

1. A progressive decrease in *Fungi* and *Actinomycetes* when water-logging increases.
2. Increase of *Bacteria* and *Clostridium* during the last period, where humidity had decreased and crop residues were incorporated into the soil with little quantitative variations during the other periods.
3. Relative stability of phosphorus solubilizer numbers during the period of observation, with an increase in the latter part of it.

341

Balance of species denotes that *Bacillus* are the most predominant bacteria throughout crop development, with the dominance of *B. mycoides. Pseudomonas* were present in the first and last samples, and disappeared during the second and third, seeming to be correlated with change in aerobic conditions.

Presence of *Azotobacter chroococcum* was detected in Pikovskaya and starch—minerals—agar medium. *Actinomycetes* with aerial mycelium of clear colour, mainly white, were predominant in this soil. It is remarkable that numbers of *Actinomycetes* decreased during water-logged conditions and began to increase again during the last period where humidity was reduced and crop residues were incorporated into the soil.

Fungi exhibit more variety of genera and species in the first sample, which represents more or less the soil in natural conditions, denoting that during rice crop development, soil fungi change, not only quantitatively but also qualitatively.

Inorganic phosphorus solubilizers maintain very little quantitative variation but, on the contrary, show qualitative differences between initial and last samples. *Bacillus* sp. predominates at the beginning, together with some *Streptomyces* colonies whilst, on the contrary fungi are absolutely dominant in the later periods.

Isolated strains tested in Pikovskaya liquid medium showed that *A. terreus* and *A. niger* are better solubilizers than strains of bacteria isolated from this soil.

It is of economic and scientific interest to elucidate when rice crop is more susceptible to phosphorus fertilization and when solubilization of inorganic phosphorus by soil microflora makes it more ready to assimilate for the crop.

SUMMARY

Considering the evolution of a Tropical Gley Soil left undisturbed for 5 years, under grass, we note a remarkable influence of rice cultivation upon the microflora, the role of water-logging being of main importance.

Finally, the incorporation of plant residues after harvest seems to restore the *Actinomycetes* number and stimulate aerobic and anaerobic bacteria.

ACKNOWLEDGEMENTS

To engineers Adrian Fernández, Dimas R. Cuenca and Armando Vuelta and to the workers from the Jucarito Rice Experimental Station. To Daisy Lobo and Angel López from the University of Oriente for their valuable laboratory work.

REFERENCES

Jackson, M. L. (1964): *Análisis quimico de suelos.* Omega, Barcelona.
Macura, J. (1965): *Symposium on Plant—Microbes Relationship,* CSAV, Prague,
Sorokina, T. A. (1965): *Symposium on Plant—Microbes Relationship,* CSAV, Praguei, p. 42—47.
Tardieux, P. and Roche, H. (1964): *Ann. Inst. Pasteur,* **107**, 565—567.

QUANTITATIVE STUDIES OF FUNGI AND *ACTINOMYCETES* IN THE PRIMARY SOILS OF WEST-SPITZBERGEN

by

J. ZABAWSKI and Maria ŽURAWSKA
Institute of Plant Biology and Biophysics, Agricultural Academy,
Wroclaw, Poland

The idea of Polish polar expeditions reappeared at the end of the sixties, after the successful Spitzbergen Expeditions organized within the framework of the International Geophysical Year. Since 1970 owing to the efforts of the Commission of Geophysical Expeditions of the Polish Academy of Sciences a new series of expeditions to West Spitsbergen and the region of Hornsund was started. The themes studies carried out centred around the sphere of interests of the organizer — The Committee of Geological and Geographical Sciences of the Polish Academy of Sciences; hence, biological studies constituted a relatively limited section of these works.

The literature on soil microflora has only few data on polar zones (Cooke 1959, di Menna 1960, Flint and Stout 1960, Kobayasi *et al.* 1967, Lind 1934, Tsyganov *et al.* 1970, Zhukova 1956). From the region of West-Spitzbergen the flora of the actinomycetes has been elaborated (Krzywy *et al.* 1961, Wieczorek *et al.* 1964). Well-known are also those studies concerning the flora of higher fungi, including that of pathogenic fungi of vascular plants (Hagen 1941, Lind 1928, Skirgiełło 1968). The lack of information on soil fungi of the region under discussion, as well as on the determination of mutual quantitative relations between the particular groups of micro-organisms induced the authors to carry out the present study.

The aim of the present study was to determine the intensity of the microflora cover of the Spitzbergen soils, its qualitative and quantitative differentiation depending on the character of the bedding and the distance from the snout of the glacier.

MATERIAL AND METHODS

The materials for the analyses were collected during the Arctic summer in 1972 and 1973. The localization of the sites at which the samples were taken is presented in the enclosed sketch (Fig. 1). The soil samples were divided into five groups, representing different habitats.

The I-group of samples (Nos 1–8) consisted of soil samples taken on the forefield of the Werenskiold Glacier, at various distances from its snout down to its sea-terrace. This glacier retreats for years, uncovering new parts of the forefield. The oldest part of the forefield is gradually covered by moss and vascular plants, whereas the younger, closest to the glacier snout, is poorly covered or deprived of vegetation (Fabiszewski 1975). The gravel-clay soil material of the forefield is constantly washed and shifted by waters from the melting glacier in summer.

The II-group of samples (Nos 9–13) was taken in the mineral tundra persistently sodden by mosses and vascular plants, (covering 80–100% of the surface). The samples come from the feet of the Rotjesfjellet, Skoddefjellet and Sofjekammen mountain massifs.

The III-group of samples (Nos 14–25) was taken from the peat-tundra extending on the Ralstranda sea terrace at Rotjesfjellet and from the area of Skoddefjellet and Sofjekammen (covered by plants by 100% of the surface).

The IV-group of samples (Nos 26–28) was taken from the so-called cryokonits of ice fields of the Werenskiold and Hans Glaciers. This was mineral and organic material drifted from the surrounding elevations and set into the ice.

The V-group of samples (Nos 29–31) comes from three nunataks situated in the middle of the ice-fields. The nunataks consist of subfossil materials from the dead peat-tundra covered secondarily by a 50 cm thick layer of rocky rubble. All the samples were taken on principle from the level of 0–10 cm. In these samples the number of fungi and actinomycetes were determined. The quantitative analysis of these micro-organisms was carried out by means of dish dilutions and for the fungi additionally the method described by Krzemieniewska and Badura (1954) was used. The initial medium for actinomycetes was ammonium-starch agar, whereas for the fungi the glucose-potato agar, the actinomycetes were incubated in a temperature of 28 °C for 10–20 days — the fungi in a temperature of about 20 °C for 3 days. After the incubation period, the appearance on the initial substrates of colonies of the micro-organisms was counted and then isolated. Detailed data on the methods used can be found in previous papers of the authors (Zabawski 1967, 1975, Żurawska 1975).

In all the soil samples under study the concentration of hydrogen ions in H_2O and KCl were measured potentiometrically and the percentage weight loss after heating at 400 °C was determined. Moreover, in samples of group III (Nos 14–25) the contents of phosphorus, potassium, calcium and sodium were indicated. The mentioned elements were determined quantitatively in a 0.5 n HCl soil-extract, phosphorus by means of colorimetry and potassium, calcium and sodium photo-metrically.

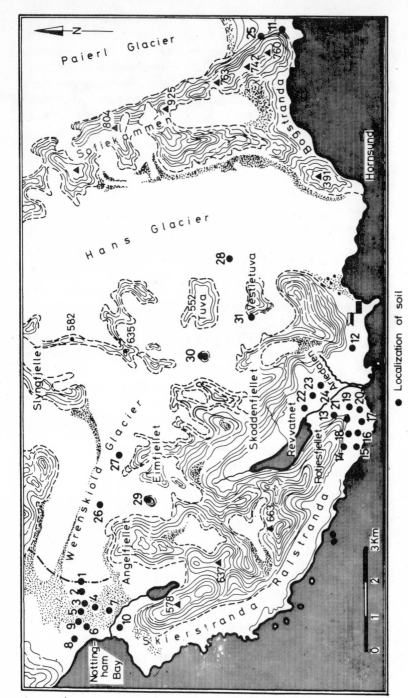

Fig. 1. Sketch of the Hornsud region (West-Spitzbergen)

● Localization of soil

RESULTS

The quantitative microbial analysis has shown the occurrence of micro-organisms in all the soil samples studied, regardless of the site of their collection. The fungi and bacteria occurred on dilution plates of all the samples, and actinomyces in most of them (22 samples). The study had been limited to a quantitative analysis of fungi and actinomycetes. The obtained results are presented in histograms (Figs 2 and 3) and the result of chemical analyses (Tables 2,3)

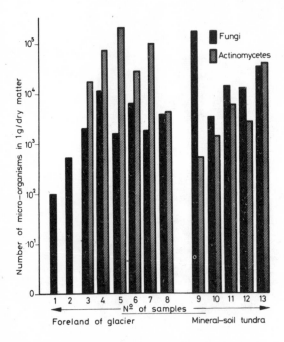

Fig. 2. Actinomycetes and fungi in the foreland of glacier and mineral soils of tundra

The mutual quantitative relation of fungi and actinomycetes in the particular groups of the soil samples studied was differentiated. In samples of the forefield glacier the actinomycetes distinctly predominated over the fungi (samples 3—8). Only samples taken closest to the snout of the glacier (Nos 1 and 2) were without actinomycetes, and the numbers of the fungal colonies obtained were the lowest among all the samples of the five habitats studied.

Samples representing the mineral-soil tundra showed a slight quantitative predomination of fungi. Only in sample No. 13 the numbers of both the groups of micro-organisms studied were more or less the same.

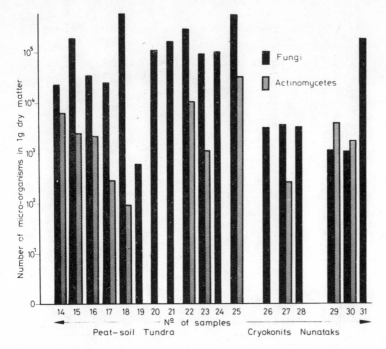

Fig. 3. Actinomycetes and fungi in different soils of West-Spitsbergen

Soil samples of the peat tundra were characterized by the highest number of fungi, among all the sites studied, these being the most predominat. In some of these samples (Nos 19, 20, 21 and 24) the actinomycetes did not occur at all.

In the materials from the cryokonits, the actinomycetes occurred only in one sample and the number of fungi here was the same in all the three samples.

Two samples from the nunataks (Nos 29 and 30) showed similar numbers of fungi and actinomycetes with the latter predominating slightly, and in the third sample a relatively large number of fungi was found, whereas actinomycetes were lacking (sample No. 31).

The qualitative analysis of the micro-organismic flora of the soils studied has indicated also differentiation according to the habitats (Table 1). The richest as regards the multiplicity of fungal forms were the peat samples. Altogether 80 fungal species were isolated here. Especially numerous here were the species from the group *Ascomycetes* (15 species altogether), mainly of the genus *Podospora* and *Chaetomium*, all well as *Ascobolus, Coniochaeta, Sporormiella* and *Rhodotorula.* Equally numerous here were the group of *Phycomycetes* (18 species), especially the genus *Mortierella*, as many as 10 species, and among them three new for the flora, as well as of the genus *Mucor, Spinalia, Syncephalis* and others.

In the mineral tundra, altogether 60 fungal species were found. In a relatively smaller number of *Ascomycetes* (6 species) and *Phycomycetes* (11 species) than in

347

Table 1
Number of fungal species belonging to various groups isolated from soils of West-Spitsbergen

Groups of fungi	Groups of soil samples			
	I forefield of glacier	II mineral tundra	III peat-tundra	IV–V cryokonits and nunataks
Phycomycetes	3	11	18	3
Ascomycetes	1	6	15	2
Fungi Imperfecti	6	37	31	12
Unidentified species	10	6	8	4
Total number of isolated fungial species	20	60	72	21

the peat samples, there were relatively more of various representatives of *Fungi Imperifecti* as genera *Cephalosporium, Cladosporium, Acremonium, Arthrobotris, Phialophora, Trichoderma* and numerous species of the genus *Penicillium.*

The poorest, with respect to the multiplicity of fungal species, were the samples taken closest to the snout of the glacier, especially Nos 1 and 3, and samples from cryokonites and nunataks. Here most frequently the *Fungi Imperfecti* and cosmopolitic species of the genus *Penicillium* occurred and of the yeasts *Rhodotorula* sp., were quite numerous the *Phycomycetes* in the samples of the middle parts of the glacier forefield were fewer. In this group of samples about 20 different fungal species were isolated.

From among the various isolated actinomycetes of the genus *Actinomyces* (Streptomyces), 7 different groups (series) have so far been isolated, namely: *Griseus, Aurantiacus, Globisporus, Chromogenes* and *Fradiae*. The studies, especially with regard to the actinomycetes, are not yet completed.

The results of the chemical analyses carried out (Tables 2 and 3), indicate a differentiation of the soil samples with respect to their percentage content of organic substances (ignition loss by heating at 400 °C) and their pH values. The contents of the organic matter in the group of samples from the glacier forefield varied from 5 to 11%, whereas the contents in samples from the mineral soil tundra were more differentiated, 9–30% or even 72%, and all of them exceeded the values assessed for samples of group I.

The relatively high percentage of organic substance was found in peat samples (group III) from about 30 to as much as 96%. The contents of organic matter in the particular samples of the cryokonits and nunataks showed a high differentiation depending on their origin.

Table 2
Some properties of soil samples from West-Spitzbergen

No. of point	No. of soil samples	Distance from glacier/m.	% loss ignition (organic matter)	pH	
				H$_2$O	1 n KCl
1	2	3	4	5	6
forefield of glacier					
1	1	4	6.63	7.60	7.00
2	2	40	5.76	6.95	6.60
3	3	400	8.07	7.60	6.60
4	4	400	32.87	5.00	4.20
5	5	700	5.97	7.70	6.60
6	6	1200	10.96	7.25	6.30
7	7	500	6.34	7.20	6.85
8	8	1400	9.22	7.40	6.50
9	9	1000	29.63	7.35	6.35
mineral – soil tundra					
10	10	1000	13.09	6.03	4.46
11	11	1200	72.77	7.20	6.60
12	12	2000	11.32	7.16	6.10
13	13	2000	27.25	6.60	6.36
cryokonits					
14	26	0	9.72	6.80	5.30
15	27	0	8.50	6.70	5.50
16	28	0	69.81	6.90	–
nunataks					
17	29	30	81.26	5.70	–
18	30	5	24.97	6.40	–
19	31	30	49.20	7.10	6.10

In samples of groups I and II (forefield of glacier and mineral tundra) the pH values were rather similar and showed either a neutral or a slightly alkaline reaction, whereas in samples of group III and V the acidic reaction predominated. Exceptions were only the samples Nos 20, 25, 31, having a neutral reaction.

The quantitative determinations of phosphorus and potassium carried out only in peat soils (group III of soil samples) did not show high differences between the particular samples. The contents of the components based on the standards elaborated by Polish Agrochemical Stations, were evaluated as low and average for phosphorus and average for potassium. Determinations of CaCO$_3$-contents in peat were varied highly and none, without distinct trend could be discerned.

Table 3
Some properties of peat-soil samples from West–Spitsbergen

No. of point	No. of soil sample	Distance from glacier/m.	% loss ignition (organic matter)	pH H$_2$O	pH 1 n KCl	Na (mg/dry matter) %	K$_2$O	P$_2$O$_5$	CaO
							(in mg/100 g dry soil matter)		
1	2	3	4	5	6	7	8	9	10
1	14	2,500	41.88	5.2	4.1	1.29	75.2	44.6	35.0
2	15	2,500	52.22	6.1	4.8	0.04	80.0	49.0	17.0
3	16	2,500	89.67	5.9	4.7	1.18	64.0	25.6	95.0
4	17	2,500	52.72	6.1	5.0	1.74	72.0	30.4	16.5
5	18	2,500	96.78	4.1	3.1	0.99	80.0	36.0	3.5
6	19	2,500	76.73	5.8	4.8	1.40	53.2	24.6	55.0
7	20	2,500	89.76	6.8	5.8	1.44	67.2	35.0	165.0
8	21	2,500	86.20	–	–	0.11	117.6	53.0	95.0
9	22	1,500	57.55	5.8	4.7	0.90	100.0	61.3	19.0
10	23	1,500	29.48	5.2	4.6	0.22	83.2	45.2	29.0
11	24	1,500	29.23	5.1	4.5	0.26	67.2	54.8	3.0
12	25	1,000	72.30	7.3	6.2	0.70	104.0	72.8	250.0

DISCUSSION

The relatively frequent occurrence of micro-organisms observed in the present study on soils of West-Spitsbergen is in accordance with the results obtained previously (Krzywy *et al.* 1961, Wieczorek *et al.* 1964, Zabawski and Żurawska 1975). This phenomenon is well-founded by the studies of Rudolph (1970) on the dissemination of spores of cryptogamous plants by means of air transport. This mechanism enables the microflora to habitate even the subpolar region (Corte and Daglio 1964, Rudolph 1970).

However, to connect the amount of micro-organisms in the soils under study with the distance from the snout of the glacier (Krzywy *et al.* 1961, Wieczorek *et al.* 1964). seems rather problematical. Admittedly, the exceptionally small numbers of spores in samples collected closest to the snout of the glacier (samples 1 and 2), and in the materials from the cryokonits may suggest a direct influence of the glacier on the abiotic and biotic factors determining the amount of microflora, however, already at a distance of less than 100 m from the glacier, numerous micro-organisms were observed, whereas in certain samples collected at considerably large distances their number was smaller. It seems that attention should be turned also towards other factors affecting the development of microflora in the soils of Spitsbergen.

The abundance of mineral components (P, K, Ca and Na) did not explain the quantitative differentiation of the microflora studied. Our results of abundance determination concerning the peat-tundra samples, as well as the data of Szerszen (1965, 1968) for mineral soils of the glacier forefield may be regarded, based on standards assessed by Polish Agrochemical Stations, as low or average. The poor differentation of the above-mentioned mineral components in all the samples studied does not suggest a direct influence on the number of micro-organisms. The number-determinants probably have to be searched for elsewhere.

The interpretation of the mutual quantitative relations between the particular group of micro-organisms is a rather difficult task. Undoubtedly, in all the soil samples studied, bacteria predominated. This is in accordance with data concerning the artic soils of the USSR (Mishustin 1966, Zhukova 1956). The present paper is not concerned with a detailed analysis of this group of micro-organisms,

Generally the highest number of fungi were found in materials of the peat tundra and the lowest in the samples from the glacier forefield. The number of fungi, as well as their species variety showed positive correlations with the contents of organic substances. Strong acidity, as well as the large amount of poorly decayed organic substances in the peat-tundra were probably the decisive factors for the high number of fungi, determining their quantitative predominance over the actinomycetes. Similar results concerning the number of fungi and their dominance over actinomycetes were obtained also for some peat soils (Burzyńska-Czekanowska 1967, Zabawski 1967, Żurawska 1975).

As opposed to fungi the number of actinomycetes was the highest in the older parts of the glacier forefield, lower in the mineral tundra, and the lowest in the peat-tundra. It may seem that the most advantageous habitat for actinomycetes is the mineral tundra because of the rather good aeration of the substrate, the neutral or slightly alkaline reaction, as well as the constant soddy cover conditioning the successive inflow of organic matter into the substrate. These conditions are generally accepted as favourable for the development of actinomycetes (Lacey 1973). But it was found that actinomycetes occurred in highest numbers and dominated just at the glacier forefield, where apart from the pH value (neutral or slightly alkaline) it was difficult to find conditions favouring the development of this group of micro-organisms. A similar predominance of actinomycetes over fungi in some of the samples from soils of the Antarctic was found by Tsyganov *et al.* (1970).

The low number of actinomycetes or their absence in peat-tundra samples can be explained by the poor aeration of the substrate, connected with the flooding of peatlands and its acidation, factors not counterbalanced by the higher amount of organic matter. Similar low numbers of actinomycetes were found in the soils of the subalpine bog (Žurawska 1975).

Thus, in the light of the obtained results and on the basis of the data of the literature it seems, that one of the more important factors determining the quantitative relations between the particular groups of micro-organisms, their number in the soils under study and probably also in similar primary soils, is not so much the high contents of organic matter, but the character of this substance.

SUMMARY

The analysis included 31 soil samples representing five different habitats in the Hornsund region (West Spitzbergen). In all the samples micro-organisms were found. The studied samples differed in number of fungi and actinomycetes. The authors found that actinomycetes predominated over fungi in soils of the glacier forefield, whereas there were slightly more fungi than actinomyces in samples from the mineral tundra and marked predominance over actinomycetes in samples from the peat-tundra.

The number of micro-organisms and their development in primary polar soils is undoubtedly in correlation with the presence of organic substances in the substrate. Instead, differences in predominance of fungi or actinomycetes should be explained by the character of the organic substance rather than by its percentage amount.

REFERENCES

Burzyńska-Czekanowska, E. (1967): *Zesz. Prob. Post. Nauk Roln.* **76**, 313–353.
Cooke, W. B. (1959): *J. Ecol.* **47**, 529–449.
Corte, A. and Daglio, C. A. (1964): *A mycological study of the Antarctic air.* In. "Antarctic Biology" SCAR Symposium, Paris 1962. Carrick R., Holdgate M. and Prevost J. eds. 115–120.

di Menna, M. E. (1960): *J. Gen. Microbiol.* **23**, 295–300.

Fabiszewski, J. (1975): (Spitsbergen Zachodni). *Mat. z Symp. "Polskie Wyprawy na Spitsbergen 1972–1973 r."*, wyd. Uniw. Wrocławskiego, pp. 81–88.

Flint, E. A. and Stout, J. D. (1960): *Nature.* **188**, 767–768.

Hagen, A. (1941): *Norges. Sval. og Ishavs. Unders.* **49**, 1–11.

Kobayasi, J. *et al.* (1967): *Rep. Inst. Fermentation, Osaka* **3**, 1–138.

Krzemieniewska, H. and Badura, L. (1954): *Acta Soc. Botan. Polon.* **23**, 545–587.

Krzywy, T., Szerszeń, L. and Wieczorek J. (1961): *Arch. Immun. i Terapii Dośw.* **9**, 253–260.

Lacey, J. (1973): *"Actinomycetales: characteristics and practical importance"*, In: G. Sykes and F. A. Skinner, Acad. eds. Acad. Press. London–New York: 231.

Lind, J. (1928): *Skriften om Sval. og Ishav.* **13**,

Lind, J. (1934): *Kgl. Danske Vidensk. Selsk. Biol. Medd.* **11**, (2): 1–152.

(Mishustin, E. N.) Мишустин, Е. Н. (1966): *Микрофлора почв северной и южной частей СССР.* АН СССР, Москва.

Rudolph, E. D. (1970): *Antarctic Ecol.* **2**, 812–817.

Skirgiełło, A. (1968): *Higher fungi collected in 1958 at Hornsuns (Westspitsbergen).* Summary of Scientific Results Polish Spitsbergen Expeditions 1957–1960, ed. K. Birkernmayer. Pol. Ac. of Sci. pp. 114–116.

Szerszeń, L. (1965): *Zesz. Wyższ. Szk. Roln. we Wrocławiu, Roln.* **29** (60), 39–82.

Szerszeń, L. (1968): *Some properties of sub-fossil mineral and organic deposits from the Region Werenskioldbreen, Vestspitsbergen.* Summary of Scientific Results Polish Spitsbergen Expeditions 1957–1960, ed. K. Birkenmayer. Pol. Ac. of Sci. pp. 240–247.

(Tsyganov, V. A., Konyev, Yu. E., Kamishko, O. P., Riabinin, I. F. and Podolian, L. A.) Цыганов, В. А., Конев, Ю. У., Камышко, О. П., Рябинин, И. Ф., Подолян, Л. А. (1970): *Микробиол.* **39**, 821–826.

Wieczorek, J. *et al.*, (1964): *Arch. Immun. et Therap. Exper.* **12**, 14–24.

Zabawski, J. (1967): *Zesz. Prob. Post. Nauk Roln.* **76**, 355–400.

Zabawski, J. (1975): *Zesz. Nauk. Akad. Rolniczej we Wraclawiu. Roln.* **31**, (109): 9–17.

Zabawski, J. and Żurawska, M. (1975): Mikroflora pierwotnych gleb rejonu Hornsudu i Lodowca Werenskiolda (Zachodni Spitsbergen) (badania wstępne), materialy z sympozjum Polskie Wyprawy na Spitsbergen 1972 i 1973 r Wroclaw 29–30 marca 1974. Wyd. Uniw. Wroclawski. pp. 101–107.

(Żhukova, R. A.) Жукова, Р. А. (1956): *Микробиол.* **25**, 569–573.

Żurawska M. (1975): *Zesz. Nauk. Akad. Rolniczej we Wrocławiu. Roln.* **31**, (109): 19–25.

ANAEROBIC SOIL BACTERIA

by

V. T. EMTSEV
Timiryazev Agricultural Academy, Department of Microbiology,
Moscow, USSR

Anaerobic bacteria are widespread in various soils, in water and in bottoms of lakes, rivers, seas and oceans, in cavities of man, animals, insects and so on, etc. They take part in biological cycles of carbon, nitrogen, sulphur and a number of other elements. Certain anaerobes can cause dangerous infectious diseases in man and animals. Some anaerobic bacteria are used to produce chemical substances by butyric and acetobutylic fermentation.

However, the role of anaerobes in the processes of transformation of organic and mineral substances in the soil has not yet been fully solved.

The most important prerequisite for successful elucidation of the role of anaerobic bacteria in the transformation of different substances is the profound and thorough study of nature and the patterns of their vital activity in the soil.

To have a clear idea of the biology of anaerobic bacteria one should know the ecological and geographical regularities of living individual species of anaerobes in the soil.

The investigations carried out by us up till now (Emtsev 1965, 1974, Emtsev and Dzadzamiya 1969, 1970, 1971, Emtsev *et al.* 1969, 1974, Emtsev and Zakharova 1970, 1973, Emtsev and Razvozhevskaya 1971, Emtsev and Pokrovsky 1973) have shown that soil and climatic conditions determine specific composition of aerobic nitrogen-fixing flora of different soil types and influence the biological properties of these organisms.

In the work that has been done lately we continued to study the conditionality of the physiological peculiarities of the bacteria of the genus *Clostridium,* and first of all butyric bacteria, not only by specific conditions of different soil types but also by the **anthropogenic factor.**

MATERIAL AND METHODS

The objects of our investigation were butyric *(Cl. pasteurianum* and *Cl. butyricum)* and acetobutylic *(Cl. acetobutylicum)* bacteria. The quantitative calculation and isolation of anaerobes were done from the irrigated and over-

1 soils of Georgia. The soils used were cinnamonic forest soil requiring ~~~on (town of Mtzkheta, village of Tzerovany) and meadow-boggy soil (town of ~ty, village of Khorga). The microbiological study of the two soils mentioned was conducted in the following treatments: virgin soil (check), the soil prepared for corn with and without meliorative practices (irrigated and drained treatments respectively). Drainage was done with filtrating filling, drain spacing being 10 m. Soil samples were taken from the depth of 0–25 cm.

The number of cells of butyric *(Cl. pasteurianum* and *Cl. butyricum)* and acetobutylic *(Cl. acetobutylicum)* bacteria in the soils was determined by the use of optimum differential media (Emtsev 1965).

The isolation of anaerobes from the soil and obtaining pure cultures *(Cl. butyricum* and *Cl. acetobutylicum)* were done according to our method (Emtsev and Dzadzamiya 1969, Emtsev *et al.* 1969).

The response of isolated pure cultures of *Clostridium* to different sources of carbon and combined nitrogen was studied by the method described in our papers (Emtsev and Dzadzamiya 1970, 1971).

The determination of the activity of the dehydrogenases in the cultures of the bacteria was done by the **Fahmy and Walsh method (Fahmy and Walsh 1952).**

Volatile acids and alcohols in the cultures of *Clostridium* were determined by the method of gas-liquid chromatography with the use of Chrom-31 chromatograph (Czecho-Slovak Socialist Republic). (Emtsev and Dzadzamiya 1970).

Nitrogen-fixing activity of *Cl. butyricum* and *Cl. acetobutylicum* was determined by Emtsev and Zakharova method (1970).

The effect of various rates of combined nitrogen on the growth and nitrogen-fixing activity of *Cl. butyricum* and *Cl. acetobutylicum* was studied in the Vinogradsky medium (Rodina 1965) of 1% glucose, 0.5% $CaCO_3$, 0.05% sodium thioglucolate and 1 ml/l of microelements according to Fedorov. The combined nitrogen in the form of casein hydrolysate and ammonium sulphate was applied in the medium mentioned above in the following amounts: 0.25, 0.5, 1.0 and 2.0%.

The intensity of nitrogen fixation of *Cl. butyricum* and *Cl. axetobutylicum* in media of various nitrogen rates being determined, the neutral red (0.004%) and Sörensen's buffer mixture (1 : 4) were applied to the Winogradsky medium. The test was conducted in 100 ml Erlenmeyer flasks: the inoculant was prepared according to our method (Emtsev and Dzadzamiya 1970, Emtsev and Zakharova 1970). Cultures of *Cl. butyricum* were incubated at 27 °C, while that of *Cl. aceto-butylicum* – at 37 °C during 15–20 days.

The Kjeldahl micromethod was used for determining nitrogen, Betrand's method for determining sugar.

The method of pyrolysis – gas-chromatography used by us to study strains of *Clostridium* is described in the paper (Emtsev *et al.* 1965).

RESULTS AND DISCUSSION

The data of *Clostridium* spreading in the soils of Georgia mentioned above are given in Table 1. The analysis of the data obtained shows that though butyric and acetobutylic anaerobes have been found in the soils of both types, their ratio varies considerably. It has been determined that in cinnamonic forest soil there are more acetobutylic bacteria while in meadow-boggy soil butyric bacteria are predominant. Such ratios of anaerobes in two soil types can be explained by different amounts of relatively available organic compounds as well as by soil moisture.

It is known that meadow-boggy soils tend to accumulate considerable supplies of organic compounds, which along with high moisture favours rapid multiplication of butyric bacteria. The results obtained confirm the previous observations.

One more fact that has been established during the investigations is of interest. That is the role of the **anthropogenic factor** in spreading anaerobes. It has been found that anaerobic bacteria respond favourably to the meliorative practices used.

Table 1
Dynamics of the number of butyric and acetobutylic bacteria in irrigated and overmoistened soil (in thousands per gram of dry soil, 1972–1973, Georgian SSR)

Months	Soil					
	cinnamonic forest			meadow-boggy		
	soil condition					
	virgin	cultivated (non-irrigated)	cultivated (irrigated)	virgin	cultivated (non-drained)	cultivated (drained)
Cl. pasteurianum						
April	280.0	726.0	15900.0	740.0	4540.0	36400.0
July	230.0	272.5	585.0	437.5	2951.0	26520.0
October	750.0	768.0	7920.0	1044.0	1410.0	28600.0
January	82.2	134.5	756.1	115.2	1482.2	6100.0
Cl. butyricum						
April	28.0	302.5	7800.0	3700.0	13620.0	45500.0
July	57.5	272.5	585.0	1050.0	5635.0	14080.0
October	162.5	166.4	7920.0	1044.0	7050.0	15500.0
January	34.3	76.2	756.1	148.4	793.8	1464.0
Cl. acetobutylicum						
April	672.0	3025.0	3025.0	435.0	1410.0	1320.0
July	69.0	1417.0	2925.0	105.0	563.5	1224.0
October	750.0	1664.0	3300.0	88.8	1362.0	1274.0
January	134.25	752.0	1560.7	122.0	321.1	610.0

357

The number of all species of *Clostridium* in such soil plots is many times more (sometimes 100–200 times) than the number of these organisms in virgin and unimproved soils. The irrigation of cinnamonic soil favours rapid development of *Cl. pasteurianum Cl. butyricum* and especially of *Cl. acetobutylicum*. The drainage of meadow-boggy soil increases the development of only *Cl. pasteurianum* and *Cl. butyricum* which can be explained by the influence of moisture on soil micro-organisms (Emtsev *et al.* 1974). We have determined that 80 per cent moisture is the optimum for the development of anaerobes. When moisture is 100 per cent, that is, when soils are under conditions of complete flooding, the vital activity of anaerobic bacteria is badly inhibited.

In addition, it has been shown that moisture does not affect the development of different species of anaerobic bacteria of the genus *Clostridium* in the same way. The optimum development of *Cl. pasteurianum* is observed at 80 and 90 per cent moisture, while that of cellulose decomposing anaerobes takes place at 90 per cent moisture.

Thus, each physiological group of micro-organisms has its own optimum moisture level.

The experiments have also shown that under conditions of complete flooding (100% moisture) not only the vital activity of aerobic but also anaerobic micro-organisms is badly inhibited. Under the conditions of complete anaerobiosis caused by the flooding of the soil the products of anaerobic metabolism are likely to be accumulated, which results in the depression of micro-organic development.

Hence, irrigation (increase in soil moisture) and drainage (decrease in soil moisture) establish the optimum moisture level that stimulates the growth and development of anaerobic nitrogen-fixing bacteria (Debrivnaya 1970).

Thus, the observations have shown that under the conditions of meadow-boggy soils butyric bacteria predominate while in cinnamonic forest soils acetobutylic bacteria are the most numerous. Agromeliorative practices increase the number of anaerobic bacteria in the soils studied without changing their specific composition.

Are there any differences in the physiological peculiarities of butyric and acetobutylic bacteria living in different soils that have been subjected to various agromeliorative practices?

Pure cultures of *Cl. butyricum* and *Cl. acetobutylicum* isolated from meadow-boggy and cinnamonic soils were studied from the standpoint of the following physiological indices: responce to different sources of carbon and nitrogen, the products of fermentation, dehydrogenase and nitrogen-fixing activity.

The data showing the use and intensity of the development of *Clostridium* on different sources of carbon are given in Table 2.

It is seen that the intensity of the development of *Cl. butyricum* and *Cl. acetobutylicum* isolated from different soil types on different sources of carbon varies greatly, the growth of various strains on the same carbohydrate in most cases being different. *Cl. butyricum* isolated from meadow-boggy soil (where they dominate over *Cl. acetobutylicum*) develop on different sources of carbon better

Table 2

Development of pure cultures on different sources of carbon

Soils	Treatments	No of strains	Optical density, measured at 440 mmk × 5							
			glucose	lactose	starch	glycerine	mannite	salicin	amygdalin	pyruvic acid
Cl. butyricum										
Cinnamonic forest	Virgin	11.13	0.04	0.27	0.08	0	0.15	0.18	0	0.21
	Non-irrigated	32.33	0.08	0.43	0.16	0	0.30	0.23	0	0.33
	Irrigated	51.53	0.32	0.52	0.45	0	0.51	0.28	0	0.52
Meadow-boggy	Virgin	71.72	0.14	0.18	0.12	0	0.45	0.30	0	0.14
	Non-drained	91.92	0.18	0.39	0.24	0	0.50	0.32	0	0.38
	Drained	112.113	0.72	0.57	0.66	0	0.58	0.35	0	0.55
Cl. acetobutylicum										
Cinnamonic forest	Virgin	22.23	–	0.14	0.10	0	0.07	0.07	0.05	0
	Non-irrigated	41.43	0.61	0.19	0.23	0	0.08	0.14	0.06	0
	Irrigated	61.64	0.84	0.30	0.49	0	0.18	0.41	0.14	0
Meadow-boggy	Virgin	81.82	0.38	0.08	0.10	0	0.03	0.09	0.02	0
	Non-drained	103.105	0.38	0.11	0.19	0	0.05	0.13	0.04	0
	Drained	121.123	0.49	0.16	0.32	0	0.08	0.16	0.08	0

than those isolated from cinnamonic forest soil. Just the opposite is observed in *Cl. acetobutylicum*. The strains of this organism isolated from cinnamonic forest soil (where they predominate over *Cl. butyricum*) develop much better on different kinds of carbohydrate than those isolated from meadow-boggy soil. However, not only does the soil type influence the response of *Clostridium* to different sources of carbon and to the intensity of their use. An essential effect is produced by agro-meliorative practices. So, the strains of *Cl. butyricum* (and *Cl. acetobutylicum*) isolated from irrigated and drained soils develop better on most tested sources of carbon as compared with those isolated from non-irrigated (non-drained) and especially virgin soils.

The results of the study of the nature of the glucose products of fermentation and their ratio in cultures of *Clostridium* are given in Table 3.

As it is seen from the Table, the strains of *Cl. butyricum* isolated from meadow-boggy soil produced more butyric acid than those isolated from cinnamonic forest soil which contains a larger amount of acetic acid and neutral (butanol and ethanol) products. This is especially clearly seen if we compare the ratio of volatile acids (butyric and acetic) and neutral products (butanol and ethanol) excreted by the cultures of *Cl. butyricum* from meadow-boggy and cinnamonic forest soils. So, in the culture of *Cl. butyricum* (strain 113) isolated from meadow-boggy soil the percentage of acids to alcohols was 19.4 (such proportion is typical of true butyric bacteria), while in the culture (strain 53) isolated from cinnamonic forest soil it was 4.4. Similar proportion of acids to alcohols was found in the cultures of *Cl. acetobutylicum* as well. In the culture isolated from meadow-boggy soil (strain 82), for example, it amounted to 7.8, while in that from cinnamonic forest soil (strain 22) – 6.4. Hence, the butyric anaerobe of *Cl. butyricum* from cinnamonic soil that is the zone of the optimum growth of *Cl. acetobutylicum* possesses an altered metabolism similar to that of acetobutylic bacteria. Such phenomenon has been found in *Cl. pasteurianum* (Emtsev and Dzadzamiya 1970). The amount of acids and alcohols produced by *Cl. acetobutylicum* changes depending on the soil type to a less extent than that produced by *Cl. butyricum*.

From all the meliorative practices it is drainage of meadow-boggy soil that was produced a great effect on the percentage of acids to alcohols in *Clostridium*, mainly in *Cl. butyricum*. Thus, in the culture of *Cl. butyricum* (strain 71) isolated from the virgin soil the percentage of acids to alcohols was 12.7 while in the culture (strain 112) from drained soil it makes 18.6. Such proportion of the products of fermentation is typical of butyric bacteria (Winogradsky 1952). Hence, the drainage of the soil "normalizes" the metabolism of these organisms.

Interesting results have been obtained in studying dehydrogenase activity of *Clostridium* (Table 4). Certain differences have proved to be present in dehydrogenase activity of *Cl. butyricum* and *Cl. acetobutylicum*, the former having higher dehydrogenase activity. However, considerable differences have been observed mainly between strains of the species mentioned above isolated from different soil types. The strains of *Cl. butyricum* isolated from meadow-boggy soil had two times as much dehydrogenase activity as those isolated from cinnamonic forest soil. In *Cl. acetobutylicum,* on the contrary, a higher dehydrogenase activity was observed in strains isolated from cinnamonic forest soil than that in strains isolated from meadow-boggy soil. The differences between strains of *Cl. acetobutylicum* from different soil types were not, however, so great as those between strains of *Cl. butyricum.*

From the Table it is also clear that cultivation of soils (irrigation, drainage) considerably increases the dehydrogenase activity of anaerobes. This is typical of both species of *Clostridium,* but especially of *Cl. butyricum.* The strains of this anaerobe isolated from irrigated and drained soils have two and sometimes three times as much dehydrogenase activity as that of the culture isolated from virgin soils.

The investigation of nitrogen-fixing activity of *Clostridium* has shown that it varies greatly in *Cl. butyricum* of different origin, mamely, the strains isolated from meadow-boggy soil had higher activity than those isolated from cinnamonic forest soil. No considerable differences in nitrogen-fixing activity have been revealed in the strains of acetobutylic bacteria (Table 5).

The results of the determination of the intensity of nitrogen combining of *Clostridium* have also shown that the highest activity is typical of the strains of *Cl. butyricum* and *Cl. acetobutylicum* isolated from irrigated cinnamonic and drained meadow-boggy soils, the strains of *Clostridium* isolated from drained meadow-boggy soil possessing the maximum nitrogen-fixing activity. The favourable water-air regime established by irrigating cinnamonic and drained meadow-boggy soil is likely to cause not only rapid multiplication of *Clostridium* but also their high activity. It should be noted, however, that more optimum conditions are created for anaerobic micro-organisms in drained meadow-boggy soil than in a cinnamonic one because the former has a large supply of relatively available organic substances than the latter. That is why in meadow-boggy soil the butyric bacteria develop better and their activity is higher.

The cultures of *Clostridium* we had were also investigated by means of gas-chromatography after pyrolysis. The pyrograms of the cultures of *Cl. butyricum* of different origin differed from each other, which indicates a certain specificity of their composition. It should be noted that pyrograms of the cultures of *Cl. aceto-butylicum* were more alike than those of the strains of *Cl. butyricum* obtained from different soils.

Thus, the results of the experiments have shown that the composition of the anaerobic flora of the soil and the physiological peculiarities of its species are greatly influenced not only by the geographical but also by agrosoil factors. The natural microbic coenosis, biological peculiarities of individual species of anaerobes undergo certain changes with the cultivation of the soil (especially irrigation and drainage). The cultivation of the soil does not deteriorate, however, distinguishing features develop peculiar to coenosis of anaerobic micro-organisms of a certain soil type. It should be noted that there is a considerably greater variability of butyric bacteria compared with that of acetobutylic ones.

361

Table 3

Products of glucose* fermentation by different cultures of *Clostridium*

Soil	Treatments	Strains	Volatile acids g/100 ml of medium		Alcohols g/100 ml of medium	
			butyric	acetic	buthanol	ethanol
		Cl. butyricum				
Cinnamonic	Virgin	11	0.610	0.250	0.142	0.073
forest		13	0.594	0.265	0.160	0.082
	Irrigated	51	0.675	0.190	0.138	0.059
		53	0.705	0.180	0.130	0.068
Meadow-	Virgin	71	0.920	0.100	0.043	0.037
boggy		72	0.890	0.120	0.048	0.039
	Drained	112	0.990	0.090	0.030	0.028
		113	0.960	0.085	0.034	0.025

*Initial glucose-content in the medium is 2%.

Table 4

Dehydrogenase activity of pure cultures of *Clostridium*
(in mg TFF per 1.5 mlrd cells during 24 hours)

Soils	Treatments	*Cl. butyricum*			
		strains	glucose	lactose	strach
Cinnamonic	Control,				
forest	virgin	11.13	0.175	0.247	0.158
	Non-irrig-				
	ated	32.33	0.202	0.388	0.295
	Irrigated	51.53	0.562	0.660	0.788
Meadow-	Control,				
boggy	virgin	71.72	0.368	0.364	0.328
	Non-drained	91.92	0.660	0.638	0.752
	Drained	112.113	0.958	0.788	0.900

Relation of acids to alcohols	Strains	Volatile acids g/100 ml of medium		Alcohols g/100 ml of medium		Relation of acids to alcohols
		butyric	acetic	buthanol	ethanol	
Cl. acetobutylicum						
4.0	22	0.500	0.210	0.042	0.056	6.4
3.5	23	0.520	0.230	0.048	0.064	6.6
4.3	61	0.570	0.195	0.046	0.042	8.6
4.4	64	0.585	0.205	0.048	0.048	8.2
14.7	81	0.605	0.260	0.043	0.056	8.7
11.6	82	0.603	0.253	0.045	0.064	7.8
18.6	121	0.650	0.240	0.038	0.072	8.09
19.4	123	0.636	0.234	0.040	0.068	8.05

		Cl. acetobutylicum					
mannite	pyruvic acid	strains	glucose	lactose	starch	mannite	pyruvic acid
0.225	0.202	22.23	0.180	0.135	0.152	0.100	0
0.422	0.375	41.43	0.318	0.175	0.180	0.202	0
0.638	0.570	61.64	0.522	0.202	0.225	0.318	0
0.375	0.422	81.82	0.175	0.125	0.145	0.088	0
0.718	0.602	103.105	0.295	0.152	0.175	0.158	0
0.825	0.788	121.123	0.410	0.180	0.212	0.180	0

Table 5
Fixation of atmospheric nitrogen by cultures of *Clostridium* isolated from irrigated and over-moistened soils (Georgian SSR)

Soils	Soil condition	fixed atmospheric nitrogen in mg per 1 g of glucose (average of three strains)	
		Cl. butyricum	*Cl. acetobutylicum*
Cinnamonic forest	virgin	5.47	3.24
	cultivated (non-irrigated)	5.62	3.27
	cultivated (irrigated)	6.77	4.13
Meadow-boggy	virgin	5.71	2.66
	cultivated (non-drained)	6.47	2.93
	cultivated (drained)	9.96	4.17

In conclusion it must be said that the conducted investigations of geographical and ecological aspects of the biology of soil anaerobes of the genus *Clostridium* have allowed us to clear up only some of many various questions pertaining to the problem discussed. But at the same time, some new problems have arisen including those that are not yet ready to be solved because of lack of necessary facts. We can hope that the recent increased interest on the part of microbiologists in the problems of geography and ecology of anaerobic micro-organisms will result in the intensification of investigations that will provide us with data necessary for exhaustive solution of theoretical and applied aspects of the biology of anaerobes as a whole.

SUMMARY

The study of spreading anaerobic nitrogen-fixing bacteria of the genus *Clostridium* in some soils of Georgia has shown that butyric bacteria *(Cl. pasteurianum, Cl. butyricum)* predominate in meadow-boggy soil, while aceto-butylic bacteria are mostly found in cinnamonic forest soil. Agronomeliorative practices increase the number of anaerobic bacteria in the soils studied, without changing their specific composition.

Essential differences have been revealed in the response of the strains of *Cl. butyricum* and *Cl. acetobutylicum* to the sources of carbon and nitrogen, in their products of fermentation, as well as in the dehydrogenase and nitrogen-fixing activity. These differences depend not only on the type of the soil from which this or that strain has been isolated but also on the agromeliorative practices that have been used.

The depressing effect of combined nitrogen compounds upon nitrogen-fixing activity of *Clostridium* varies both with the rate and form of nitrogen applied into the medium and with the species of the micro-organisms and the place of its isolation.

It has been found that combined forms of organic and especially of mineral nitrogen exert a stronger inhibiting effect upon the nitrogen fixation by *Cl. butyricum* than upon the nitrogen fixation by *Cl. acetobutylicum*. The differences revealed can be explained by greater variability and, hence, the sensitivity of butyric bacteria *(Cl. butyricum)*.

The degree of depression of nitrogen-fixing activity of *Cl. butyricum* as well as *Cl. acetobutylicum* isolated from virgin and cultivated cinnamonic and meadow-boggy soils is different due to the application of organic and mineral nitrogen to the medium. It is lower in the strains from the virgin soils than in those from cultivated soils (irrigated and drained).

REFERENCES

(Debrivnaya, I. E.) Дебривная, И. Е. (1970): *Азотфиксирующие бактерии ризосферы риса, культивируемого в условиях юга УССР.* Диссертация, Киев.

(Emtsev, V. T.) Емцев, В. Т. (1965): *Доклады ТСХА.* **109**, 123–130.

(Emtsev, V. T.) Емцев, В. Т. (1967): *Анаэробные фиксаторы молекулярного азота..* in: Биологический азот и его роль в земледелии. Наука, Москва.

(Emtsev, V. T.) Емцев, В. Т. (1974): *Успехи микробиол.* **9**, 153–182.

(Emtsev, V. T. and Dzadzamiya, T. D.) Емцев, В. Т., Дзадзамия, Т. Д. (1969): *Изв. ТСХА* **4**, 33–40.

(Emtsev, V. T. and Dzadzamiya, T. D.) Емцев, В. Т., Дзадзамия, Т. Д. (1970): *Изв. ТСХА* **6**.

(Emtsev, V. T. and Dzadzamiya, T. D.) Еицев, В. Т., Дзадзамия, Т. Д. (1971): *Доклады ТСХА.* **162**, 251–257.

(Emtsev, V. T. and Pokrovsky, V. P.) Емцев, В. Т. и Покровский, В. П. (1973): *Изв. ТСХА* **4**, 212–214.

(Emtsev, V. T. and Razvozhevskaya, Z. S.) Емцев, В. Т., Развожевская, З. С. (1971): *Изв. ТСХА* **4**, 18–26.

(Emtsev, V. T. and Zakharova, S. N.) Емцев, В. Т., Захарова, С. Н. (1970): *Доклады ТСХА.* **160**, 174–178.

(Emtsev, V. T. and Zakharova, S. N.) Емцев, В. Т., Захарова, С. Н. (1973): *Изв. ТСХА,* **3**, 108–113.

(Emtsev, V. T., Razvozhevskaya, Z. S. and Dzadzamiya, T. D.) Еицев, В. Т., Развожевская, З. С., Дзадзамия, Т. Д. (1970): *Изв. АН СССР, сер. биол.* **5**, 705–712.

(Emtsev, V. T., Dzadzamiya, T. D., Murzakov, B. G. and Gostenkov, M. F.) Еицев, В. Т., Дзадзамия, Т. Д., Мурзаков, Б. Г., Гостенков, М. Ф. (1971): *Изв. АН СССР, сер. биол.* **3**, 465.

(Emtsev, V. T., Nemova, L. T. and Ignatova, N. N.) Емцев, В. Т., Немова, Л. Т., Игнатова, Н. Н. (1974): *Влияние уровней аэрации на динамику размножения аэробных микроорганизмов в дерново-подзолистой почве.* in: Динамика микробиологических процессов в почве и обуловливающие ее факторы, Москва 83–84.

Fahmy, A. K. and Walsch, O. F. (1952): *J. Biochem.* **51**.

(Rodina, A. G.) Родина, А. Г. (1965): *Методы водной микробиологии.* Наука, Москва.

(Winogradsky, S. N.) Виноградский, С. Н. (1952): *Микробиология почвы. Проблемы и методы.* Изд-во АН СССР, Москва.

CH-OXIDIZING SOIL BACTERIA AS INDICATORS
OF HYDROCARBON ACCUMULATIONS

by

SZOLNOKI, J. and Ágnes K. MENDLIK
Geochemical Research Laboratory of the Hungarian Academy of Sciences,
Budapest, Hungary

The direct microbiological hydrocarbon exploration as an extraordinarily simple and inexpensive method is becoming more and more widespread all over the world. The method is primarily gaining ground in the Soviet Union (Mogilevsky *et al.* 1974), in some socialist countries (Karaskiewicz 1970, Wagner 1968) and in the U. S. A. (Davis 1967). Only in the Soviet Union, more than 800.000 km^2 area was examined using the microbiological method with favourable results.

The fundamental principles of the microbiological prospecting method are given by the vertical migration of gaseous and volatile hydrocarbons. As a result of this migration, the hydrocarbons in the layers and in the waters near the surface get relatively enriched, resulting in a local accumulation of micro-organisms utilizing hydrocarbons as sole source of carbon. The method is particularly effective in case of hydrocarbon-accumulations found at small depth. The hydrocarbon-oxidizing micro-organisms are able to assimilate the significant part of gases and volatiles diffusing toward the earth surface (Kuznetsov *et al.* 1962). According to some investigations (Slavnina 1964) a single bacterium-cell in one hour is able to assimilate $2-5 \cdot 10^{-12}$ ml of gaseous hydrocarbon. Under optimal conditions the activity of bacteria might be so intensive, that it results in a "gas-minimum" with a "bacterial-maximum". In such cases the gas-anomalies may be found in a ring-shaped strip around the contour of the reservoirs (Mogilevsky 1967, Mogilevsky *et al.* 1968).

Although the list of CH-oxidizing bacteria grows continuously (Iizuka *et al.* 1966, Leadbetter and Foster 1960, Rozanova and Kuznetsov 1974, ZoBell 1950), the greater part of the gaseous hydrocarbon-utilizing micro-organisms belong to the genera of *Pseudomonas* and *Mycobacterium*. Some of them, are able to decompose selectively certain gaseous- or higher carbon atomic number alkanes (Karaskiewicz 1970). For the development of hydrocarbon-utilizing, about 10^{-6} vol.% of gas-concentration is sufficient (Rushakova 1960). Since the concentration of gaseous components migrating near the surface is often comparable to the mentioned one, in consequence of continuous diffusion of volatile hydrocarbons, the number of micro-organisms utilizing those may be very high; also in such areas, where the gas-chromatographic analyses cannot indicate or indicate traces of hydrocarbons in the soil or water. So the direct microbiological prospecting method is many times more sensitive than other usual physical or chemical methods.

Whereas methane is the main component of the natural gas, generally the methane-oxidizing bacteria are not accepted as indicator-organisms, since the methane may originate not only from hydrocarbon-reservoirs, but from the recent microbiological decomposition of organic materials too. Therefore from gaseous hydrocarbon-utilizing microbes chiefly the propane- and 'butane-oxidizing micro-organisms are accepted as indicator ones (Smirnova 1964), (Kersten 1964, 1966, Mogilewsky 1966).

Since the direct microbiological method forms a supplement to the seismic and gravitational methods, it is advisable to use it simultaneously or in succession. Namely, while the seismic and gravitational methods are primarily suitable for determining the location and extension of possible reservoirs, by using the direct microbiological method, it can be settled with a great probability whether the structure contains any hydrocarbons or not.

MATERIAL AND METHODS

The area examined is situated in the district of Mórahalom, Southern Hungary. In this area two interesting seismic measuring lines (MJ-3-726 and MJ-4-726) were taken as a basis. Along these lines soil samples were taken aseptically at small depth (1.5 m), and water samples coming from dug wells (1 m from water surface), situated in the environs of the lines were examined.

The soil samples were suspended in sterilized water and from both sorts of samples dilution-series were made. Media containing inorganic salts (Kuznetsov and Romanenko 1963) and as a sole carbon-source, respectively gases releasing from crude oil, propane-butane gas, pentane and hexane, were inoculated and incubated at 30 °C.

During microbiological investigations semiquantitative bacteria counting was carried out by the end-point dilution method (Oberzill 1967), partly bacterial activity examination was performed by observation of pellicle developed on the surface of media (Mogilevsky et al. 1974), and by gaschromatographic determination of the quantity of CO_2 produced by the microbiological oxidation of used hydrocarbons. For the microbiological examinations with rubber-stopperr and aluminium-cap closed glass injection-flacons (Mogilevsky et al. 1974) were used.

The investigated area was evaluated statistically according to the number and activity of that bacteria. Results have been summarized and delineated on a map.

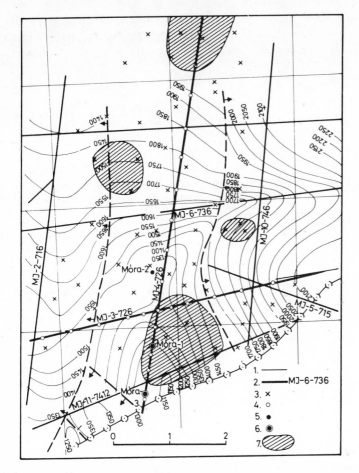

Fig. 1. Mórahalom. *Anomalous map of the microbiological tests.*
Legend: 1. depth in metres, 2. line of the seismic survey,
3. sampling points (water), 4. sampling points (soil),
5. barren well, 6. productive wells, 7. strong positive anomalies

RESULTS

Data obtained by all microbiological methods are summarized graphically on Figure 1 where also the seismic measuring data, as well as the points of wells drilled after the microbiological examinations, are shown. From the map it can be stated that there is a strong positive anomaly in the neighbourhood of the intersection point of the MJ-3-726 and MJ-4-726 lines as well as south of that which is proved also by drilling results obtained so far. A strong positive anomaly can be found at the northern end of the MJ-4-726 line and in its vicinity too. Two smaller positive anomalies appear in the N—W and S—E direction from the intersection point of the MJ-4-726 and MJ-6-738 lines, however, these are not significant.

DISCUSSION

From the data and interpretation of the direct microbiological hydrocarbon prospecting — carried out on the basis of previous seismometry — it can be stated that a markedly positive anomaly appears in the environs of the intersection point of the afore-mentioned seismic lines and south of that, which is proved also by the data of the Móra-1. and Móra-3. productive wells drilled after the examinations.

In the examined area the microbiological prospecting method proved to be successful. In as much as the further examinations — being in progress lately — should give similarly favourable results it could be used as a supplement to the usual seismic, gravitational and geochemical exploration, especially by the information survey of large regions, because this method involves a low cost impact.

SUMMARY

Direct research was carried out for microbiological prospecting of hydrocarbon accumulation. In South Hungary one of the probable oil-bearing areas was examined and surveyed on the basis of analyses of soil- and water samples, derived from small depths, for crude petroleum-gas-, propane-butane-gas-, as well as pentane and hexane-oxidizing bacteria. The investigated area was evaluated on the basis of number and activity of that bacteria. The results were summarized and delineated on a sketch map. Contours of CH-accumulation were well-defined by the micro-biological prospecting method. The success was justified by the data and results of productive oil-wells drilled after the examinations.

ACKNOWLEDGEMENTS

The authors wish to express their appreciation to Mr. I. Fisch (Research Laboratory for Oil and Gas Industry) and to Mr. J. Trompler (Univ. E. L. T. E., Dept. of Inorganic and Analytical Chem.) for gas-chromatographic analysis.

REFERENCES

Davis, J. B. (1967): *Petroleum microbiology.* Elsevier, New York.
Iizuka, H., Tsuru, S. and Seato, N. (1966): *On the microflora of oil and natural gas-fields in Japan.* In: Vorträge d. Internat. Symp. "Erdölmikrobiologie", Brno. 1964. Akad. Verl. Berlin.
Karaskiewicz, J. (1970): Badania nad zastosowaniem metod mikrobiologicznyeh w poszukivwaniu zloz ropu naftowej i gazu ziemnego *Slask.* Katowice.

370

(Kersten, D. K.) Керстен, Д. К. (1964) : *Микробиол.* 33, 31–37.

(Kersten, D. K.) Керстен, Д. К. (1966) : *Автореферат дисс.* Москва.

(Kuznetsov, S. I., Ivanov, M. V. and Lialikova, N. N.) Кузнецов, С. И., Иванов, М. В., Ляликова, Н. Н. (1962) : *Введение в геологическую микобиологию.* А. Н. СССР, Москва.

(Kuznetsov, S. I. and Romanenko, V. I.) Кузнецов, С. И., Романенко, В. И. (1963) : *Микробиологическое изучение внутренных водоемов.* А. Н. СССР. Москва.

Leadbetter, E. R. and Foster, J. W. (1960): *Arch. f. Microbiol.* 35, 92–104.

Mogilevsky, G. A. (1966): *Analyse der Ergebnisse bei Anwendung gas-mikrobiologischen Methoden zur Prospection von Erdöl und Erdgas unter verschiedenen geologischen Bedingungen.* In: Vorträge d. Internat. Symp. "Erdölmikrobiologie" Brno 1964. Akad. Verl. Berlin.

(Mogilevsky, G. A.) Могилевский, Г. А. (1967) : *Об изменении и новообразовании углеводородных газов в зоне гипергенеза.* Сб. Доклады представленные на Всесаюзное совещание по генезису нефти и газа. Недра Москва.

(Mogilevsky, G. A., Bogdanova, V. M., Kitsatova, S. N. and Slavina, G. P.) Могилевский, Г. А., Богданова, В. М., Кичатова, Ш. Н. Славнина, Г. П. (1968) : *Бактериальный фильтр в зоне нефтяых и газовых месторождений, его особенности и методы изучения.* In: Vorträge zu geochemischen und chemisch-physikalischen Problemen der Erdöl-Erdgas Erkundung und Förderung. Deutsch. Verl. f. Grundstoffeinindustrie, Leipzig.

(Mogilevsky, G. A., Bogdanova, V. M., Zaikin, N. G., Sapunova, G. G., Telegina, Z. P. and Tserkinskaya, V. P.) Могилевский, Г. А., Богданова, В. М., Заикин, Н. Г., Сапунова, Г. Г. Телегина, З. П. Черкинская, В. П. (1974) : *Инструктивные указания по проведению газобиохимических поисковых работ на нефт и газ.* Научно-техн. информ. Москва.

Oberzill, W. (1967): *Mikrobiologische Analytik.* Verl. H. Carl, Nürberg.

(Rozanova, E. P. and Kuznetsov, S. I.) Розанова, Е. П., Кузнецов, С. И. (1974) : *Микрофлора нефтянных месторождений.* Наука, Москва.

(Rushakova, G. M.) Рушакова, Г. М. (1960) : *Микробиол.* 29, 715–720.

(Slavnina, G. P.) Славнина, Г. П. (1964) : *Влияние микроэлементов на развитие бактерий окисляющих углеводороды.* Сб.: Проблема нефтяной геологии и методика лабораторных исследований. Недра, Москва.

(Smirnova, Z. S.) Смирнова, З. Ш. (1964) : *К вопросу о специфичности пропаноокисляющих бактерий.* Сб.: Прямые методы поисков нефти и газа. Недра, Москва.

Wagner, M. (1968): *Gommern.* 19, 6–10.

ZoBell, C. E. (1950): *Adv. Enzymol.* 10, 443–486.

THE ROLE OF SOIL ORGANISMS
IN THE SOIL FORMING PROCESS

SOME SOIL BIOLOGICAL PROBLEMS IN THE RECULTIVATION OF OPEN-CUT MINE BANKS

by

J. SZEGI,[1] F. GULYÁS,[1] J. OLÁH[2] and Ibolya N. VÖRÖS[1]
[1] Research Institute for Soil Science
and Agricultural Chemistry of the Hungarian Academy of Sciences,
Budapest, Hungary
[2] Recultivation Department of the "M. Thorez" Open-Cut Mines,
Visonta, Hungary

Development, maintenance and continuous improvement of soil fertility on open-cut mine banks is an extremely important problem of environmental control and agriculture. In the last two decades, numerous studies have been devoted to these problems; works done in western countries (particularly in England, USA and Federal Republic of Germany) were reviewed by Doubleday (1974). Nevertheless, these problems are intensively studied in the socialist countries as well, for example Izhevskaya and her co-workers in the Soviet Union (1974), Knabe (1952), Brünning (1959) in German Democratic Republic, Nastya *et al.* (1974) in Rumania, Jonás (1974) in Czechoslovakia or Strzyszcz (1974) in Poland should be mentioned here. In Hungary, Szabó and Gordienko (1974), Szabó *et al.* (1974) have achieved important results in this field.

Unfortunately, due to the considerable differences observable in the physical and chamical composition of mine banks, it is almost impossible to develop optimal methods for recultivation of open-cut mine banks, if the planning is based solely on data available in the literature.

The bulk of the coal mine wastes is often composed of clay shale. Sandstone, volcanic tuff and various incrustations, infiltrations may also occur. Topsoil and loess is mixed with these materials in varying amounts in open-cut mine banks.

The methods of recultivation are determined by the physical and chemical composition of the tips. If carbonates are predominant, the pH is neutral or slightly alkaline, while presence of pyrite results in the development of acidity causing formation of acidic weathering products. Accumulation of toxic cations (Fe^{2+}, Al^{3+}) is extremely disadvantageous and might inhibit plant growth for years. Colliery spoil heaps regraded by heavy, rubber-tyred vehicles are often almost impermeable to moisture and air. Therefore, deep loosening and continuous improvement of physical properties of the spoil is indispensable in such cases.

In spite of the undisputable priority of these problems, careful study of biological processes occurring in colliery spoil is also important.

Following from the above-mentioned considerations, the aim of our work was the study of biological processes and development of methods of artificial stimulation.

Colliery spoil heaps of the "M. Thorez" Open-Cut Mines (Visonta, Hungary) were chosen for these studies, since several thousand hectares are disturbed by mining in that area and further increase is planned. Moreover, preliminary measurements are in progress for opening a new, much more larger open-cut mine in the vicinity of the mine mentioned. Recultivation of the spoil heaps of these mines is extremely important, since this area is famous for its vine production; being one of the best, traditional grape vine-producing areas of the country, it is exceptionally valuable land.

MATERIAL AND METHODS

Spoil heaps of the site in question are mainly composed of pannon sand and two types of clay. Besides a common, yellowish form, bluish-grey, reduced, strongly gleyic type also occurs. Considerable amounts of weathered andesitic tuff and holocenic alluvial deposits are mixed in these materials. Generally, the bluish-gray clay lies in contact with the lignite, (at a depth of 25–50 m), followed by the yellowish clay and pannon sand. Andesitic tuff is distributed irregularly in the overburden, from 10–12 m down to the lignite layer. Several data of these materials is summarized in Table 1.

As the data show, all of these materials and the topsoil are neutral or slightly alkaline, probably due to their relatively high calcium carbonate-content, which is generally above 10% or even exceeds 25% in the bluish-gray clay. Total amount of soluble salts is relatively low, ranging from 0.02 to 0.07%. Humus-content is practically zero in these layers (with the exception of the topsoil, of course). The relatively high "organic matter"-content of the bluish-gray clay is attributable to contaminating lignite particles.

Physical properties of the main components are presented in Table 2. Physical clay-content of the pannon sand is below 10%, while its amount is over 70% in the other cases. Obviously, mixing of pannon sand with the other materials will result in improvement of their physical properties. The same also holds true for the andesitic tuff showing extreme porosity (indicated by the high h_y value in Table 2).

Establishment and promotion of microbial life in the fresh spoil is a crucial problem of recultivation (Müller, 1965). Total activity of the microflora is frequently characterized by soil respiration measurements; in the present study, CO_2-production of the variously treated soil samples was determined acidimetrically. Details of the experimental apparatus used were described by Szegi (1973). Erlenmeyer flasks containing soil samples moistened to 60% WHC were connected to CO_2-trapping flasks containing 1N NaOH. Flow of air and the gases evolved was achieved by a small membrane pump. The whole apparatus was incubated (28 °C) for 49 days; aliquots from the CO_2-trapping flasks were titrated weekly using an automatic titration equipment (Radiometer, Denmark). Samples of the above-mentioned four main types of spoils were treated with various additives in the following combinations: 1, untreated control, 2, enriched with 1% cellulose, 3, enriched with fertilizers abd 1%

Table 1
Chemical data of samples

Sample	pH		CaCO₃ %	Humus %	Total salts %	N mg/100 g		P₂O₅ mg% available***	K₂O
	H₂O	KCl				total*	available**		
Topsoil	7.6	6.9	1.3	3.45	0.070	91.08	1.73	3.4	28.8
Pannon sand	8.0	7.4	12.4	0.07	0.005	0.041	0.52	2.1	2.8
Yellow clay	8.5	7.5	15.4	0.09	0.020	0.084	0.42	4.4	11.0
Bluish-gray clay	7.8	7.4	25.6	0.79	0.040	0.076	2.31	4.8	3.6
Weathered andesitic tuff	7.7	6.7	1.3	0.11	0.080	0.037	0.53	5.6	19.0

*   Kjeldahl method
**   Bremner method
*** Egner–Riem–Domingo method.

Table 2
Physical data of samples

Sample	Water holding capacity	Sticky point acc. to Arany	hy	Mechanical composition %							Physical sand : Physical clay
				0.25	0.25–0.05	0.05–0.02	0.02–0.01	0.01–0.005	0.005–0.002	0.002	
Topsoil	63.4	63	4.03	2.4	7.7	16.5	10.8	8.9	7.7	46.0	37.4 : 62.6
Pannon sand	35.8	40	0.84	2.2	68.5	15.7	4.4	2.0	2.0	5.2	90.8 : 9.2
Yellow clay	74.5	68	4.34	1.2	2.0	6.9	15.3	21.4	17.7	35.5	25.2 : 74.4
Bluish-gray clay	59.3	55	2.39	–	3.6	11.3	24.6	21.4	18.5	20.6	38.5 : 61.5
Weathered andesitic tuff	86.1	66	6.75	3.2	11.3	6.0	8.9	10.9	15.3	44.4	29.4 : 70.6

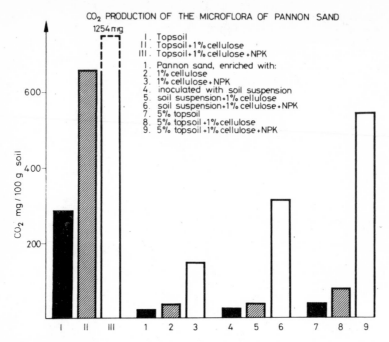

Fig. 1. CO_2 production of the microflora of pannon sand

cellulose 4, inoculated with soil suspension 5, inoculated with soil suspension and enriched with 1% cellulose 6, inoculated with soil suspension and enriched with fertilizers + 1% cellulose 7, inoculated with 5% topsoil 8, inoculated with 5% topsoil and enriched with 1% cellulose 9, inoculated with 5% topsoil and enriched with fertilizers + 1% cellulose. The soil suspension used resulted in 0.25 g alien soil/100 g of sample under investigation; amount of fertilizers added was equal to 576 kg N, 640 kg P_2O_5 and 640 kg K_2O per hectare.

As Figures 1–4 show, the four main components of the spoil exhibited rather different biological activities. The two clay types originating from 25–40 m depth, showed no significant activity. Presence of reduced compounds probably inhibited the propagation of micro-organisms introduced by addition of topsoil or soil suspension. Oxidation of these compounds probably requires more time; microbial decomposition of cellulose will start only at a certain stage of oxidation.

Pannon sand and weathered andesitic tuff showed intensive microbial activities under the effect of inoculation with topsoil or soil suspension. The definite discrepancies in the activities can be explained by differences existing between concentrations of inocula used (0.25% soil suspension *versus* 5% topsoil). According to the data obtained, spontaneous infection of the practically sterile spoil is negligible and does not result in significant microbial decomposition of the cellulose added. Enrichment with topsoil or irrigation with soil suspension is essential in this respect.

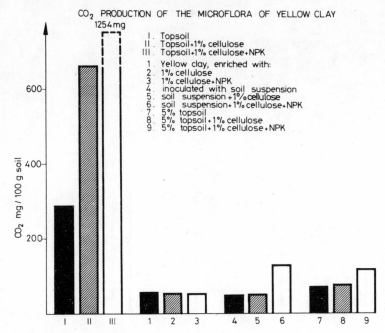

Fig. 2. CO_2 production of the microflora of yellow clay

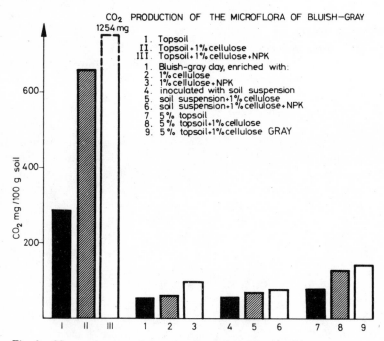

Fig. 3. CO_2 production of the microflora of bluish-gray clay

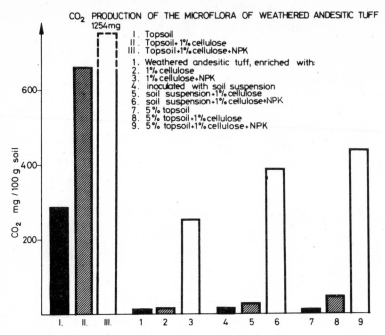

Fig. 4. CO_2 production of the microflora of weathered andesitic tuff

Under normal conditions, however, during regradation of tips, topsoil is often mixed with the biologically less active materials originating from deeper layers.

Another group of experiments was designed to estimate the biological activity of spoil heaps cultivated for several years; particular attention was paid to the effects of different cultivated plants on microbial activity of the soil.

15 g of filter paper strips (Whatman No. 1) were sown into loosely woven synthetic stuff. These bags were placed into plastic boxes, 10 mm below the surface of 400 g soil sample moistened to 60% WHC either with distilled water or with a solution containing 44 mg N, 50 mg P_2O_5 and 50 mg K_2O per 400 g soil. Quadruplicates of each treatment were kept at 28 °C. After three months of incubation, decomposition of cellulose was measured gravimetrically. Results were expressed in terms of a quotient calculated from numerical data obtained in the two treatments. Soil samples were collected in May, at the experimental station of the mine company. Four plots were selected; two of them received (in 1969) 22 t powderized lignite, 317 kg N, 112 kg P and 112 kg K per hectare. Afterwards, in the following years, these plots were fertilized with 160 kg N, 60 kg P and 60 kg K per hectare per year; monocultures of wheat and maize were grown on these plots over four years. The third plot, used as a vineyard since 1967, received 170 t powderized lignite, and 40 t farmyard manure per hectare in the first year, followed by 300 kg N, 150 kg P and 150 kg K in each year. Recultivation of the fourth plot was started in 1973, when this plot received the

Table 3

Decomposition of cellulose in the different components of the spoil and in the soil of various cultivated plants

Experimental plots	Amount of decomposed cellulose						Cellulolytic quotient
	Untreated			Fertilized (NPK)			
	decomposed		% of the control	decomposed		% of the control	
	mg	%		mg	%		
Undisturbed soil	920	61.3	100	1100	73.3	100	1.2
Bluish-gray clay	70	4.7	8	350	23.3	32	7.0
Yellow clay	50	3.3	5	540	36.0	49	10.8
Pannon sand	100	6.7	11	860	57.7	78	8.6
Winter wheat	570	38.0	38	960	64.0	87	2.5
Maize	660	44.0	72	870	58.0	79	1.3
Rye-common vetch mixture	740	49.3	80	960	64.0	87	1.3
Vine (1967)	1150	76.7	125	1100	73.3	100	0.96
Vine (1969)	780	52.0	85	990	56.7	90	1.2
Vine (1973)	460	30.7	50	600	40.0	55	1.3
Pot-garden (vegetables)	960	64.0	104	1020	68.0	93.0	1.06

same dressings as the first and second plots mentioned above. In that year rye was produced and was ploughed into the soil during the flowering stage; then vine was planted there.

As Table 3 shows, cellulolytic activity is minimal in the fresh spoil. During recultivation, due to application of various agrotechnical methods (fertilization, organic manuring, loosening, etc.), cellulolytic activity increased considerably, up to 70% of the activity exhibited by the undisturbed topsoil. Moreover, values above 80% were measurable in samples of fertilized plots. According to the literature (Unger 1968, Gamal-El-Din 1976, Gamal-El-Din et al. 1977, Szegi et al. 1976), cellulolytic activity might reflect – within certain limits – the nutrient status of the soil. As our data show, cellulolytic quotient was 1.19 in the case of the undisturbed, control areas. This low value suggests a high level of available nutrients. In the soil of wheat monoculture, cellulolytic activity differed significantly from data of soil under maize; this difference is explained by the fact that the two plants were in different periods of their life-cycles at the time of sampling. While wheat was in the early stage of ripening, maize was young, having 4–5 leaves per plant. Therefore, the latter probably did not yet exploit the available nutrients of the soil as wheat did.

Samples of the vineyard planted in 1967–1969 showed vigorous cellulolytic activity; the cellulolytic quotient is low in each treatment. Green manuring with rye ploughed into the soil during its flowering stage resulted in a somewhat higher quotient (i.e. lower cellulolytic activity). This is probably explained by the consideration that available nutrient were accumulated in the living matter of micro-organisms decomposing the large amount of plant residues.

DISCUSSION

Geologically different layers of colliery spoil have different biological properties – as it is clear from data presented in this paper. Biological processes are quickly initiated and established in the light-textured pannon sand, especially if it is inoculated with soil. Andesitic tuff has similar properties, development of a microflora is also slow in this material without inoculation. Consequently, if materials of deeper layers are not mixed with topsoil during regradation, inoculation of the fresh colliery spoil with minimal amount of topsoil is recommendable.

Yellow and bluish-gray clay are poor carriers of microbial life due to their physical and chemical properties. If it is possible, these materials should be covered by (or at least mixed with large amounts of) pannon sand and andesitic tuff.

Analysis of cellulolytic activity of soil samples taken from field experiments carried out on colliery spoil heaps pointed out the primary importance of mineral nutrients and organic matter of the mineralizable plant residues, not with standing the not negligible physical and chemical effects of the spoil. Characteristics and tendencies of microbial life and transformation of soil organic matter are different under various higher plants. Monocultures of wheat and maize result in large amounts of plant residues remaining in the soil each year. Consequently, considerable amounts of

382

mineral nutrients are also accumulated in living structures of micro-organisms decomposing these plant residues. On the other hand, cellulolytic activity is high in vineyard soil, where much less organic matter is accumulated. Green manuring by ploughing rye into the soil promotes biological recultivation of the spoil. In our opinion, this method is useful for the development of deep, fertile soil layer necessary for orchards and vineyards. Our soil biological experiments support the results of field experiments; covering of fresh spoil with a humic layer — at least in Visonta — is not an absolutely necessary requirement in the recultivation of colliery spoil heaps.

SUMMARY

Soil biological problems related to the recultivation of colliery spoil heaps ("M. Thorez" Open-Cut Mines, Visonta, Hungary) were studied. Main components of this spoil are pannon sand, weathered andesitic tuff and two types of clay. Microbial processes develop quickly in the former two materials, while clays — due to their disadvantageous physical and chemical properties — are poor carriers of microbial life. Inoculation of the fresh spoil with small amounts of topsoil resulted in vigorous decomposition of organic matter (cellulose) when added to the spoil; this cellulolytic activity was stimulated by mineral fertilizers. Recultivated areas, according to the degree of recultivation show different biological activities, which mainly depends on the kind of plants cultivated.

REFERENCES

Brünning, E. (1959): *Untersuchungen zur Frage der Begrünung teriär Rohbodenkippen des Braunkohletagebaues, dargestellt am Beispiel der Hochabsetzerkippe* 18, Böhlen, Thesis, Leipzig.

Doubleday, G. P. (1974): *Outlook on Agriculture.* 8, 156−162.

Gamal-El-Din, H. (1976): *Activity of cellulolytic micro-organisms in some Hungarian soils.* Thesis, Budapest.

Gamal-El-Din, H., Gulyás, F. and Kádár, I. (1977): *Soil Biology and Conservation of the Biosphere.* Budapest (in print).

Izhevskaya, T. I., Savich, A. I. and Cheklina, V. N. (1974): *Trans. X^{th} Int. Congr. Soil Sci.* Moscow, IV. 427−431.

Jonás, F. (1974): *Trans. X^{th} Int. Congr. Soil Sci.* Moscow, IV. 390−396.

Knabe, W. (1952): *Wiedernutzbarmachung des Kippengelädes, SKT 26,* Techn. Verl., Berlin.

Müller, G. (1965): *Bodenbiolgie.* Fischer Verl. Jena.

Nastya, S., Reutse, K. Marin, N. and Blazha, I. (1974): *Trans. X^{th} Int. Congr. Soil Sci.* Moscow, IV. 414−419.

Stryszcz, Z. (1974): *Trans. x^{th} Int. Congr. Soil Sci.* Moscow, IV. 398−403.

Szabó, B. and Gordienko, N. (1974): *Agrártud. Közl.* 33, 157−160.

Szabó, B., Gordienko, N. and Debreczeni, B. (1974): *Trans. x^{th} Int. Congr. Soil Sci.* Moscow, IV. 433−439.

(Szegi, J.) Сеги, И. (1973): *Разложение клетчатки и плодородие почвы,* Докт. диссерт. Москва.

Szegi, J., Gamal-El-Din, H., Gulyás, F. and Kádár, I. (1976): *Trans. VIIIth Int. Fertilizer Congr.* Moscow, 2, 143−150.

Unger, H. (1968): *Tagungsberichte DAL.* Berlin, 98, 19−34.

DESULPHURICATION, AS A FACTOR OF PEDOGENESIS IN SALT-AFFECTED SOILS

by

T. PÁTKAI
Research Institute for Soil Science
and Agricultural Chemistry of Hungarian Academy of Sciences,
Budapest, Hungary

The control of desulphurication is most desirable in many cases. For example, damages of underground pipelines due to desulphurication costs more than 800 million dollars per year only in the United States. There are no data available on the expenses of their disadvantageous effects on soils, but the growing demand for high yields has led to the extensive use of irrigation systems in semiarid and arid regions of the world. Extensive, not properly planned or performed irrigation has caused secondary salinization and alkalinization in many cases; rice production also suffers serious losses frequently by sulphide production of sulphate-reducers in those water-logged soils. Concerning other aspects, particularly the development of alkalinity and formation of soda in certain soils, estimation, prognosis and the mathematical description of these processes in order to prevent or control them have became an urgent problem. The automatization of big irrigation systems can not be realized without these preconditions.

In the past two decades a great number of papers have appeared on ecological, industrial and economic activities of sulphate-reducing bacteria as well as on their physiology and biochemistry. The accumulation of information has repeatedly called for the compilation of general or special reviews about these bacteria, which have been done from Baars (1930) to Postgate (1965). In this paper, several aspects of desulphurication will be discussed in relation to their role.

THE SULPHATE-REDUCING BACTERIA

The sulphate-reducing bacteria are not rare organisms in their natural habitats. However, the term "natural" has a very wide meaning; in this case, sulphate-reducers tolerate some of the most extreme terrestrial conditions of heat, cold, pressure and salinity. Therefore, enrichment is not too difficult, and many properly outlined procedures are described in the literature. As far as classification of sulphate-reducing bacteria is concerned, in spite of its tentative features, the system proposed by Postgate and Campbell (1966) is considered to be valid and incorporated into the eight edition of the Bergey's Manual (1975). It should be noted there, that the probability of further introductions is rather high because of the limited number of strains investigated so far. Surveying growth and nutrition of these bacteria, there are no data on their *pressure tolerance*, but they were also found in deep oil-borings in several cases. (ZoBell 1946, 1958). Deducing from this fact and taking into consideration the pressure tolerance of other bacteria (ZoBell 1946), one can suppose that their activity can be expected under the pressures of several hundred atmospheres. This ability might be important in soil-forming processes as it was suggested by Kovda (1964). Concerning heat resistance and temperature relationships, these bacteria can undoubtedly survive temperatures from far below 0 °C to above 100 °C. Within this range, depending on species or strain, optimal values are between 20—55 °C. The limits are not too sharp and especially growth at suboptimal temperatures is very interesting and important from a biogeochemical point of view.

The *osmotic pressure* is a significant ecological factor in sea-shore environments and in salt-affected soils. Many strains, isolated from such natural habitats exhibit relatively high capability in this respect, growing in media containing several per cent of salt, up to 10% NaCl or more. *D. salexigens* has a well-expressed requirement for salts, but almost every strain is able to grow in sea water or in media of similar osmotic properties. Dostalek and Kvet (1964) developed a method for studying subterranean waters, based on the osmotolerance of sulphate-reducing bacteria. Indigenousity of these bacteria in brines from the Romaskhina oil-field was discussed (Kuznetzova *et al.* 1962, 1964) on the basis of osmotical properties of isolates.

The *pH-limits* of desulphurication are 4.2—10.5 in nature. *In vitro* these figures are somewhat different, the minimum value is about pH 6, maximum around pH 9. Broadly speaking, the pH-range is narrower on artificial media which is important with respect to estimating their activities in salt-affected soils.

The *redox potential* of the environment is a crucial point for sulphate-reducing bacteria. Data available in the literature, especially the higher values are often misleading or incorrect. Redox potential changes with pH and temperature which facts should be considered thoroughly, E_h value without pH and temperature records is useless. Probably most of the data stating that sulphate-reducers are able to grow above -100 mV are incorrectly measured and/or calculated. This review will return to this point later, we can suggest here that the upper limit is about -100 mV (pH 7, 20 °C) in pure culture and somewhat higher in nature. It is important to be familiar with the phenomenon that there is no lower limit for desulphurication as far as E_h is concerned. Phenomena resulting in the increase of pH and simultaneous decrease of E_h value affect these bacteria substantially through the pH change. These events will result in an alkaline lysis above pH 9, when E_h is below -300 mV or around -400 mV.

Partial pressure of O_2 in the environment must be very low for the normal life of sulphate-reducing bacteria. Above 30 p.p.m. O_2-content, dissolved oxygen increases the E_h in most of the media used to a harmful level. Therefore, from a physicochemical point of view, oxygen acts by its redox properties. Moreover, oxygen is poisonous via the non-physiological "Knallgas" reaction due to the autooxidizability of cytochrome C_3 (Postgate 1959).

Inorganic nutrition of sulphate-reducing bacteria differs not too much from that of other bacteria. Generally, with several exceptions, the common macro- and micro-elements are needed. For example, Hata (1960) found that his marine *Desulfovibrio* strain did not require Ca^{2+} and Br^- for growth. Requirement for HCO_3^- in complex media (Postgate 1956) and for growth on choline (Senez and Pascal 1961) was recorded. Definite requirement for iron is observed by several authors, the optimal concentration is about $10-15\ \mu g$-atoms of Fe per litre (Postgate 1956). Group VI anions (MoO_4^{2-} SeO_4^{2-} WO_4^{2-} CrO_4^{2-}) as structural analogues of SO_4^{2-} are inhibitory for these bacteria.

Facultive autotrophy was a widely accepted misbelief for a long time about sulphate-reducing bacteria. Using labelled CO_2, it was pointed out by different authors that only 15 to 25% incorporated into cellular material almost independently from "autotrophic" or heterotrophic conditions. Heterotroph bacteria usually do not fix more than $3-8\%\ CO_2$ during growth, therefore figures for sulphate-reducers are relatively high. Moreover, Sorokin (1961) studied a strain which fixed 30% of its cell carbon from the carboxyl group of labelled lactate.

Organic nutrition of this group has not yet been elucidated in detail. Complex organic nutrients such as yeast extract, peptone and casein hydrolysate are often used as ingredients of media. The role of these materials has been studied by replacement experiments involving amino acids and growth-stimulating micronutrients. Chelating effect of ornithine, serine and isoleucine, in relation to iron requirement was discussed by different authors. Stimulation of growth and sulphide production by complex mixtures of amino acids was found by many authors. In our laboratory, experiments with *D. vulgaris* (Hildenborough strain) also support these findings (Fig. 1).Generally, sulphide yields depend stoichiometrically on the carbon source. E_h and chelating agents may affect the results, therefore evaluation is difficult. Summarizing these observations, we can conclude that amino acids, simple organic compounds support the growth of sulphate-reducing bacteria. The stimulative effect of micronutrients (and iron in this respect) requires careful re-examination.

In different media *Desulfovibrio* show linear or exponential growth-curves depending on the circumstances. If the possibility of nutrient and sulphate-limitation is excluded (which is regularly the case), the limiting factors have to lie on the side of metabolic end-products. (Accumulation of sulphide, precipitation of iron by it, and pH-changes due to its volatilization.) The effect of sulphide accumulation has not yet been properly analyzed. Concerning the other factors mentioned above, Campbell and Postgate (1965) pointed out that with the incorporation of chelating agents – EDTA or citrate – and under continuously renewed CO_2-containing atmosphere, the growth is exponential. In these experiments the minimum doubling time was about 3 hours, final cell yield 0,75 mg dry weight/ml. Senez (1962) reported similar results; on different media the doubling times were 2,0–4,5 hours, and final cell yield (with strain Berre S) was around 0,60 mg/ml as a maximum. On the other hand, recently Hallberg

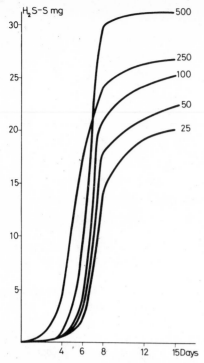

Fig. 1. Effect of yeast extract on sulphide production by *D.*
vulgaris (Holdenbrough strain).
Medium: Vitamin Free Yeast
Base (DIFCO), two-fold
diluted. SO_4^{2-}–content 1.91
g/liter

(1970) described a continuous culture apparatus for the cultivation of
sulphate-reducing bacteria. With the aid of this new apparatus, it was possible to
determine the effect of energy source limitation. Halo- and thermotolerant strain
(Canet 41) of *D. desulficians* at μ_{max} = 0.08 maximal specific growth rate,
– theoretical maximum according to the Fencl-equation – where S_0 (lactate) was
3.7 mg/ml (S_0 = the concentration of the growth limiting carbon source in the total
added substrate) showed 8.5 hours doubling time.

Details of *energy yielding metabolic processes* – being out of our present scope –
will not be dealt with here. From an ecological point of view, many papers have
discussed the importance of the role of electron acceptors, electron donors and the
dismutation of several organic substances.

1) Effects of climate. Water properties and the organo-mineral complex

From the excellent reviews of Kovda (1964, 1969) on salt-affected soils, it is clear that all over the world these soils occur, sulphate-reducing bacteria, as far as temperature reactions are concerned — may live too. From the permafrost areas of Antarctica to the extreme tropics there is no temperature limitation for this group of bacteria. Of course, the temperature range of their maximal activity is narrower — especially towards the lower limit — however, under moderate or warmer climates where the vast majority of salt-affected soils does occur, preconditions for normal growth are usually provided at least in certain periods of the year. It is noteworthy, that slow growth at suboptimal temperatures results in the fractionation of sulphur isotopes (Jones *et al.* 1957, Nakai *et al.* 1960, Kaplan *et al.* 1964). These traces make it possible to follow their biogeochemical activities in the remote past, in geological epochs more than 800 million years ago. The important gap in our knowledge is the failure of exact data about water relationships of these bacteria. In the laboratory, using liquid or solid media this is no problem at all — consequently it is hardly studied. Approaching from an other angle, we can say, that the lower limit of microbial life is around 85% relative humidity of air enclosed in the pores of soils. On the other hand, the most favourable situation for bacteria is when soil particles are covered with an approximately 20–40 μm thick water layer. However, for sulphate-reducing bacteria these figures are not valid because they are obligate anaerobes. As a consequence, the air (and E_h) relations must be taken into consideration at the same time. In unsaturated soils pore space is filled with air at least partly, depending on the water-content of the soil. In spite of this, in wet soil crumbs having a diameter of more than about 3 millimeters, the concentration of oxygen is below $3 \cdot 10^{-6}$ M, practically zero. With increasing water-content the number of pockets, microsites where there is no free oxygen will increase even in coarse- or medium-textured soils. These considerations explain the universality of strict anaerobes along soil profiles, while the occurrence of aerobes diminishes with depth.

The main physical and chemical properties of alkali soils together with water and air relations resulting from them, act in many ways favourable for sulphate-reducing bacteria. Among these properties one of the most important is — in several cases the extremely high — the colloid content; physical clay often amounts up to 40–60% (weight) in the upper horizons. Soils with high colloid content tend to hold large amounts of water because of hydratation of small particles. The clay minerals take up water in their crystal lattices and swell considerably, resulting in a practically impermeable soil which is extremely unfavourable for natural fertility. However, for sulphate-reducing bacteria these events are advantageous. The movement of soil solution becomes restricted, and pore spaces filled with it loose their air content quickly by the activity of micro-organisms. Drying out takes a comparatively long time in these soils, therefore favourable preconditions for sulphate-reducers are provided after only one short wet period. In water-logged soils these circumstances may exist for long periods and, if other factors fulfil the requirements, the vigorous activity of these bacteria may control the dynamics of these soils.

2) The soil solution, effects of its concentration and chemical composition

Following from the salt-tolerance of sulphate-reducing bacteria mentioned previously, in saturated or water-logged soils the concentration of the soil solution rarely reaches such levels which are not tolerable at least for certain strains. During drying, the situation is different. The soil solution becomes more and more concentrated and ultimately most halotolerant forms cease their activity above 10 per cent of total salt concentration. It is not too easy to decide whether the direct effect of increased ionic strength or osmotic pressure, the "physiological drought" are responsible and considerations referring to this will not be discussed here. Common mineral macronutrients are rarely missing or reach harmful levels in these soil solutions therefore they are also negligible — with the exception of sulphate, of course — for the moment. Effects caused by the concentration of sulphate will be discussed later. Only that point should be mentioned here that, at least in Hungarian soils the sulphate-content is not so high that it could be inhibitory — if specific inhibitory effect of sulphate does exist at all.

Because of the good solubility of alkali- and the relatively good solubility of alkali earth sulphates, the uptake from the soil solution is not problematic. On the contrary, in soils having high colloid content with high absorptive capacity, the availability of micronutrients is frequently restricted. For example, waters rich in dissolved or peptized humic material may contain more than 5 mg/l Fe, (which otherwise would be toxic), in this case is not toxic at all, moreover, biologically hardly available. Figures with manganese are essentially the same.

3) Effects of certain electrochemical properties of submerged soils

The importance of this point is clearly realizable from the general picture that emerges from the survey of $pH-E_h$ relations of natural environments summarized in Fig. 2. On this graph the area circumscribed by pH- and E_h-requirements of sulphate-reducing bacteria covers groundwater, as well as fields of water-logged soils, euxenic marine environments and organic-rich saline waters. All of these environments are isolated from the atmosphere by water. This reflects well that factors influencing advantageously the activity of sulphate-reducing bacteria are also very important for the development and dynamics of salt-affected soils.

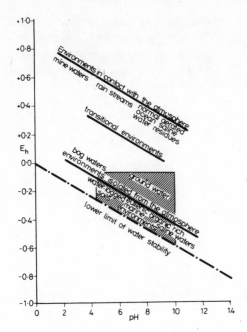

Fig. 2. Approximate position of some natural environments as characterized by pH and E_h. The shadowed area represents the limits of desulphurication

Analyzing the boundaries it is conspicuous that the natural pH-limits of desulphurication (pH 4.2–10) are fairly close to the border values of these environments. In pure cultures, however, the pH-range is narrower, as that was mentioned before. To solve this problem, several considerations should be kept in mind. The data characterizing water-logged soils include values measured in acidic soils which are beyond the scope of this paper. The universally accepted concept of micro-environments provides an explanation, which is reassuring if the whole microflora is taken into consideration. Concerning the upper limit, the beneficial effect of other microorganisms is not so well-expressed, but the Hartley-Roe theory of pH in colloid systems will clarify the situation. On the charged surfaces of soil colloid particles, the effective pH is lower than the pH of the bulk solution:

$$pH_s = pH_b + \rho/60 \text{ at } 25\ ^\circ C$$

where pH_s = the effective pH on the surface, pH_b is the pH of the bulk solution and ρ symbolizes the electrokinetic potential of the particle. The effect of this phenomenon explains the several tenth's of difference in the limiting pH values observed *in vitro* or in nature.

391

Studying the environments in question, we can assume than the pH of underground waters is controlled mostly by inorganic reactions. Below the water table, pH tends to rise because of the hydrolysis of silicates containing ferrous iron, such as biotite, chlorite, amphyboles, pyroxenes and others, thus the environment becomes alkaline and reducing. Feldspars, feldsparthoids, nephelines and syenites also have an effect in the development of alkalinity.

The salt-content of these waters is generally not high, therefore they are potential environments for sulphate-reducing bacteria. The limiting factor is the absence of organic matter. Sometimes these waters may lie very deep down, coming into contact with oil deposits which may result in organic matter supply. Thus, we have returned to ZoBell's provoking question whether the sulphate-reducing bacteria are really indigenous in oil wells. Whether they are or not, these waters rising upwards reach soil profiles in many cases (Kovda 1964) providing good possibilities for these bacteria.

In water-logged soils the pH is influenced by inorganic, organic and microbial events. Inorganic and organic reactions do not need explanation, the hydrolysis of different compounds and their influence on the pH is known. Microbial effects depend on the quantity and, to some extent on the quality of soil organic matter in close interaction with air supply. Without air, different types of fermentations may prevail producing organic acids and carbon dioxide. The result will be the lowering of pH, which is favourable both for sulphate-reducers and for alkaline soils.

Regarding the third group, organic-rich saline waters with high pH (around 10 or more) are again under the control of inorganic reactions. They are unsuitable for life without drastic exogenous influences, thus as environments, these habitats are out of consideration. Euxenic marine environments, although important biotopes of sulphate-reducing bacteria, will not be discussed here because they are not too closely related with our alkali soils.

Another determinative electrochemical parameter of desulphurication is the redox potential of soils. A soil may be considered as a very complex mixture of redox systems involving the entire range from oxygen to hydrogen. These systems may be inorganic — such as ferric-ferrous, managanic-manganous, sulphate-sulphide, etc. — as well as organic ones.

The redox potential shows linear dependence on pH, that is theoretically -0.059 volts/pH unit a 25 °C. The slope of E_h pH curves of soils are rather diverse, ranging from about -0.05 to -0.10 in well-oxydized soils, however, the slope of this curve appears to be steeper in submerged soils, ranging from -0.11 to 0.23 volts per pH unit. Temperature also influences the redox potential either directly or indirectly. The direct effect is not so important as the activity changes of the microflora, which usually decrease the E_h. At a certain point, aerobic bacteria have to cease their activities because of the decreasing oxygen concentration, giving the floor to facultative or strict anaerobes capable of using either inorganic ions or organic compounds formed in the foregoing steps. At that time, the production of carbon dioxide, methane, hydrogen, organic acids and alcohols will prevail, the redox potential may sink close to the water stability limit. This is the true range of sulphate-reducing bacteria, their sulphide production contributes considerably to the lowering of the redox potential.

During reduction of a soil, the concentration of many inorganic and organic compounds may change. As it was mentioned before, iron supply is an essential problem for sulphate-reducing bacteria, because of their own sulphide production. Moreover, in reduced neutral or alkaline soils (and in all soils poor in organic matter), the concentration of soluble Fe^{2+} is low at any time. Only a small fraction of the reduced iron is in the soil solution, the bulk of it is in the solid phase as ferroso ferric hydroxide, ferrous hydroxide, carbonate, sulphide (just because of desulphurication!) and exhangeable Fe^{2+}. If we take into consideration competition of microbes, the desirable 10—15 μg-atoms/liter is not a negligible requirement at all.

4) *Problems of the "readily utilizable" organic matter*

Alkali soils in many cases contain comparatively low amounts of organic matter. The production itself may be rather low, while loss and decay due to physical, chemical and microbial factors relatively high. In places having richer vegetation — swamps or similar water-logged formations — the organic matter content is usually higher, which is favourable for desulphurication. However, it is not utilizable directly, without complex interaction of a number of biotic and abiotic factors. Cellulose is a prominent example of this situation. It is not yet known about even a single strain of sulphate-reducers if it would be able to decompose and utilize cellulose. In spite of this, *in nature,* in close co-operation with other members of the microflora it is one of the best substrates for these bacteria (Rubentschik 1928, Abd-el-Malek *et al.* 1963, Timár and Pátkai 1967). As Figs 3 and 4 show, these processes can readily be reproduced under laboratory conditions.

FORMATION OF ALKALI SOILS BY DESULPHURICATION

The contribution of desulphurication to the development of alkalinity and to the formation of soda in certain soils may play an important, or in special cases, decisive role in the formation and dynamics of these soils.

The concentration of sulphates varies widely in salt-affected soils, from zero to 25 per cent (Kovda). The highest concentration in water-extracts of Hungarian soils is around 30 m.eq./100 g of soil. Within this range, the correlation between concentration of sulphate and sulphide formation, the increase in pH and titratable alkalinity was found to be linear in a model experiment of our laboratory. (Timár and Pátkai 1967, Fig. 5). Above this range, up to about 80—90m.eq./150mg% (SO_4^{2-}–S) sulphide production retained its linear character. Therefore, we can suppose that at least in Hungarian soils, the inhibitory effect due to high sulphate concentration normally does not exist.

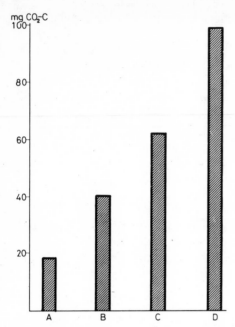

Fig. 3. The effect of various treatments on the CO_2 –production in the soil.
A) sterile soil;
B) soil + 0.5% cellulose;
C) soil + 0.1% cellulose + 20 mg% SO^{2-} – S
D) soil + 0.5% cellulose + 200 mg% SO^{2-} – S

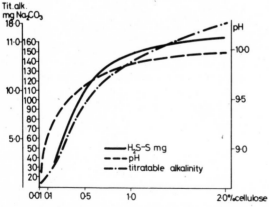

Fig. 4. The effect of increasing amounts of cellulose on sulphate reduction, pH and titratable alkalinity of the soil

394

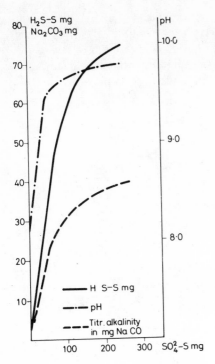

Fig. 5. The effect of increasing amounts
of sodium sulphate on sulphate
reduction

On the other hand, it is necessary to emphasize that biological soda-formation — in spite of its amazing examples — is not the dominating process for the formation of Na_2CO_3 in alkali soils: an extraordinary possibility, not a rule. From the strictly microbiological point of view, if we consider the biochemical aspects, the formation of sodium carbonate due to the activity of sulphate-reducing bacteria is not absolutely necessary. The utilization of organic compounds as terminal electron acceptor is a much more common feature of many strains than it was supposed only several years ago and results in considerable amounts of carbon dioxide, but for soda-formation CO_2 alone is not enough. Their classic peculiarity — reduction of sulphate — may also be performed without the formation of sodium carbonate. The most simple case is if there is no sodium in the medium at a necessary level. If there is an "acceptor" for the sulphide formed, it gives other possibilities. Heavy metals, first of all iron, may form practically insoluble sulphides thus, in extreme cases, the so-called sulphide facies of sedimentary iron ores is thought to be of microbiological origin by many geologists. A further group of possibilities is if the volatilization of sulphide is prevented by microbiological processes. For example, if sulphide formed in soil profile diffuses slowly upwards to aerobic layers or to the surface, where an active population of

Thiobacillus may live oxidizing it to sulphate again. Or, under water-logging, different photosynthetizing sulphur bacteria can do that with the same result. There is the possibility of the combination of all effects mentioned above resulting in one of the most beautiful natural phenomena, the notable sulphureta association of microbes in which the complete microbial cycle of sulphur compounds is represented.

REFERENCES

Abd-El-Malek, Y. and Rizk, S. G. (1963): *J. Appl. Bacteriol.* 26, 7–13.
Abd-El-Malek, Y. and Rizk, S. G. (1963): *J. Appl. Bacteriol.* 26, 14–19.
Abd-El-Malek, Y. and Rizk, S. G. (1963): *J. Appl. Bacteriol.* 26, 20–26.
Baars, J. K. (1930): *Over sulfa-atreductive door bacterien*, Thesis, Meirema, Delft, The Netherlands.
Bergey's *Manual of Determinative Bacteriology*, (1975) Eighth edition, The Williams and Wilkins Co., Baltimore.
Campbell, L. L. and Postgate, J. R. (1965): *Bacteriol. Reviews* 29, 359–363.
Dostalek, M. and Kvet, R. (1964): *Folia Microbiol.* (Prague) 9, 103–114.
Hallberg, R. O. (1970): *Antonie van Leeuwenhoek* 36, 241–254.
Hata, Y. (1960): *J. Shimonoseki Coll. Fisheries* 9, 55-67.
Jones, G. E. and Starkey, R. L. (1957): *J. Appl. Microbiol.* 5, 111–118.
Kaplan, I. R. and Rittenberg, S. C. (1964): *J. gen. Microbiol.* 34, 195–212.
Kaplan, I. R. and Rittenberg, S. C. (1964): *J. gen. Microbiol.* 34, 213–218.
Kovda, V. A. (1964): *Alkaline soda-saline soils.* The FAO/UNESCO Soil Map of the World Project. UNESCO(NS)NR 48. WS(0364.203)NS
Kovda, V. A. and Samoilova, E. M. (1969): *Agrokémia és Talajtan 18.* (Supplement) 21–36.
(Kuznetsova, V. A. and Pantskhava, E. S.) Кузнецова В. А., Пантскава Е. Ш. (1962) : *Микробиол.* 31, 129–132.
(Kuznetsova, V. A., Li, A. D. and Tiforova, N. N.) Кузнецова В. А., Ли А. Д, Пантскава Е. Ш. (1964) : *Микробиол.* 32, 683–689.
Nakai, N. and Jensen, M. L. (1960): *J. Earth Sci. Nagoya Univ.* 8, 181–196.
Postgate, J. R. (1956): *J. gen. Microbiol.* 14, 545–572.
Postgate, J. R. (1959): *Nature (Lond.)* 183, 481.
Postgate, J. R. (1965): *Bacteriol. Reviews* 29, 425–441.
Postgate, J. R. and Campbell, L. L. (1966): *Bacteriol. Reviews* 30, 732–738.
Rubentschik, L. (1928): *Zbl. Bakt. (Abt. 2.)* 73, 438.
Senez, J. C. and Pascal, M. C. (1961): *Z. Allgem. Mikrobiol.* 1, 142–149.
Senez, J. C. (1962): *Bacteriol. Reviews* 26, 95–107.
Sorokin, Y. I. (1961): *Proc. 5th Int. Congr. Biochem.*, Moscow, p. 22.
Timár, M. and Pátkai, T. (1967): *Agrokémia és Talajtan* 16, 151–160.
ZoBell, C. E. (1946): *Bull. Am. Assoc. Petrol Geol.* 30, 477–513.
ZoBell. C. E. (1958): The ecology of sulphate-reducing bacteria *in: Sulphate-reducing bacteria. and their relation to the secondary recovery of oil.* St. Bonaventura Univ., New York. pp. 1–24.
ZoBell, C. E. and Morita, R. Y. (1957): *J. Bacteriol.* 73, 563–569.

EFFECTS OF MOLASSES ON MICROBIAL ENZYME PRODUCTION AND WATER-STABLE AGGREGATION IN SOILS

by

M. DRĂGAN-BULARDA and S. KISS
Babes-Bolyai University, Department of Plant Physiology
Cluj-Napoca, Romania

Studying the amelioration of a saline-sodic soil by use of molasses, Pérez Escolar (1966) established a direct relationship between the polysaccharide content of molasses and water stable aggregation of soil particles. Weber and Van Rooyen (1971) also proved the instant and long-term effectiveness of molasses meal and its superiority to other ameliorants (gypsum, sulphur, potassium sulphate and manure) for saline-sodic soils. They concluded that the aggregating powers of the polysaccharides in molasses meal may be stronger than the dispersing forces of the sodium ions adsorbed in these soils. Moreover, they assumed that a part of the easily digestible carbohydrates in the molasses meal must have been transformed to microbial polysaccharides which acted in addition to the polysaccharides already present in this material. But no experiments were carried out to verify the assumption.

We consider that this verification can easily be performed by correlating the effect of molasses on the production of enzymes catalyzing the synthesis and hydrolysis of microbial polysaccharides with its effect on the aggregation of soil particles. Among microbial polysaccharides, levan and dextran deserve special attention for several reasons.

Levan and dextran were proved to have an aggregating effect on soil particles (Geoghegan and Brian 1948). Soils contain enzymes synthesizing levan [levansucrase] (Kiss 1961) and dextran [dextransucrase] (Drăgan-Bularda and Kiss 1972b), and hydrolyzing levan [levanase] (Kiss *et al.* 1965) and dextran [dextranase] (Drăgan-Bularda and Kiss 1972a). Levan synthesis predominates over levanolysis (Kiss and Drăgan-Bularda 1968). Amendment of soils with sucrose increases the bacterial production of levansucrase (Kiss 1961). Molasses should act similarly as it contains considerable amounts of sucrose. Amendment of soil with levan (Kiss *et al.* 1965) and dextran (Drăgan-Bularda and Kiss 1972a) leads to increased microbial production of levanase and dextranase, respectively.

Thus, a significant correlation between levansucrase activity and aggregate stability in molasses-treated soils indicates that the sucrose present in molasses induced the formation of levansucrase which synthesized levan and this levan constributed to the aggregation of soil particles. A similar correlation between levanase activity and aggregate stability also indicates that levan synthesis did occur and the levan induced the formation of levanase. At the same time, an increased dextranase activity suggests that, besides levan, dextran was also synthesized in the molasses-treated soils.

Based on these considerations we carried out laboratory experiments to verify Weber and Van Rooyen's assumption specified above.

MATERIAL AND METHODS

Soils. Three soils were studied: a solonchak, an alluvial soil and a leached chernozem containing 6.55, 4.22 and 3.75% humus, 0.30, 0.25 and 0.23% total nitrogen, and having pH 7.3, 7.2 and 6.4, respectively.

Molasses. Sugar beet molasses containing 46% sucrose was used. It was suspended in hot distilled water. Heat treatment was applied to inactivate enzyme traces, if any, in the molasses used.

Urea. It was of analytical grade.

Experimental variants. Freshly collected 100 g soil samples (air-dry) were treated with 0—4 g molasses in aqueous suspension, with no or 1% urea (molasses basis) in aqueous solution and with distilled water up to 60% of the water holding capacity of each soil (Table 1). The soils were incubated at room temperature for 30 days. During incubation soil humidity was kept constant. After incubation the soils were allowed to air-dry, then analyzed to determine their enzyme activities and water-stable aggregation.

Enzyme analysis. Levansucrase, levanase and dextranase activities were determined according to the methods already described (Drăgan-Bularda and Kiss 1972a, Kiss 1961; Kiss, Boaru and Constantinescu 1965). The reaction mixtures consisted of 3 g soil, 2 ml toluene and 10 ml aqueous solution of enzyme substrate (sucrose 10% w/v, levan 0.25% w/v, and dextran 2% w/v, respectively), and were incubated for 10 days at 37 °C. Thereafter, the reaction products (levan, fructose and oligofructosides, and glucose and oligoglucosides, respectively) were determined quantitatively. Levansucrase activity is expressed as mg levan, levanase activity as mg fructose, and dextranase activity as mg glucose produced by 3 g soil in 10 days at 37 °C.

Determination of water stable aggregation of soil particles was carried out by using Kazó's method (1958) as adopted by Csapó-Miklósi and co-workers (1964).

Statistical analysis. Correlation coefficients, their significance and the significance of differences were calculated. For calculation of significance the *t* test was applied (Sachs 1968).

RESULTS AND DISCUSSION

The results of enzyme analysis and determination of water stable aggregation are summarized in Table 2, and those obtained in the statistical analysis are presented in Tables 3—5.

Table 1
Characterization of the experimental variants

Experimental variant	Soil (g)	Molasses (g)	Urea (g)
1	2	3	4
1	100	–	–
2	100	–	0.0400
3	100	0.10	–
4	100	0.10	0.0010
5	100	0.25	–
6	100	0.25	0.0025
7	100	0.50	–
8	100	0.50	0.0050
9	100	1.00	–
10	100	1.00	0.0100
11	100	2.00	–
12	100	2.00	0.0200
13	100	4.00	–
14	100	4.00	0.0400

A general examination of the results obtained in all experimental variants (Table 2) makes it evident that the three soils studied present, in respect of their enzyme activities and water stable aggregation, the following order: solonchak $<$ alluvial soil $<$ chernozem.

Table 3 shows that there is a significant correlation between the amount of molasses added to soil and the water stable aggregation of soil particles in each of the three soils studied. This observation confirms the similar findings by Pérez Escolar (1966) and Weber and Van Rooyen (1971). Table 3 also shows that the correlations between levansucrase activity, molasses amount and water stable aggregation are highly significant in each soil. This means that, as expected (Kiss 1961) the sucrose present in molasses induced the microbial production of levansucrase and this inducing effect was proportionate to the amount of sucrose (molasses). The levan synthesized by levansucrase took part in binding of soil particles which explains the correlation found between levansucrase activity and water stable aggregation. Levanase activity also correlates well with molasses amount and water stable aggregation in each soil. This is another evidence of the synthesis of levan and, implicitly, of its aggregating effect, since the induction of microbial levanase production in soil is conditioned by the presence of levan (Kiss *et al.* 1965). The significant correlations between dextranase activity, molasses amount and water stable aggregation suggest that dextran was also synthesized in molasses-treated soils (and it contributed to the aggregation of soil particles), because dextran is the inductor for microbial dextranase production in soil (Drăgan-Bularda and Kiss 1972a).

Table 3 also indicates that levansucrase activity correlates well with levanase activity. The correlation between dextranase and levanase activities is also highly

Table 2
Enzyme activity and water stable aggregation in molasses-treated soils

Experimental variant	Levansucrase activity (mg levan)			Levanase activity (mg fructose)			Dextranase activity (mg glucose)			Water stable aggregation (%)		
	Solon-chak	Alluvial soil	Cherno-zem	Solon-chak	Alluvial soil	Cherno-zem	Solon-chak	Alluvial soil	Cherno-zem	Solon-chak	Alluvial soil	Cherno-zem
1	2	3	4	5	6	7	8	9	10	11	12	13
1	3.00	5.00	7.50	2.50	4.30	4.00	0.150	0.350	0.550	27.3	40.3	51.0
2	3.10	5.20	7.80	2.80	4.05	4.10	0.155	0.360	0.545	27.3	39.7	51.6
3	3.30	6.50	9.50	2.90	5.50	5.80	0.160	0.365	0.570	29.6	41.0	53.5
4	3.25	7.00	10.00	2.95	5.50	6.30	0.165	0.375	0.590	31.3	42.3	52.6
5	3.50	8.00	12.50	2.92	5.80	6.30	0.162	0.370	0.720	35.3	43.6	54.0
6	3.75	8.10	13.80	3.00	6.30	6.30	0.178	0.390	0.690	38.3	45.0	52.9
7	4.00	9.00	15.90	3.10	6.30	7.90	0.167	0.387	0.835	43.0	43.7	57.6
8	4.20	11.00	17.30	3.20	6.30	6.80	0.190	0.400	0.906	45.0	47.3	68.3
9	4.30	12.00	22.50	3.50	8.30	7.80	0.198	0.401	0.948	47.3	48.6	75.8
10	4.50	12.50	23.00	3.50	8.30	6.80	0.214	0.425	1.025	53.0	59.6	77.8
11	5.10	13.00	23.10	3.60	9.30	7.85	0.210	0.415	1.050	59.3	66.0	81.0
12	6.00	12.60	23.60	3.80	9.30	8.30	0.240	0.450	1.200	59.0	71.5	78.3
13	5.80	13.50	24.50	3.90	9.80	9.00	0.235	0.430	1.750	61.0	76.3	82.3
14	6.40	14.00	25.50	4.00	11.10	9.00	0.280	0.500	1.240	61.3	80.0	84.6

Table 3
Correlations between enzyme activities, molasses amount and water
stable aggregation in soils

Correlated values		Soil	Correlation coefficient	Significance
1		2	3	4
Molasses amount	Water stable aggregation	Solonchak	0.5978	0.05 > P > 0.02
		Alluvial	0.9523	0.001 > P
		Chernozem	0.8406	0.001 > P
Levansucrase activity	Molasses amount	Solonchak	0.9407	0.001 > P
		Alluvial	0.9254	0.001 > P
		Chernozem	0.7774	0.01 > P > 0.002
	Water stable aggregation	Solonchak	0.9527	0.001 > P
		Alluvial	0.8733	0.001 > P
		Chernozem	0.9825	0.001 > P
Levanase activity	Molasses amount	Solonchak	0.9681	0.001 > P
		Alluvial	0.6722	0.02 > P > 0.01
		Chernozem	0.8483	0.001 > P
	Water stable aggregation	Solonchak	0.9653	0.001 > P
		Alluvial	0.9431	0.001 > P
		Chernozem	0.8174	0.001 > P
Dextranase activity	Molasses amount	Solonchak	0.9535	0.001 > P
		Alluvial	0.8249	0.001 > P
		Chernozem	0.8879	0.001 > P
	Water stable aggregation	Solonchak	0.9160	0.001 > P
		Alluvial	0.9216	0.001 > P
		Chernozem	0.9348	0.001 > P
Levansucrase activity	Levanase activity	Solonchak	0.9661	0.001 > P
		Alluvial	0.9573	0.001 > P
		Chernozem	0.9264	0.001 > P
Levanase activity	Dextranase activity	Solonchak	0.9552	0.001 > P
		Alluvial	0.9340	0.001 > P
		Chernozem	0.8904	0.001 > P
Dextranase activity	Levansucrase activity	Solonchak	0.3071	0.3 > P > 0.25
		Alluvial	0.4464	0.3 > P > 0.25
		Chernozem	0.9870	0.001 > P

significant. However, a similar correlation between dextranase and levansucrase
activities is lacking in two of the three soils studied.

All these observations support the validity of the assumption made by Weber and
Van Royen (1971) that the microbial polysaccharides synthesized in molasses-treated
soils contribute to the amelioration of these soils.

Table 4
Comparison of levansucrase activity with levanase activity in soils

Soil	Mean values of enzyme activities		Difference	Significance
	Levansucrase	Levanase		
1	2	3	4	5
Solonchak	4.30	3.26	1.04	0.01 > P > 0.002
Alluvial	9.80	7.15	2.65	0.02 · > P > 0.01
Chernozem	16.90	6.87	10.03	0.001 > P

Table 5
Comparison of enzyme activities in soils treated and not treated with urea

Soil	Enzyme	Mean values of enzyme activities		Difference	Significance
		Soil treated with urea	Soil not treated with urea		
1	2	3	4	5	6
Solonchak	Levansucrase	4.45	4.14	0.31	0.7 > P > 0.6
	Levanase	3.32	3.20	0.12	0.7 > P > 0.6
	Dextranase	0.20	0.18	0.02	P > 0.9
Alluvial	Levansucrase	10.10	9.60	0.50	0.9 > P > 0.8
	Levanase	7.26	7.04	0.22	0.9 > P > 0.8
	Dextranase	0.41	0.39	0.02	P > 0.9
Chernozem	Levansucrase	17.30	16.50	0.80	0.9 > P > 0.8
	Levanase	6.80	6.95	−0.15	0.9 > P > 0.8
	Dextranase	0.88	0.83	0.05	0.8 > P > 0.7

One can see from Table 4 that the sequential induction of microbial levansucrase and levanase productions in molasses-treated soils affects stronger the levansucrase production than the levanase production, i.e. levan synthesis predominates over levanolysis. This is in good agreement with the data obtained in soils treated with pure sucrose and levan (Kiss and Drăgan-Bularda 1968).

Addition of a small quantity of urea to molasses-treated soils (1% urea on molasses basis) does not enhance significantly the effect of molasses on microbial enzyme production (Table 5). In other words, the micro-organisms developing in molasses-treated soils do not require additional nitrogen sources to produce levansucrase, levanase and dextranase.

SUMMARY

Samples of three soils (a solonchak, an alluvial soil and a leached chernozem) were treated with different amounts of molasses and incubated under laboratory conditions for 30 days, then analyzed to determine their levansucrase, levanase and dextranase activities and the water stable aggregation of soil particles. The results show that the sucrose present in molasses induced sequentially the microbial production of these enzymes. The inducing effect was proportionate to the amount of molasses. Enzyme activities correlate significantly with water stable aggregation. The correlations support the idea that in molasses-treated soils the enzymatically synthesized polysaccharides levan and dextran contribute to the water stable aggregation of soil particles; amelioration of molasses-treated soils is partly due to soil enzyme activities.

REFERENCES

Csapó-Miklósi, J., Dobai, R. and Kain, J. (1964): *Trans. 8th Int. Congr. Soil Sci. (Bucharest).* **2**, 243–250.

Drăgan-Bularda, M. and Kiss, S. (1972a): *Soil Biol. Biochem.* **4**, 413–416.

Drăgan-Bularda, M. and Kiss, S. (1972b): *Third Symp. Soil Biol. (Bucharest),* 119–128.

Geoghegan, M. J. and Brian, R. C. (1948): *Biochem. J.* **43**, 5–13.

Kazó, B. (1958): *Agrokém. és Talajtan.* **7**, 141–150.

Kiss, S. (1961): *Naturwissenschaften.* **48**, 700.

Kiss, S. and Drăgan-Bularda, M. (1968): *Ştiinţa Solului.* **6**, (2–3). 54–59.

Kiss, S., Boaru, M. and Constantinescu, L. (1965): *Symp. Methods Soil Biol. (Bucharest),* 129–136.

Pérez Escolar, R. (1966):*J. Agr. Univ. Puerto Rico.* **50**, 209–217.

Sachs, L. (1968): *Statistische Auswertungsmethoden.* Springer-Verlag. Berlin-Heidelberg-New York.

Weber, H. W. and Van Rooyen, P. C. (1971): *Geoderma.* **6**, 233–253.

EFFECT OF HEAVY METALS ON BIOLOGICAL ACTIVITY OF SOIL AND THEIR ACCUMULATION BY PLANTS

by

J. KOBUS and A. KABATA-PENDIAS
Institute of Soil Science and Plant Cultivation,
Pulawy, Poland.

A continuous growth of a concentration of heavy metals in soils due to the technological activity of man leads to several irreversible changes of their chemical composition and biological activity. Those changes are especially visible in the vicinities of metallurgic industry, where various metals are concentrated in the soil (Purves 1967), Burkitt, Lester and Nickless (1972), De Koning (1974), Kabata-Pendias (1976), Lagerwerff et al. (1975).

Copper seems to be a metal of a relatively low toxicity when compared to other metalic contaminants of industrial complexes.

Accordingly to Wu (1972) an operation of the copper refinery in Lancashire for 73 years has caused a high increase of this metal in the top soil (up to 5000 ppm). Various plants and especially grasses are tolerant to a high concentration of copper and can grow in a medium with 4830 ppm Cu (Wu 1972) and in a solution of above 500 ppm Cu (Kabata-Pendias and Wiacek, 1974).

Agricultural utilization of wastes from the copper mine is also a source of copper and other heavy metals.

Skaar, Ophus and Cullvag (1973) have found that lead is accumulated mainly in the nucleus and mitochondria of both kinds of plant and animal cells.

There is evidence that other heavy metals are also concentrated in those cell parts which are reflected by a disorder of biological functions of cells (Welch 1975, Murray and Kidby 1975).

MATERIAL AND METHODS

Two kinds of wastes of two ponds "Lubin" and "Polkowice" from the copper mine of Lower Silesia have been used for the experiments.

Total chemical analyses of these wastes have been made by ASA and spectrophotometric methods (Table 1).

Mineralogical identification of separated granulometric fractions was done using X-ray diffraction method. A detailed description of analytical methods is given elsewhere (Kabata-Pendias (1976).

Table 1
Physical and chemical properties of waste material after copper extraction

Locality	Mechanical composition		Chemical composition		pH	
	Size in mm	%	Component	%	KCl	H_2O
Lubin	> 0.2	95	SiO_2	69.56	7.8	8.4
	0.2 −0.02	4	Al_2O_3	5.00		
	0.02−0.002	1	Fe_2O_3	0.59		
			FeO	0.15		
			MgO	3.72		
			CaO	9.09		
			Na_2O	0.10		
			K_2O	1.17		
			SO_3	0.92		
			P_2O_5	0.02		
			CO_2	8.94		
			C-org	0.30		
			N	0.07		
Polkowice	> 0.2	72	SiO_2	27.32	7.8	8.6
	0.2 −0.02	22	Al_2O_3	4.20		
	0.02−0.002	6	Fe_2O_3	0.97		
			FeO	0.47		
			MgO	11.43		
			CaO	23.10		
			Na_2O	0.15		
			K_2O	2.45		
			SO_3	1.20		
			P_2O_5	0.04		
			CO_2	27.12		
			C-org.	0.48		
			N	0.14		

The following experiment was done for investigation of micro-organism development and their biochemical activity.

Experimental series:

1. Waste + NPK.
2. Waste + NPK + 2% wheat straw.
3. Waste + NP + 2% clover hay.

These materials were inoculated with soil and *Azotobacter chroococcum* (10 g of aluvial soil and 90 ml of water containing pure culture of *Azotobacter*).

After different periods of incubation at 25 °C the initial and progressive change in the number of bacteria and actinonomycetes on agar plates with soil extract and K_2HPO_4 was detected.

The total number of fungi was estimated on agar plates using Martin medium. Azotobacter count was carried out on agar plates without nitrogen.

The number of anaerobic N-fixers was estimated by serial dilutions of soil in distilled water (from 1 : 10 to 1 : 10^8). One ml of each dilution was distributed among tubes containing 5 ml of nutrient medium. After its solidification 20 ml of liquid agar was added, then 2 ml of mineral oil for protection against O_2 diffusion.

Cellulolytic micro-organisms were detected by using the Winogradsky method (Table 2).

Amylolytic activity was measured by the method of Hofmann and Hoffmann (1965).

Dehydrogenase activity by Lenhard method, modification of Casida, Klein and Santore (1964).

Content of $N-NH_4$ and $N-NO_3$ was determined by colorimetric analysis. The greenhouse experiment (described in detail previously by Kabata-Pendias, 1976) was conducted with the following plants grown on the wastes pricklyseed spinach, garden radish, broad bean, maize, brome grass, common dandelion and great plantain (Table 3). The plants grew successively in the order given above.

Each pot was watered with 10 ml Hoagland solution of major nutrients only once a week, and normal watering was carried out when needed.

DISCUSSION

Mechanical composition of the wastes presented in Table 1, indicates a predominance of small size fractions (< 0.2 mm) resulting in a poor growth of the roots especialy in the "Polkowice" waste.

All the fractions were composed mainly of quartz and dolomite. Clay minerals represented by illite and kaolinite occurred in negligible amounts and in the finest fractions only.

Chemical composition of the slurries differed for each pond. There was a predomination of SiO_2 in "Lubin" waste, while CaO and MgO yielded altogether 32% in "Polkowice" waste containing copper and manganese at about 2000 ppm levels. In "Lubin" waste 1000 ppm Cu and 300 ppm Mn occurred. Lead content is about 200 ppm, while zinc and nickel are present at 10 ppm level and cadmium with molibdenum at 1 ppm level (Table 3).

Microbiological investigations indicated that initial waste materials had only a very small number of fungi. However, an addition of straw or hay together with soil inoculation produced an intense development of micro-organisms in both wastes (Figs 1 and 2).

Azotobacter introduced into waste material together with soil inoculation did not develop properly and disappeard completely after two weeks of incubation.

Also anaerobic bacteria fixing free nitrogen were very few. *Clostridium* could also developed for the first three weeks only. Two kinds of bacteria, *Cellvibrio* and *Cytophaga* only representatives of micro-organisms decomposing cellulose, were mainly active in the wastes, especially in the "Polkowice" type. In this soil, *Stachybotrys* genus occurred very seldom (Table 2).

407

Table 2
Number of micro-organisms decomposing cellulose (10^{-1}/g soil)

Experimental series	Time of incubation days	Number of colony									
		Lubin					Polkowice				
		Cyto-phaga	Cell-vibrio	Cell-falci-cula	Actino-mycetes	Stachy-botrys	Cyto-phaga	Cell-vibrio	Cell-falci-cula	Actino-mycetes	Stachy-botrys
Waste material	0	0	8	10	2	2	0	4	0	24	0
	7	0	16	0	0	0	0	18	0	8	0
	14	8	12	0	0	6	6	0	0	0	0
	21	10	0	0	0	6	14	40	0	2	0
	28	22	18	0	0	28	30	0	0	0	0
	60	0	0	0	0	16	32	68	0	0	0
	90	0	0	0	0	14	0	10	0	2	0
	120	0	0	0	0	30	0	0	0	0	0
Waste material + 2% of wheat straw	0	8	00	0	6	10	0	8	0	28	0
	7	24	0	0	0	0	0	94	0	0	0
	14	0	>200	0	0	0	40	60	0	0	0
	21	0	>200	0	0	0	0	>200	0	0	0
	28	0	60	0	0	0	0	>200	0	0	20
	60	0	62	0	0	0	10	40	0	0	20
	90	10	0	0	0	14	56	0	0	0	12
	120	12	0	0	0	31	34	0	0	0	
Waste material + 2% of clover hay	0	0	8	0	0	12	6	0	0	22	0
	7	0	86	0	0	0	40	0	0	0	0
	14	24	50	0	0	0	56	0	0	0	0
	21	0	>200	0	0	0	0	104	0	0	0
	28	0	68	0	0	6	0	>200	0	0	0
	60	0	60	0	0	0	20	60	0	0	16
	90	0	>200	0	0	0	58	0	0	0	10
	120	0	>200	0	0	0	30	0	0	0	16

Table 3
Effect of heavy metal contents in waste material on their accumulation in tops and roots of different plants (in ppm)

Plants	Experimental series	Heavy metals content in waste material								Heavy metals content in the plants							
		Total				Dissolved in 0.1 N HCl				Tops				Roots			
		Mn	Cu	Pb	Cd	Mn	Cu	Pb	Cd	Mn	Cu	Pb	Cd	Mn	Cu	Pb	Cd
Pricklyseed Spinach (Spinacia oleracea)	Control									123	15	7	0.5	65	17	25	0.3
	Waste – Lubin	582	1131	181	0.30	250	630	68	0.23	479	136	24	0.6	257	1020	157	1.1
	Waste – Polkowice	2033	1966	153	0.30	200	442	39	0.25	109	82	25	0.5	525	2817	472	0.2
Garden Radish (Raphanus sativus)	Control									50	4	4	0.8	10	6	3	0.5
	Waste – Lubin									162	105	22	0.5	265	756	140	0.3
	Waste – Polkowice									106	99	25	0.7	408	1184	150	0.3
Broad Bean (Vicia faba)	Control									200	5	1	0.2	–	–	–	–
	Waste – Lubin									158	15	2	0.2	–	–	–	–
	Waste – Polkowice									129	18	1	0.2	–	–	–	–
Maize (Zea mays)	Control									75	7	4	0.4	–	–	–	–
	Waste – Lubin									120	110	11	0.6	–	–	–	–
	Waste – Polkowice									71	80	8	0.5	–	–	–	–
Brome grass (Bromus inermis)	Control									17	5	1	0.1	–	–	–	–
	Waste – Lubin									53	19	3	0.2	–	–	–	–
	Waste – Polkowice									48	18	1	0.4	–	–	–	–
Common Dandelion (Taraxacum officinalis)	Control									800	17	8	1.7	–	–	–	–
	Waste – Lubin									364	132	30	0.3	–	–	–	–
	Waste – Polkowice									–	–	–	–	–	–	–	–
Great Plantain (Plantago maior)	Control									64	8	2	0.7	–	–	–	–
	Waste – Lubin									66	45	9	0.4	–	–	–	–
	Waste – Polkowice									43	53	8	0.4	–	–	–	–

27 Szegi

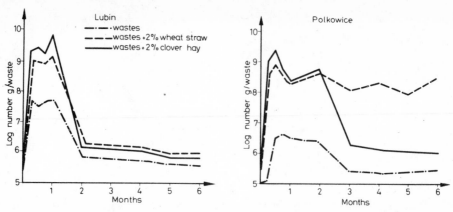

Fig. 1. Effect of wheat straw and clover hay on total number of bacteria and actinomycetes in wastes

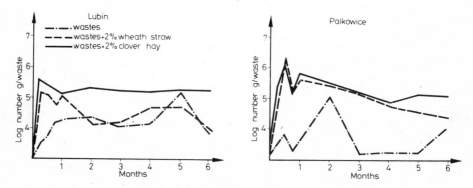

Fig. 2. Effect of wheat straw and clover hay on total number of fungi in wastes

The presence of NH_4^+ and NO_3^- was used as a test for processes of ammonification and nitrification. A smaller amount of $N-NH_4$ has been found in the "Lubin" waste than the "Polkowice" type (Fig. 3).

A distribution of $N-NO_3$ was diverse (Fig. 4). In the "Lubin" waste, process of nitrification was normal, however, in the "Polkowice" waste NH_4^+ did not nitrified. Presumably a higher concentration of Cu and Mn was harmful to nitrifying bacteria. Tandon and Mishra (1969) established that manganese did not affect nitrification up to 5000 ppm concentration in the substratum. Therefore, it seems to be possible that copper is more toxic for nitrifying bacteria than manganese.

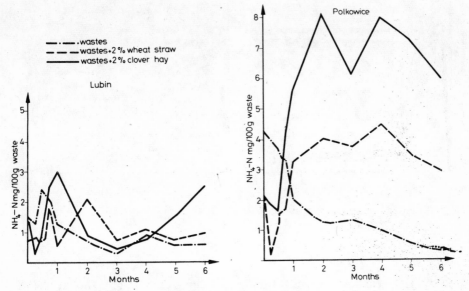

Fig. 3. Effect of wheat straw and clover hay on ammonium accumulation in wastes

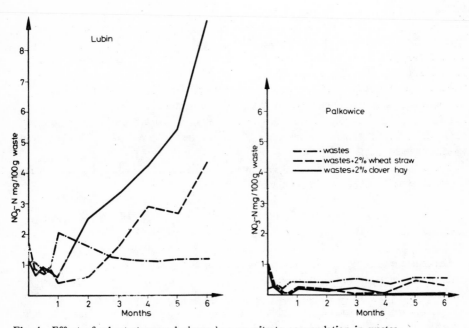

Fig. 4. Effect of wheat straw and clover hay on nitrate accumulation in wastes

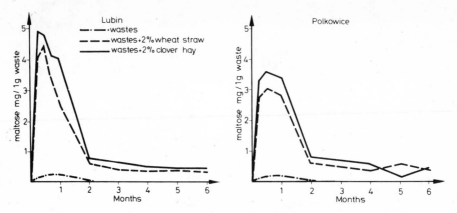

Fig. 5. Effect of wheat straw and clover hay on amylase activity in wastes

Heavy metals influenced also the amylolytic activity of soil (Fig. 5). The amylolytic activity was smaller in "Polkowice" than in "Lubin" waste. Dehydrogenase seems to be also very sensitive to a higher concentration of heavy metals. TTC was not reduced in both wastes.

The chemical composition of plants grown on the wastes is presented in Table 3. There is a significant difference in the uptake of heavy metals by various plants. The highest concentration of these metals have been noticed in spinach, radish and dandelion, especially in spinach roots and edible parts of radish. Bromgrass and corn accumulated much lower amounts of heavy metals.

There was a relatively high uptake of Mn, Cu and Pb but no significant difference was observed in accumulation of Cd. Heavy metal uptake by plants seems to be a function of 0.1 N HCl-soluble amount of these metals in the substratum. On the other hand, the concentration of heavy metals in roots was in correlation with their total amount in the wastes.

The accumulation of copper and lead reached a hazardous level for the food chain in both tops and roots of several experimental plants.

CONCLUSIONS

The concentration of heavy metals in wastes of the copper mine is toxic to several kinds of micro-organisms, especially for *Azotobacter, Clostridium, Nitrosomonas* and *Nitrobacter.* Heavy metal content in wastes was inhibitory for dehydrogenase activity.

Plants grown on the wastes are able to accumulate a high amount of heavy metals, however a great proportion of these metals is accumulated in root tissues and is not transported to the tops.

Ability of plants to uptake heavy metals differed, being the highest for spinach and radish and the lowest for grasses.

An agricultural utilization of wastes of the copper mine may be hazardous to health because of the introduction of lead and copper to the food chain.

ACKNOWLEDGEMENT

The authors are indebted for the partial financial support made available by USPA under the project Pl-ARS-24.

REFERENCES

Burkitt, A., Lester, P. and Nickless, G. (1972): *Nature*. **238**, 327–328.
Casida. L. E., Klein, D. A. and Santore, T. (1964): *Soil Science,* **98**, 371–376.
De Koning, W. H. (1974): *Water, Air and Soil Pollution*, **3**, 63–70.
Hofmann, E. and Hoffmann, G. (1965): *Ztsch. für Pflanzenernährung, Dügung, Bodenkunde.* **70**, 97.
Kabata-Pendias, A. (1976): *Heavy metals accumulation of plants grown on gangue slurrnes of the copper mine, (in press).*
Kabata-Pendias, A. And Wiacek, K. (1974): *10th Inter. Congress Soil. Sci.* Moscow **4**, 185–193.
Lagerwerff, J. V., Brower, D. L. and Biersdorf, G. T. (1975): *Abst.* 9th *Ann. Conf. Trace Subst. Environment. Health,* p. 32.
Murray, A. D. and Kidby, D. K. (1975): *J. of General Microbiol.* **86**, 66–74.
Purves, D. (1967): *Plant and Soil.* **26**, s. 380–381.
Skaar, H., Ophus, E. and Cullvag, B. M. (1973): *Nature.* **241**, 215–216.
Tandon, P. S. and Mishra, M. M. (1969): *Ztbl. für Bact.* **123**, 399–402.
Welch, W. R. and Dick, D. L. (1975): *Environmental Pollution.* **8**, 15–21.
Wu L. (1972): *Nature.* **238**, 167–169.

CLOSING REMARKS

We have come to the end of our VII Soil Biology Meeting. The participants have done a great job, for by discussing the aspects of environmental protection of soil biology have had a formidable task the results of which are invaluable to mankind with regard to the future.

Recently numerous organizations have been devoted to actual problems of environmental protection not only at congresshalls and at symposia but even the representatives of the world have debated it in the United Nations.

This complicated and rather divergent problem can only be solved by the closest collaboration of nations and in this the research workers have a basic role.

The research field of environmental protection encompasses a rather wide spectrum from sociology to medicine through architecture to agricultural sciences. A very important task within the latter is relegated to researchers in the soil, since fertile soil ensures the nutrients and clothing for mankind. Therefore the protection of the fertile soil from different environmental dangers is vital for mankind especially with the population explosion.

I am convinced that the Soil Biological Section of our Soil Science Society could not have found a more timely theme for the VII Scientific Session at an international level. This is indicated by the great interest shown in the symposium. The lectures and debates following prove that the significance of soil biology in the protection of agricultural environment is not overestimated.

There is not a branch in soil science which would be so tightly connected with the most diverse problems of environmental protection as soil biology. Whether we consider chemical plant protection or large dose fertilization or the area of soil cultivation, these can only by determined properly if we are aware of the direction and intensity of the biological processes occurring in the soil. Only in this way will it be possible to influence the organisms living in the soil according to our aims.

The Presidential committee greatly appreciates the work of the meeting organized by the Soil Biology Section of the Soil Science Society and it will likewise in the future give every support to any similar meeting.

The VII Scientific Session was more extensive than any previously held. In fact here at Keszthely more than 100 specialists of which at least half were from abroad took part and with more than 54 lectures have reported on their results indicating that our scientific meeting has contributed to the better collaboration of soil biologists of different countries and to deepening the scientific connections. The research methods presented here have been valuable and the discussions, exchange of experience and critical evaluation of the conclusions have been useful for further work.

Allow me as president of the Hungarian Agricultural Science Society and on behalf of the organizing Committee to thank all those who by participating have promoted the realization of our aims.

To all those visitors from foreign countries who with their lectures and discussions have added to a better understanding of each others' work thereby promoting a fruitful international collaboration, we hope you have enjoyed your stay in Hungary and are looking forward to meeting you again at our next symposium.

Finally I should like to thank the Rector and Dean of Keszthely Agricultural University and the whole University Board for making it possible to hold our scientific meeting at this agricultural institution of historical renown and to have received every support for this.

I extend our cordial greetings to you all and wish you much luck in the realization of your research goals, wishing you all good health until we meet at the next Scientific Meeting of the Soil Biology Society.

K. György
Secretary General of the Hungarian
Association of Agricultural Sciences

AUTHOR INDEX

417

418

Frommer, W. 265, 270
Furusaka, C. 239, 240, 243
Füleki, Gy. 14

Gabe, D. R. 315, 317
Gafar, A. Z. 92, 93
Garcia-Peña, r. 14
Galgóczy, B. 14
Gamal El Din, H. 7, 14, 229, 233, 382, 383
Galstian A. 145, 149
Gamble, S. J. R. 111, 117
Garkavenko, A. J. 201, 202, 203, 205
Gärtner-Bánfalvi, A. 5, 14, 79 85, **95**
Geoghegan, M. I. 397, 403
Gere, G. 319, 327
Gergely, Z. 6, 14, **111**, 117
Gerrsten, F. C. 149
Gesheva, P. 201, 205
Getzin, L. W. 59, 60, 70, 71
Giambiagi, N. 136, 137
Gibbons, N. E. 160
Giddnes, J. 111, 117
Gillberg, B. O. 106, 109
Gloser, J. 332, 335
Golebiowska, J. 95, 101
Golovieva, L. A. 312
Gordienko, N. 375, 383
Goss, O. M. 103, 109
Gosselink, J. G. 122, 127
Gostenkov, M. F. 365
Gould R. F. 71
Graff, O. 260
Gray, P. H. H. 135, 137
Gray, T. R. G. 260
Grechin, I. 73, 78
Green, L. 207, 211
Greenland, D. J. 271, 275
Gregory, K. F. 265, 270
Grimes, D. W. 232
Gruev 140
Gulidov, A. M. 78
Gulyás, F. 7, 8, 14, 68, 71, 111, 117, **229, 265,**
   375, 383
Gunner, H. B. 59, 60, 61, 70, 71
Gupta, U. C. 261, 263
Gurinovits, E. 117
György, K. 8, 415
Gyurkó, P. 7, 14, 117, 293

Hadyivalcheva, E. M. 14
Hagen, A. 343, 353

Hahn, B. E. 232
Haider, K. 7, 14, **245,** 249, 262, 263, 270, 276
Hale, M. G. 111, 117
Hallberg, R. O. 387, 396
Hamatová-Hlavacková, E. 215, 216
Hamdi, Y. A. 92, 93, 96
Hamed, A. S. 6, 14, **103,** 104, 106, 109
Hamissa, M. R. 199
Hanway, J. J. 232
Harder, A. 134, 137
Hardy, R. W. F. 187, 191
Hargitai, L. 5, 4, **59,** 63, 67, 71, 319, 327
Harris, C. R. 60, 71
Hartenstein, R. 326, 327
Hata, Y. 387, 396
Hattori, T. 239, 240, 243
Hauke-Paczewiczowa, T. 111, 117
Hearne, E. F. 275
Heim, A. H. 265, 270
Helmeczi, B. 14
Henry, A. W. 103, 106, 109
Hildebrand, D. C. 178
Hlebarova, S. I. 14
Hoglund, M. P. 227, 326
Hofmann, E. 146, 149, 407, 413
Hofmann, G. 407, 413
Holdgate, M. 352
Holstein, R. C. 191
Hopkins, T. L. 61, 71
Hormaeche, E. 159, 160
Hörmann, W. D. 85
Hugh, R. 157, 158 159, 160
Hulcher, F. H. 117
Humphry, B. 210, 211
Hynes, H. B. N. 126, 127

Ibañez, B. S. 136, 137
Ibrahim, A. N. 5, 14, **87,** 199
Ieruzalimsky, N. D. 239, 243
Igmándy, Z. 277, 286
Ignatova, N. N. 365
Iizuka, H. 367, 370
Ilyaletdinov, A. N. 111, 117
Imre, J. 14
Isensee, A. K. 59, 71
Isepy, I. 319, 320, 321, 327
Iswaran, V. 193, 199
Ivanov, M. V. 371
Ivanova, E. P. 14
Iwasaki, I. 53, 57
Izhevskaya T. I. 375, 385